Progress in Mathematics

2   EXTENSION

Progress in Mathematics

Pupils' Book 1G	Pupils' Book 1C
Pupils' Book 2G	Pupils' Book 2C
Pupils' Book 3G	Pupils' Book 3C
Pupils' Book 4G	Pupils' Book 4C
Pupils' Book 5G	Pupils' Book 5C

Pupils' Book 1E
Pupils' Book 2E

The remainder of the 'extension' books are in preparation.

For each pupils' book, there are:
Mental Tests and Phase Tests
Copy Masters
Answers

Progress in Mathematics

2 EXTENSION

Les Murray BA
Formerly Senior Teacher and Head of Mathematics, Garstang County High School

Stanley Thornes (Publishers) Ltd

© Les Murray 1988

First published in 1988 by Stanley Thornes (Publishers) Ltd, Old Station Drive, Leckhampton, Cheltenham GL53 0DN, UK

British Library Cataloguing in Publication Data

Murray, Les.
  Progress in mathematics
  1. Mathematics—Questions & answers—For schools
  I. Title
  510'.76

  ISBN 0–85950–730–0

Typeset by Tech-Set, Gateshead, Tyne & Wear.
Printed and bound in Great Britain at A. Wheaton & Co. Ltd., Exeter.

Preface

This book is the first of the higher level series. It is not intended that it should be worked through from cover to cover.

Although the order of contents is a suitable one to follow, the discretion of the teacher will determine the order of work and whether or not one chapter should be completed before another is attempted. The starting point for a pupil or class will not necessarily be at the beginning of a chapter. Numerous carefully graded questions have been provided to allow plenty of freedom — again the teacher must be selective. Few worked examples are given, thus allowing for alternative methods of introducing topics.

The material has been carefully planned to allow for the use of a calculator, but total dependence on calculator-use is not encouraged.

Photocopy masters are available for exercises where pupils may benefit by their provision, such exercises have been labelled **M** . The use of masters helps to eliminate laborious, time-wasting tasks, such as the copying out of tables; more time can be spent doing mathematics.

The completion of this book has been dependent on the valued help and advice given to me by many people, in particular Mr Clive Horsford of Lancaster Royal Grammar School, who painstakingly worked through the text and provided the answers and Mr J. Britton, Head of Mathematics at Copthall School, London, for his welcome advice and most useful comments.

My thanks also go to Casio Electronics and Texas Instruments for the loan of a selection of calculators, thus enabling me to consider the different characteristics of calculators in my writing; to Ken Gunn and Joe Heatley for providing invaluable information; to Mr John Patrick and Mr Fred Watson of Pandoro Ltd, Fleetwood, for their help with the section on containers; and to Lona Bond, Sharan Jeet Shan and Wilbert Garvin for providing lists of names.

Les Murray
1988

To BAM and LM

Acknowledgements

The author and publishers are grateful to the following:
Black and Decker for the photograph on p. 175.
British Railways Board for the timetable, on p. 148.
Dover Publications Inc. for the hieroglyphic notation, on p. 45.
Guinness Superlatives for the records of memorising π on p. 242,
   and for the miscellaneous records on p. 374.
Mathematical Pie for the mnemonics for π on p. 243.
Royal Greenwich Observatory for the information taken from
   The Astronomical Almanac on p. 155.

Contents

1 Sets

Exercise 1

1. Here is the set of odd numbers that lie between 12 and 34. Two *members* (or *elements*) of the set are missing. What are the missing members?

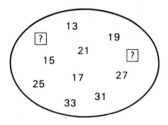

2. Consider the set of factors of 30. The set can be listed in curly brackets, { }, sometimes called *braces*. Copy the set and fill in the two missing members:

   The set of factors of 30 = {1, 2, 3, [?], 6, 10, [?], 30}

3. List these sets. Use curly brackets.
   (a) the set of even numbers that lie between 17 and 31,
   (b) the set of factors of 36,
   (c) the set of multiples of 4 that are less than 45,
   (d) the set of letters of the alphabet that have more than one line of bilateral symmetry (use the capital letters in Appendix 1, p. 433).

4. If $J = \{\text{months that begin with the letter J}\}$, then list the members of set J. Use curly brackets. Set out your answer like this: $J = \{ \qquad \}$

5. List these sets as in question 4:
   (a) $M = \{\text{months that have 30 days}\}$
   (b) $N = $ the set of natural numbers* that are less than 12
   (c) $D = \{\text{divisors of 40}\}$
   (d) $L = \{\text{multiples of 5 that are less than 42}\}$
   (e) $E = $ the set of even numbers that are factors of 100

*See the glossary, p. 446.

1

6. Describe these sets in words:

    (a) $V = \{a, e, i, o, u\}$

        $V = $ the set of $\boxed{?}$

    (b) $M = \{April, August\}$

    (c) $P = \{2, 3, 5, 7, 11, 13, 17, 19, 23\}$

    (d) $F = \{1, 2, 3, 4, 6, 8, 12, 24\}$

    (e) $L = \{6, 12, 18, 24, 30, 36, 42, 48, \ldots\}$

    (f) $R = \{\frac{3}{4}, \frac{6}{8}, \frac{9}{12}, \frac{12}{16}, \frac{15}{20}, \frac{18}{24}, \frac{21}{28}, \frac{24}{32}, \ldots\}$

Note   In parts (e) and (f), the lists *do not finish*. They are called *infinite sets*. The dots can be read as 'and so on'.

7. $A = \{1, 4, 6, 7\}$

List set B where $B = $ the set of four-digit even numbers formed by using all four digits in set A. (No digit should be repeated in any of these four-digit numbers.)

8. $Q = \{quadrilaterals\ with\ four\ equal\ sides\}$
List set Q.

9. Mark two points on your page about 5 cm apart.

        $B = $ the set of points that are equidistant from the two points.

Make a drawing to show set B.

10. Draw a straight line 45 mm in length. (Leave at least 25 mm to each side of the line.)

        $R = \{points\ that\ are\ 25\ mm\ from\ the\ straight\ line\}$

Make a drawing to show set R.

The Symbols $\in$ and $\notin$

$\in$ means 'is a member of' (or 'belongs to').

$\notin$ means 'is not a member of' (or 'does not belong to').

Exercise 2

For each question, write the symbol $\in$ or $\notin$ that would make the sentence correct:

1. 16 ? {2, 4, 6, 8, 10, 12, 14, 16, 18, . . .}.

2. 4 ? {factors of 60}.

3. A triangular-based prism ? {solids with six edges}.

4. 49 ? S, where $S = $ {square numbers}.

5. 48 394 ? D, where $D = $ {numbers exactly divisible by 4}.

6. 58 392 ? {numbers exactly divisible by 9}.

7. 2 ? P, where $P = $ the set of prime numbers.

8. $12 \in T$, where $T = $ {triangular numbers}.

9. 76 ? Y, where $Y = $ the set of multiples of 6.

10. Amsterdam ? {cities in Europe}.

3

The Empty Set

An *empty set* (or *null set*) is a set with no members.

It is written as $\emptyset$ or $\{\ \}$.

$\{0\}$ is not an empty set. (Zero is a member.)

$\{\emptyset\}$ is not an empty set (it has one member, namely $\emptyset$).

Exercise 3

A Which of these are empty sets? Write $\emptyset$ or $\{\ \}$ if a set is empty, otherwise write 'IS NOT AN EMPTY SET'.

1. the set of empty milk bottles

2. {triangles containing two right-angles}:
   (*a*) when drawn on a flat piece of paper,
   (*b*) when drawn on a sphere.

3. {triangles containing three right-angles}:
   (*a*) when drawn on a plane surface*,
   (*b*) when drawn on a sphere.

4. the set of quadrilaterals that, when drawn on a plane surface, have exactly three right-angles

5. {pentagons with six sides}

6. the set of polygons with eight sides

7. the set of pentagons with five acute interior angles*

8. {quadrilaterals that have three obtuse angles}

9. {straight lines that can be drawn on the curved face of a sphere}

10. {straight lines that can be drawn on the curved face of a cylinder}

B State whether each of the following is true or false:

1. {quadrilaterals with three sides} $= \emptyset$

2. {quadrilaterals with perpendicular diagonals} $= \{\ \}$

*See the glossary, pp. 447 and 445.

4

3. the set of odd numbers that are multiples of $3 = \emptyset$

4. the set of quadrilaterals containing four obtuse angles $= \emptyset$

5. the set of prime numbers that are multiples of $5 = \{\ \}$

6. {prime numbers that are factors of 192} $= \emptyset$

The Universal Set and the Complement of a Set

The *universal* set is the set of all elements being considered. The symbol $\mathscr{E}$ is used to stand for the universal set ('$\mathscr{E}$' for '$\mathscr{E}$verything'). On a Venn diagram, a rectangle is used for the universal set. Although a circle is usually used to show other sets, any shape may be used. The *complement* of a set A is the set of elements in $\mathscr{E}$ that are not in set A. It can be written as A'.

e.g.   If $\mathscr{E} = \{$natural numbers less than 12$\}$
       and $A = \{$odd numbers less than 12$\}$
       then $A' = \{$2, 4, 6, 8, 10$\}$ as shown in the diagram.

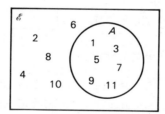

Exercise 4

A 1. (*a*) Copy the diagram.

    (*b*) If $A = \{4, 14, 20, 23\}$, write these elements on your diagram.

    (*c*) Complete the diagram where $\mathscr{E} = \{3, 4, 5, 9, 14, 15, 20, 21, 23\}$.

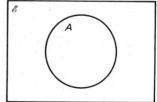

2. Draw a Venn diagram to show:

        $\mathscr{E} = \{$the last eight letters of the alphabet$\}$
        $B = \{$T, V, X$\}$

3. Draw a Venn diagram to show:

$$\mathcal{E} = \{\text{factors of } 42\} \quad C = \{1, 7\}$$

B Suggest a possible universal set for each of the following sets:

1. $\{1, 3, 5, 7, 9\}$

2. $\{2, 3, 5, 7, 11, 13, 17, 19\}$

3. $\{\text{Mon, Tue, Wed, Thur, Fri, Sat, Sun}\}$

4. $\{\text{red, blue, green}\}$

5. $\{5, 10, 15, 20, 25, 30, 35, \ldots\}$

Exercise 5

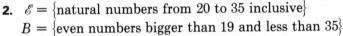

1. (a) Draw a Venn diagram as shown.

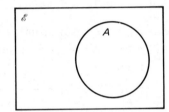

(b) Complete it where:
$\mathcal{E} = \{\text{even numbers less than 25}\}$
$A = \{16, 18, 20, 22, 24\}$
(c) List A'.
(d) Describe A' in words.

2. $\mathcal{E} = \{\text{natural numbers from 20 to 35 inclusive}\}$
$B = \{\text{even numbers bigger than 19 and less than 35}\}$
(a) Draw a Venn diagram to show these sets.
(b) List B'.
(c) Describe B' in words.

3. $\mathcal{E} = \{\text{divisors of 60}\} \quad T = \{\text{divisors of 20}\}$
(a) Show these sets on a Venn diagram. (b) List T'.

4. $\mathcal{E} = \{\text{whole numbers* less than 50}\}$
$W = \{\text{whole numbers less than 40}\}$
(a) List set W'. (b) Describe W' in words.

5. $\mathcal{E} = \{\text{letters of the alphabet}\} \quad X = \{\text{vowels}\}$
Describe X' in words.

*See the glossary, p. 448.

6. $\mathscr{E} = \{2, 4, 6, 8, 10, 12, 14, 16, 18\}$ $M = \{4, 8, 12, 16\}$
List M'.

7. $\mathscr{E} = \{\text{quadrilaterals}\}$
$T = \{\text{quadrilaterals with four equal sides}\}$
$C = \{\text{quadrilaterals in which the diagonals bisect each other}\}$
(*a*) List T'.   (*b*) List C'.

8. If $A = \{2, 3, 4, 5\}$ and $A' = \{6, 7, 8\}$, find $\mathscr{E}$.

9. If $B = \{a, e, i, o, u\}$ and $B' = \{f, c, t, s\}$, find $\mathscr{E}$.

10. $\mathscr{E} = \{x : x = 5n \text{ where } n \text{ is odd}\}*$
$A = \{\text{numbers that are bigger than } 40\}$
List set A'.

Equal Sets

Two sets are equal if they have the same members.

If $X = \{p, q, r, s\}$ and $Y = \{s, p, r, q\}$, then $X = Y$.

Note that the sets are still equal even though the members are listed in a different order.

If $P = \{\text{odd numbers less than } 9\}$ and $Q = \{1, 3, 5, 7\}$, then $P = Q$.

Note that the sets are equal even though they have been described in different ways.

Exercise 6

Write whether or not the following sets are equal:

1. $X = \{a, t, m, e, g\}$, $Y = \{m, a, g, t, e\}$

2. $P = \{v, e, r, t, i, c, a, l\}$, $Q = \{r, c, l, t, e, v, i, l\}$

3. $K = \{\text{even numbers less than } 15\}$, $L = \{8, 6, 12, 10, 2, 4, 14\}$

4. $P = \{\text{prime numbers less than } 20\}$, $Q = \{3, 11, 7, 13, 5, 19, 17\}$

5. $M = \{\text{multiples of 8 that are less than } 65\}$,
$N = \{24, 40, 16, 32, 48, 8, 64, 56\}$

*See Appendix 2, p. 435.

7

Venn Diagrams and the Intersection and Union of Sets

The *intersection* of sets A and B is the set of elements in *both A and B*. The symbol $\cap$ stands for intersection.

The *union* of sets A and B is the set of elements in *either A or B or both*. $\cup$ stands for union.

$\cap$ is often pronounced as 'cap' and $\cup$ pronounced as 'cup'.

e.g.

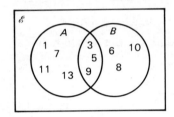

If $A = \{1, 3, 5, 7, 9, 11, 13\}$
and $B = \{3, 5, 6, 8, 9, 10\}$,
then $A \cap B = \{3, 5, 9\}$
and $A \cup B = \{1, 3, 5, 6, 7, 8, 9, 10, 11, 13\}$.

Exercise 7

1. If $A = \{1, 2, 4, 7, 8\}$ and $B = \{2, 3, 5, 8, 9\}$,
   find: (*a*) $A \cup B$ (*b*) $A \cap B$

2. If $X = \{l, m, p, s, u, v\}$ and $Y = \{p, q, r, s, t, u\}$,
   find: (*a*) $X \cup Y$ (*b*) $X \cap Y$

3. $P = \{\text{factors of } 18\}$ $Q = \{\text{factors of } 24\}$
   Find: (*a*) $P \cap Q$ (*b*) $P \cup Q$

4. $P = \{\text{prime numbers less than } 100\}$
   $A = \{\text{numbers between } 30 \text{ and } 50\}$
   Find $A \cap P$.

5. $M = \{\text{multiples of } 4 \text{ less than } 50\}$
   $Z = \{x: 30 < x \leqslant 40 \text{ where } x \text{ is a whole number}\}$
   Find $M \cap Z$.

6. $N = \{$multiples of 9 that are less than 50$\}$
$T = \{t: 26 \leqslant t < 31$ where t is a whole number$\}$
Find: (a) $N \cap T$ (b) $N \cup T$

7. $C = \{x: 20 < x < 40\}$
$D = \{x: x = 3n$ and n is even$\}$
Find $C \cap D$.

8. $Q = \{$quadrilaterals$\}$
$S = \{$polygons with at least one pair of parallel sides$\}$
List $Q \cap S$.

9. $Q = \{$quadrilaterals$\}$
$R = \{$polygons with at least two right-angles$\}$
Draw four different members of $Q \cap R$.

10. $W = \{$odd numbers that lie between 15 and 30$\}$
$X = \{$even numbers greater than 10$\}$
$Y = \{y: 17 < y < 25$ where y is a whole number$\}$
Find: (a) $W \cap Y$ (c) $X \cap Y$
      (b) $W \cup Y$ (d) $W \cap X$

Exercise 8

Combine each pair of sets as instructed. Re-arrange the letters of each answer to form a word. The seven words obtained give a message.

1. $A = \{$h, e, a, t$\}$ $B = \{$t, h, e, m$\}$ Find $A \cap B$.

2. $C = \{$w, e, a, r$\}$ $D = \{$s, a, n, e$\}$ Find $C \cup D$.

3. $F = \{$s, i, t$\}$ $G = \{$r, i, s, e$\}$ Find $F \cap G$.

4. $H = \{$h, i, t$\}$ $J = \{$g, r, i, t$\}$ Find $H \cup J$.

5. $K = \{$y, o, u, t, h$\}$ $L = \{$y, o, u, n, g, e, r$\}$ Find $K \cap L$.

6. $M = \{$h, e, a, v, y$\}$ $N = \{$h, e, a, v, i, n, g$\}$ Find $M \cap N$.

7. $P = \{$p, r, i, m$\}$ $Q = \{$d, o, v, e$\}$ Find $P \cup Q$.

Exercise 9

1. $A = \{1, 2, 3, 5, 7\}$ $B = \{2, 4, 5, 6, 8\}$ $C = \{3, 5, 8, 9\}$

Find: (a) $A \cap B$

      (b) $B \cup C$

      (c) $A \cap C$

      (d) $A \cup B \cup C$

      (e) $A \cap B \cap C$

      (f) $(A \cap B) \cup C$

      (g) $A \cup (B \cap C)$

      (h) $B \cap (A \cup C)$

      (i) $C \cap (A \cup B)$

      (j) $(C \cap A) \cup (C \cap B)$

2. $P = \{2, 4, 6, 8, 10\}$ $Q = \{3, 4, 6, 7, 9\}$ $R = \{1, 3, 5, 7, 9\}$

Find: (a) $P \cap Q$

      (b) $P \cup Q$

      (c) $P \cap R$

      (d) $P \cup R$

      (e) $Q \cap R$

      (f) $Q \cup R$

      (g) $P \cap Q \cap R$

      (h) $P \cup Q \cup R$

      (i) $P \cap (Q \cup R)$

      (j) $(P \cap Q) \cup R$

      (k) $(P \cap Q) \cup (P \cap R)$

      (l) $(P \cup R) \cap (Q \cup R)$

Exercise 10   Factors and Union of Sets

1. $A = \{\text{factors of } 42\}$

so $A = \{1, 2, 3, 6, 7, 14, 21, 42\}$

(a) List set B whose members are double those in set A.

(b) Find $A \cup B$.

(c) List the set of factors of 84.

(d) Compare the answers to parts (b) and (c), then write what you notice.

2. List all the factors of 24. Use them to find:

(a) the factors of 48,   (b) the factors of 72.

3. List the set of factors of 18. Use them to find all the factors of:

(a) 36   (b) 54   (c) 72   (d) 90   (e) 108

Exercise 11   HCF and LCM

A 1. $X = \{\text{factors of } 24\}$ $Y = \{\text{factors of } 30\}$

(a) List set X.

(b) List set Y.

(c) Find $X \cap Y$.

(d) Find the common factors of 24 and 30.

(e) What is the HCF (highest common factor) of 24 and 30?

2. $P = \{$factors of 42$\}$ $Q = \{$factors of 56$\}$
  (a) Find $P \cap Q$.
  (b) What is the HCF of 42 and 56?

3. $L = \{$factors of 36$\}$ $M = \{$factors of 45$\}$
  (a) Find $L \cap M$.
  (b) What is the HCF of 36 and 45?

B 1. $M = \{$multiples of 6 that are less than 100$\}$
     $N = \{$multiples of 10 that are less than 100$\}$
    (a) Find $M \cap N$.
    (b) What is the LCM (lowest common multiple) of 6 and 10?

2. $C = \{$multiples of 8 that are less than 100$\}$
     $D = \{$multiples of 12 that are less than 100$\}$
    (a) Find $C \cap D$.
    (b) What is the LCM of 8 and 12?

3. $V = \{$multiples of 15 that are less than 125$\}$
     $W = \{$multiples of 20 that are less than 125$\}$
    (a) Find $V \cap W$.
    (b) What is the LCM of V and W?

Exercise 12   Shading Sets   M

A For each question, write which set is shaded:

  1. A
     or B
     or $A \cup B$
     or $A \cap B$?

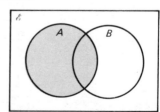

  2. C
     or D
     or $C \cup D$
     or $C \cap D$?

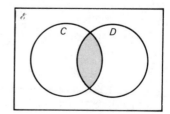

3. G
  or $F \cup G$
  or G'
  or $(F \cap G)'$?

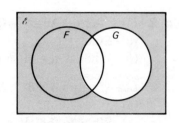

4. J
  or $J \cap K$
  or $J \cup K$
  or $J \cup K'$?

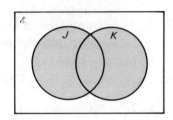

5. $L \cup M$
  or $L \cap M$
  or $(L \cap M)'$
  or $(L \cup M)'$
  or $L' \cup M'$?

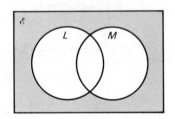

B Make eight copies of the given Venn diagram. Shade each one as instructed.

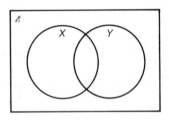

Shade:

1. X

2. X'

3. $X \cap Y$

4. $(X \cap Y)'$

5. Y'

6. $X \cup Y'$

7. $X \cap Y'$

8. $X' \cup Y'$

Exercise 13   Miscellaneous Questions

1. Using the given Venn diagram:

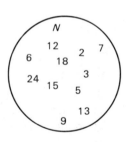

(a) List set X.

(b) List set X'.

(c) List $X \cap Y$.

(d) List $X \cup Y$.

(e) List $(X \cup Y)'$.

(f) List $X' \cap Y$.

(g) List the members of set X that are not in set Y.

(h) List $X' \cap Y'$.

2. $\mathscr{E} = \{$natural numbers that are less than 30$\}$
$P = \{$prime numbers that are less than 30$\}$
$D = \{$odd numbers that are less than 30$\}$
$S = \{$multiples of 7 that are less than 30$\}$

(a) In which set or sets is the number 19?

(b) List the members of $P \cap D$.

(c) List the members of D that are not in S.

(d) List the members of $D' \cap S$.

(e) List $S \cup D$.

(f) List $(S \cup D)'$.

(g) List S'.

(h) List D'.

(i) List $S' \cap D'$.

3. Copy the diagram. Split the set into two parts using a single line which should divide the set in such a way that each part can be described (the line need not be straight). Write why you split the set in the way you did. Describe in words the two sets obtained by your *partition* line.

4. $\mathscr{E} = \{$triangles$\}$
$R = \{$right-angled triangles$\}$ $S = \{$scalene triangles$\}$
$Q = \{$equilateral triangles$\}$ $I = \{$isosceles triangles$\}$
Where possible, draw a sketch to show each of the following. If impossible, write 'IMPOSSIBLE'.

(a) $R \cap I$

(b) $S \cap Q$

(c) $R' \cap I$

(d) $I' \cap R$

(e) $S \cap R$

(f) $S' \cap R$

Exercise 14   Logic Problems   M

A **1.** 47 people were asked if they had carrots or peas for Sunday dinner. 13 people had only carrots. 18 people had only peas. 9 people had both. These numbers are shown in the incomplete Venn diagram, where $C = \{$people who had carrots$\}$ and $P = \{$people who had peas$\}$.

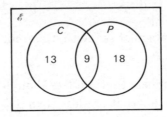

(*a*) How many altogether had carrots?
(*b*) How many had either carrots or peas or both?
(*c*) How many had neither?
(*d*) How many did not have peas?

2. Copy this Venn diagram.

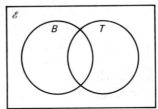

63 people were asked if they had travelled on a bus or a train during the past month. If $B = \{$people who travelled on a bus$\}$ and $T = \{$people who travelled on a train$\}$, complete the Venn diagram using the given information, then answer the questions. 38 people said they had travelled on a bus but not on a train, while 12 people said they had travelled on both a bus *and* a train. Altogether, 54 people had travelled on *either* a bus *or* a train *or* both.

(*a*) What was the total number of people who had travelled on a bus?
(*b*) What was the total number who had travelled on a train?
(*c*) How many had travelled on a train but not on a bus?
(*d*) How many had not travelled on a train?
(*e*) How many had neither travelled on a train nor on a bus?

14

B Draw Venn diagrams to help you to solve these problems (any letters may be used to label the sets):

1. In a survey, 82 people were asked whether they had a bath or a shower during last week. 37 had a bath but not a shower, 26 had a shower but not a bath, while 78 had either a bath or a shower or both.
   (a) How many had both a bath and a shower?
   (b) How many had neither a bath nor a shower?
   (c) How many altogether had a bath?

2. Yesterday, out of a number of people questioned, 14 had eaten an orange but not an apple, 5 had eaten both an orange and an apple, 48 had eaten either an apple or an orange, or both, while 17 had eaten neither an apple nor an orange:
   (a) What was the total number of people who had eaten an apple?
   (b) How many had eaten an apple but not an orange?
   (c) How many people had been questioned?

3. Out of a number of people questioned, 11 owned both a cat and a dog, 46 owned neither, 18 owned a dog but no cat, while 61 did not own a dog:
   (a) How many people were questioned?
   (b) How many did not own a cat?
   (c) How many owned either a cat or a dog or both?

4. 36 people were asked whether they could play a keyboard or a guitar. A total of 17 could play a keyboard, while 12 could play a keyboard but not a guitar. 19 could play either a keyboard or a guitar or both.
   (a) How many could play both a keyboard and a guitar?
   (b) How many could not play a guitar?
   (c) How many could play a guitar but not a keyboard?

5. Out of a number of people questioned, 41 had bacon for breakfast, 19 had bacon but no toast, 30 had toast but no bacon, while 6 had neither.
   (a) How many altogether had toast?
   (b) How many altogether did not have toast?
   (c) What was the total number of people questioned?

6. 72 people were asked whether they would like a chocolate or a caramel. 46 did not want a caramel, 19 greedily asked for both, while everyone wanted one or the other. How many did not want a chocolate?

7. In a survey, 32 people stated they collected records, while 56 said they collected tapes. 38 collected tapes but not records, while 51 did not collect records.
   (a) How many were questioned in the survey?
   (b) How many collected both records and tapes?
   (c) How many collected either records or tapes or both?

8. Some people were asked whether they drank fruit juice or milk at breakfast this morning. Altogether, 38 drank fruit juice, 63 drank either fruit juice or milk or both, 16 drank neither, while 35 drank fruit juice but not milk.
   (a) How many altogether did not drink fruit juice?
   (b) How many drank both?
   (c) How many altogether were questioned?

9. A teacher asked some pupils whether or not they had brought a protractor or a set square to school today. A total of 41 had brought a protractor, while a total of 23 had brought a set square. 8 had brought neither; 48 had brought either a protractor or a set square or both.
   (a) How many pupils were asked?
   (b) How many brought a set square but not a protractor?
   (c) How many did not bring a set square?

10. 107 pupils were asked how they had travelled to school this morning. 53 had travelled by bus only, 50 had not travelled on the bus, while 78 had travelled by either bus or car or both.
    (a) How many had not travelled by car?
    (b) How many had travelled by both car and bus?
    (c) How many had travelled by car but not by bus?
    (d) How many had travelled by neither bus nor car?

2 Number

Exercise 1　Rounding

1. Round to the nearest ten:
   (a) 39　　(b) 284　　(c) 5167　　(d) 82 375

2. Round to the nearest hundred:
   (a) 465　　(b) 5108　　(c) 23 490　　(d) 56 053

3. Round to the nearest thousand:
   (a) 8192　　(b) 7635　　(c) 12 506　　(d) 425 499

4. There were 24 879 people at a match:
   (a) Write the number in words.
   (b) Round the number correct to the nearest thousand.

5. 1348 people were at a concert. Write that number:
   (a) correct to the nearest ten,
   (b) correct to the nearest hundred.

6. Round to one significant figure:
   (a) 38　　(b) 765　　(c) 4490　　(d) 35 000

7. Altogether, 72 983 people attended an exhibition. Write that number correct to one significant figure.

8. The following numbers have been rounded correct to the nearest ten. For each one, find　(i) the smallest and (ii) the largest whole number it could have been before rounding:
   (a) 60　　(b) 240　　(c) 7810　　(d) 3400

9. The following numbers have been rounded correct to the nearest hundred. For each one, find　(i) the smallest and (ii) the largest whole number it could have been before rounding:
   (a) 700　　(b) 6200　　(c) 4800　　(d) 5000

10. The following numbers have been rounded correct to the nearest thousand. For each one, find (i) the smallest and (ii) the largest whole number it could have been before rounding:
    (a) 9000   (b) 14 000   (c) 75 000   (d) 90 000

11. If 470 people watched the play and that number had been rounded correct to the nearest ten:
    (a) What is the largest number it could have been before rounding?
    (b) What is the smallest number it could have been before rounding?

12. The area of a field was 15 200 m^2 correct to the nearest 100 m^2:
    (a) What is the largest area (as a whole number of square metres) it could have been before rounding?
    (b) What is the smallest area it could have been before rounding?

Exercise 2   Estimating

Throughout this exercise, work with one significant figure:

1. A motorist travelled 194 miles and averaged 39 m.p.h. Estimate the time taken.

2. There were 12 bottles in each box. Estimate the total number of bottles in 283 boxes.

3. Janine earned £5.15 an hour. Estimate her earnings for 27 h work.

4. A sales person drove the following distances each day: 113 km, 192 km, 218 km, 184 km and 189 km. Estimate the total distance travelled.

5. There were two cars. One car was priced at £9270 and the other at £6310. Estimate the difference in cost.

Calculations

Exercise 3

Copy the following and fill in the missing digits:

1.
```
    3 8 [?] 2
  + 2 [?] 4 [?]
  ─────────────
    [?] 5 2 1
```

2.
```
    7 0 6 5
  + [?][?][?][?]
  ─────────────
    9 4 2 3
```

3.
```
    [?] 1 8 9
    2 [?] 0 3
  + 1 6 5 [?]
  ─────────────
    8 5 [?] 0
```

4.
```
    7 [?][?] 2
  - [?] 3 4 [?]
  ─────────────
    2 6 7 7
```

5.
```
    8 1 3 4
  - [?][?][?][?]
  ─────────────
    6 7 5 8
```

6.
```
    [?] 8 0 [?]
  ×         9
  ─────────────
  [?] 4 [?][?] 3
```

7.
```
  [?][?][?][?]
  ×         7
  ─────────────
  5 9 0 2 4
```

8.
```
        2 5 3 8
  3 ) [?][?][?][?]
```

9.
```
        5 [?] 9
  5 ) [?] 7 4 [?]
```

Exercise 4

Answer these without using a calculator. Look for quick methods.

1. $9 + 18 + 11$

2. $35 + 29 + 15$

3. $78 + 39 - 28$

4. $54 - 39 + 6$

5. $783 + 389 + 217$

6. $471 - 297 + 129$

7. $846 + 372 - 146$

8. $542 - 185 - 142$

9. $3927 + 548 + 73$

10. $1039 - 265 + 261$

Exercise 5

Copy and complete:

1. $57 + 32 = \boxed{?} + 30$

2. $83 - 28 = \boxed{?} - 30$

3. $56 + 49 = 60 + \boxed{?}$

4. $72 + 56 = 70 + \boxed{?}$

5. $72 - 56 = 70 - \boxed{?}$

6. $91 - 43 = \boxed{?} - 40$

7. $61 + 89 = \boxed{?} + 90$

8. $67 - 38 = 70 - \boxed{?}$

9. $486 - 289 = \boxed{?} - 290$

10. $542 - 137 = \boxed{?} - 100$

11. $318 + 587 = 300 + \boxed{?}$

12. $847 + 975 = \boxed{?} + 1000$

13. $4019 - 2406 = 4000 - \boxed{?}$

14. $6183 + 5024 = \boxed{?} + 5000$

15. $2894 - 1457 = 2900 - \boxed{?}$

16. $1956 + 2316 = 2000 + \boxed{?}$

Exercise 6

e.g. Find: $5 + 6 + 7 + 8 + 9 + 10$

$$5 + 6 + 7 + 8 + 9 + 10$$
$$= (5 + 10) + (6 + 9) + (7 + 8)$$
$$= \quad 15 \quad + \quad 15 \quad + \quad 15$$
$$= \underline{\underline{45}}$$

Find:

1. $9 + 10 + 11 + 12 + 13 + 14 + 15 + 16$

2. $12 + 13 + 14 + 15 + 16 + 17 + 18 + 19 + 20$

3. $6 + 8 + 10 + 12 + 14 + 16$

4. the sum of the first 30 odd numbers

5. the sum of the numbers from 1 to 1000 inclusive

Exercise 7

Answer these:

A
1. $87 \div 3$
2. $145 \div 5$
3. $3843 \div 9$
4. $8964 \div 6$
5. $5712 \div 8$
6. $2863 \div 7$

20

B **1.** Three people shared 114 sweets equally amongst themselves. How many did each person receive?

2. Mrs Aspinall took four tablets each day. How many days would a supply of 252 tablets last?

3. Into how many rows could 324 chairs be placed, if nine chairs are put in each row?

4. A store had 558 eggs. How many boxes did they have if there were six eggs in each box?

5. 632 stamps were put into packets with eight stamps in each packet. How many packets would there be?

6. 504 sheets of paper were shared equally amongst seven people. How many did each person receive?

Darts

Brief rules (There are other versions.)

i Scoring starts at 301, and the total score at each turn is subtracted until zero is reached.

ii Players take it in turn to throw three darts.

iii To begin, a player must score a double.

iv Also, to end, a player must score a double.

v The bull's eye in the centre (the inner bull) scores 50 (double 25).

vi The narrow band around the bull's eye (the outer bull) scores 25.

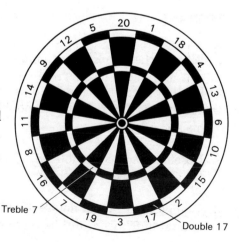

Treble 7

Double 17

A sample game showing scoring

1 John starts. He misses with his first dart and scores double 5 and 18 with his other darts.
(Score $= 10 + 18 = 28$. $301 - 28 = 273$.)

2 Jim scores double 20 and 5, which is 45, leaving 256.

3 John scores treble 20, 20 and 1, which is 81
($273 - 81 = 192$).

4 Jim scores 100 ($256 - 100 = 156$).

5 John scores 84.

6 Jim scores 79.

7 John scores 66 (42 needed to win).

8 Jim scores 38 (39 needed to win).

9 John scores 36.

10 Jim scores 7, 16 and then double 8 to win.

John	Jim
273	256
192	156
108	77
42	39
6	0

Exercise 8   **M**

1. What is the highest score a player can obtain with a single dart?

2. If Allan needs to score 58 to win using two darts and he scores 20 with his first dart, which double does he need to obtain with his second dart?

3. Rosemary scored double 18, 13 and treble 19 with three darts. What total score was that?

4. Liam scored 14 and double 17. If with his third dart he reached a total of 87, what did he score with his third dart?

5. Copy and complete the following table:

	Score from first dart	Score from second dart	Score from third dart	Total
(a)	19	double 8	9	?
(b)	double 7	?	14	39
(c)	double 9	treble 12	18	?
(d)	?	double 11	treble 5	54
(e)	double 13	17	?	69
(f)	treble 20	bull's eye	treble 5	?
(g)	?	double 15	16	84
(h)	double 19	20	?	85
(i)	treble 18	?	double 17	109
(j)	treble 19	treble 20	?	171

6. Mike scored double ?, treble ? and treble 20 with three darts. His total score was 119. List all possible scores for his first two darts.

7. Linda prefers to aim for the top part of a dart-board. She also finds the 6 sector, 11 sector and inner and outer bulls difficult. List eight possible ways for Linda to score a total of 40 using exactly two darts, if both darts score and she only scores in her preferred sectors.

8. Emyr requires 36 with three darts (all darts should score). He prefers to aim for the left-hand side of a dart-board. He also prefers the 20 sector, but not the 3 sector. List as many ways as you can for Emyr to score a total of 36, if he only scores in his preferred sectors and if he scores *exactly* one double.

23

Exercise 9

1. I have a piece of string that is 964 mm long. If I cut it into two pieces so that one piece is 246 mm shorter than the other, how long is each piece?

2. The sum of three consecutive even numbers is 888. Find them.

3. The perimeter of a rectangular piece of card is 1260 mm. Find its dimensions, if its length is twice its breadth.

4. In a certain league, there are 18 teams. If each team plays every other team twice, once at home and once away, how many games will be played altogether?

5. How much per month is £384 per week? (Note that you do not simply multiply by 4.)

6. Write the units digit that is in the answer to the calculation 437×28.

7. The product of two consecutive numbers is 1190. Find them.

8. The product of two consecutive odd numbers is 2303. Find them.

9. £156 is shared between Helen and Ann so that Ann gets three times as much as Helen. How much does Ann get?

10. $87 \times 5\blacksquare = 4698$. Unfortunately, one digit is smudged. What must it be?

11. 49 cm more string will give me a length that is 26 cm shorter than 94 cm. How long is the string that I have?

12. 9184 stamps are put into packets of 48:
    (a) How many packets will there be?
    (b) How many stamps will be left over?

13. Is 47×59 greater than or less than 3000?

14. A boy, when asked to multiply 57 by 25, divided 5700 by 4 and obtained the correct answer. Give a reason why.

15. Ian is two places in front of the last boy and four places behind Paul, who is fifth. How many are there altogether in the queue?

These are *difference tables.*
Try to work out how they have
been made.

```
                                        1
                                          4
                                        5       6
                                          10        3
                                        15      9
                                          19        3
                                        34      12
                                          31        3
1     5     15     34     65     111     65      15
   4     10     19     31     46                46
     6     9     12     15              111
        3     3     3
```

Make difference tables for the following sequences (already started).

1. 6   9   13   22   40   71   119   188

```
      3    [?]    [?]    18    [?]    [?]    [?]
        1    [?]    [?]    13    [?]    [?]
          [?]   [?]   [?]   [?]   [?]
```

2.
```
          8
            1
          9       4
            5       1
          14      5      [?]
             10      [?]
          24      7      [?]
             [?]     [?]
          41      [?]     [?]
             27      [?]
          68      [?]     [?]
             [?]      5
          109     [?]     [?]
             [?]     [?]
          169     [?]     [?]
             85      [?]
          254     [?]
             [?]
          371
```

3.

```
1
   1
2      ?
    ?     ?
4      2      1
    ?     ?     ?
8      ?     ?     ?
    ?     4     2     ?
16     ?     ?     ?
    ?     ?     ?     ?
32     ?     ?     ?
   32     ?     ?     ?
64     ?     ?     8
    ?     ?     ?     ?
128     ?     ?     ?
    ?     ?     ?
256     ?     ?
    ?     ?
512     ?
    ?
1024
```

Exercise 11   Russian Multiplication

e.g.   44 × 29

Write the two numbers side by side.
Divide one of the numbers by 2 and if
there is a remainder, ignore it. (Note
that 44 ÷ 2 = 22). Write the answer
below the number divided. Divide this
answer by 2 ignoring any remainder
(22 ÷ 2 = 11). Continue dividing by
2 and forming a column of numbers
until 1 is reached.

~~44~~	~~29~~
~~22~~	~~58~~
11	116
5	232
~~2~~	~~464~~
1	928
	1276

(*Note* $11 \div 2 = 5$ since the remainder is ignored, also $5 \div 2 = 2$
        and $2 \div 2 = 1$)

Multiply the other number by 2. Repeat and write each answer next
to the answers in the other column. Stop when you write a number
alongside the 1.

Cross out each pair of numbers where there is an even number in the
first column that was worked out.

Add the numbers that remain in the second column to be worked out.
(In the example, $116 + 232 + 928 = 1276$)

The answer obtained is the product.
(So, $44 \times 29 = 1276$)

Work out the following using the method above:

1. 34×48 **4.** 51×49

2. 52×33 **5.** 84×16

3. 64×37 **6.** 63×28

Exercise 12   Number Patterns   M

1. (*a*) Find the next number in the sequence:

$$100, \ 120, \ 138, \ 154, \ 168, \ \boxed{?}$$

(*b*) Copy and complete the given calculations (try to find a
quick method).

$$4 \times 25 = 100$$
$$5 \times 24 = 120$$
$$6 \times 23 = \boxed{?}$$
$$7 \times 22 = \boxed{?}$$
$$8 \times 21 = \boxed{?}$$
$$9 \times 20 = 180$$
$$10 \times 19 = \boxed{?}$$
$$11 \times 18 = \boxed{?}$$
$$12 \times 17 = \boxed{?}$$
$$13 \times 16 = \boxed{?}$$
$$14 \times 15 = \boxed{?}$$

2. Copy and complete the given calculations (try to find a quick method).

$$20 \times 20 = 400$$
$$19 \times 21 = \boxed{?}$$
$$18 \times 22 = \boxed{?}$$
$$17 \times 23 = \boxed{?}$$
$$16 \times 24 = \boxed{?}$$
$$15 \times 25 = \boxed{?}$$
$$14 \times 26 = \boxed{?}$$
$$13 \times 27 = \boxed{?}$$
$$12 \times 28 = \boxed{?}$$
$$11 \times 29 = \boxed{?}$$
$$10 \times 30 = 300$$
$$9 \times 31 = \boxed{?}$$
$$8 \times 32 = \boxed{?}$$
$$7 \times 33 = \boxed{?}$$
$$6 \times 34 = \boxed{?}$$

3. Make up your own list of products where one number increases while the other decreases. Try to find a pattern in your answers.

Exercise 13

For each of the following, state, whether it is 'ALWAYS TRUE', 'SOMETIMES TRUE' or 'NEVER TRUE':

1. The sum of two even numbers is even.

2. The sum of two odd numbers is odd.

3. The product of two even numbers is even.

4. The product of two odd numbers is odd.

5. The sum of two prime numbers is prime.

6. The product of two prime numbers is prime.

7. The product of two prime numbers is odd.

8. The product of an even and an odd number is even.

9. The factors of an odd number are odd.

10. The factors of an even number are even.

11. The sum of two prime numbers is even.

12. A number having no even factors must be odd.

Exercise 14

Try to find all possible three-digit numbers where the digits total 12 and which divide exactly by 12.

e.g. 732 is one such number. The sum of the digits is $7 + 3 + 2 = 12$ and 732 is exactly divisible by 12.

Exercise 15   M

In the following football matches, 3 points are awarded for a win, 1 for a draw and 0 for losing.

1. Brill United played 30 games, drew 8 of them and gained 65 points. How many games did they lose?

2. Rotten Rovers won only 6 matches after playing 24. If they gained 25 points altogether, how many games did they lose?

3. Copy and complete the following table:

	Number of games played	Number of wins	Number of draws	Number of games lost	Total points
(a)	39	?	13	?	58
(b)	?	17	?	8	57
(c)	?	?	7	12	34
(d)	42	?	?	7	81

Exercise 16

1. In certain league football matches, 3 points are awarded for a win, 1 for a draw, and 0 for losing:
   (a) If Clever United played 22 games and obtained 48 points having lost only 4 of those games, how many games did they win?
   (b) Brilliant Rovers played 41 matches and lost 8 of them. If their points totalled 79, how many of their matches were draws? How many did they win?
   (c) Pathetic City, after playing 38 matches, had lost 15 of them and gained 41 points. How many games did they win?
   (d) After playing 18 games, Midville Town had a total of 31 points. List all the possible ways that Midville could do this (*i.e.* list all possible wins, draws and losses).

2. In a Rugby league match, Rovers scored a total of 19 points. If they took only one penalty, how many tries and how many conversions did they have in that match? (A try = 3 points, a conversion = 2 points, a penalty = 2 points.)

   Note There must be the same number of (or more) tries than conversions in a game.

3. In Rugby union, a try is worth 4 points, a penalty is worth 3 points, while a conversion is worth 2 points. Again, there must be the same number of (or more) tries than conversions in a game. If the Grasshoppers obtained 26 points in a particular game, list all the possible ways they could do so.

4. Park obtained 22 points in a Rugby union match. List all the possible ways in which they could get such a score.

Exercise 17 Calculator Investigations

e.g.

A 1. Select any three digits (all different).   4, 8, 0

2. Enter on your calculator the biggest three-digit number you can make with your selected digits.   840

3. Subtract the smallest number you can make. $\frac{-\ 048}{792}$

4. Note the three digits in the answer; clear the display, then enter the largest number you can make with the digits obtained in that answer.   972

5. Subtract the smallest number you can make with these three digits. $\frac{-\ 279}{693}$

6. Continue doing this (i.e. repeat steps 4 and 5) until you keep obtaining the same three-digit number. $\frac{963}{-\ 369}$

7. What is the final three-digit number obtained?   etc.

8. Repeat the steps using different three-digit numbers.
    Note   Write the answer obtained at each stage. Watch how the first (or last) digits change in successive answers. Add the digits.

9. Write what you notice.

B **1.** Enter on your calculator the biggest four-digit number you can make using any four digits (not all the same).

2. Subtract the smallest number you can make using the same four digits.

3. Re-arrange the four digits in your answer to form the biggest possible number using all four digits. Enter this number into the calculator after clearing the display.

4. Now subtract the smallest number that can be made using the same four digits.

5. Repeat steps 3 and 4 over and over again until you repeatedly obtain the same four-digit answer.

e.g.

$$9521$$
$$\underline{-1259}$$
$$8262$$

$$8622$$

$$\underline{-2268}$$
$$6354$$

$$6543$$
$$\underline{-3456}$$
$$3087$$

$$8730$$
$$-0378$$

etc.

6. What is the final four-digit number that you repeatedly obtain?

7. Try all the steps above again using different digits (still use four digits).

C At each stage of your answers to part B:
1. Find the sum of the digits.

2. Add the first and last digits.

3. Add the middle two digits.

4. Look for patterns.

5. Try to find four digits that do not give the patterns that are usually obtained.

6. Write about your findings.

D **1.** Test five-digit and six-digit numbers as in parts A and B.

2. In each case, do you eventually obtain a certain answer whatever the starting digits?

3. Note your answers at each stage and look for patterns.

4. Write about your findings.

3 Symmetry

Bilateral Symmetry

Exercise 1 ▬▬▬▬▬▬▬▬▬▬▬▬▬ **M**

1. For each shape, write the number of lines of bilateral symmetry (the answer may be 'NONE'):

(a)

(b)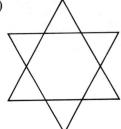

(c)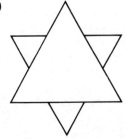

(d)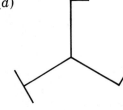

(e)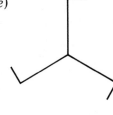

(f)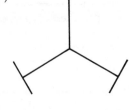

2. Copy these shapes. On your copies, draw the line (or lines) of bilateral symmetry.

(a)

(b)

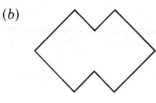

3. Copy the given shape. Complete it so that the broken line is a line of bilateral symmetry.

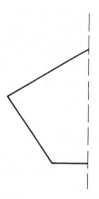

4. Copy the given drawing. Complete it so that the broken lines are lines of symmetry.

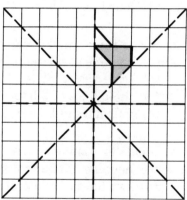

5. A symmetrical design for the handles of pieces of cutlery is shown. Design your own symmetrical pattern that is suitable for a piece of cutlery.

Throughout this exercise, if an answer does not exist, write 'IMPOSSIBLE'. Draw each part of each answer on a separate grid.

A Using 5 by 5 square grids as shown:

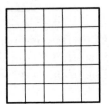

  1. Shade one small square so that the whole grid has exactly:
  - (*a*) one line of bilateral symmetry,
  - (*b*) two lines of bilateral symmetry,
  - (*c*) three lines of bilateral symmetry,
  - (*d*) four lines of bilateral symmetry.

  2. Shade two small squares so that the whole grid has exactly:
  - (*a*) one line of bilateral symmetry,
  - (*b*) two lines of bilateral symmetry,
  - (*c*) three lines of bilateral symmetry,
  - (*d*) four lines of bilateral symmetry.

  3. Shade three small squares so that the whole grid has exactly:
  - (*a*) one line of bilateral symmetry,
  - (*b*) two lines of bilateral symmetry,
  - (*c*) three lines of bilateral symmetry,
  - (*d*) four lines of bilateral symmetry.

  4. Shade four small squares so that the whole grid has exactly:
  - (*a*) one line of bilateral symmetry,
  - (*b*) two lines of bilateral symmetry,
  - (*c*) three lines of bilateral symmetry,
  - (*d*) four lines of bilateral symmetry.

B Answer part A again, but this time use 4 by 4 grids of squares (as shown).

Rotational Symmetry

This is sometimes referred to as *radial symmetry*.

Exercise 3   To Make a Windmill

1. Cut out a square from a piece of paper (about 15 cm square).

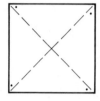

Fig. 1

2. Draw the two diagonals.

3. Cut along the diagonals from each vertex. Stop when you are about 15 mm from the centre of the square (Fig. 1).

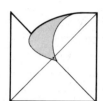

Fig. 2

4. Put pin-pricks through the paper as shown in Fig. 1.

Fig. 3

5. Fold the four parts as shown in Fig. 2 and Fig. 3 but *do not crease* the paper. These are the windmill's sails.

6. Pin, or nail the sails to a stick. If you put a small bead between the stick and the sails, the sails will turn more easily.

The windmill's sails have *rotational symmetry*. A shape has rotational symmetry if it can be rotated to a new position to fit exactly on top of itself.

When a shape is rotated, the number of times it fits exactly on top of itself is called the *order of rotational symmetry*. The windmill in Exercise 3 has rotational symmetry of order 4.

37

1. Write the order of rotational symmetry of each of these shapes:

(a)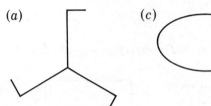

(c)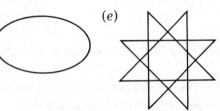

(e)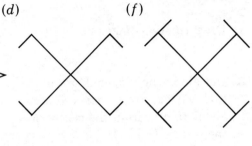

(b)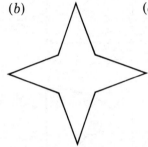

(d)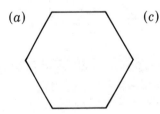

(f)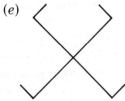

2. What is the order of rotational symmetry of:
   (a) a rectangle?
   (b) a square?
   (c) a parallelogram?
   (d) a rhombus?
   (e) a kite?
   (f) a regular octagon?

3. Copy each shape. If it has rotational symmetry of order greater than 1, mark on your copy its centre of rotation. Use a dot.

(a)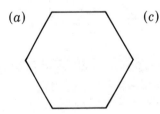

(c)

(e)

(b)

(d)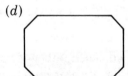

(f)

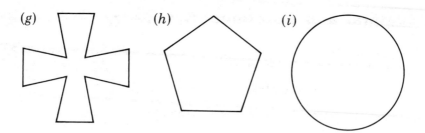

(g) (h) (i)

Exercise 5

Using this shape as many times as required, draw diagrams that have the following orders of rotational symmetry:

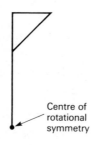

Centre of
rotational
symmetry

1. order 2 **3.** order 4 **5.** order 6

2. order 3 **4.** order 5 **6.** order 8

Exercise 6

A square looks the same if it is rotated through 90°, 180° or 270°.

1. Draw another shape that looks the same when it is rotated through 90°.

2. Draw a shape that looks the same when it is rotated through 60°.

3. Draw a shape that looks the same when it is rotated through 120°.

Bilateral and Rotational Symmetry

Exercise 7 — **M**

$\mathcal{E} = \{$letters of the alphabet written in capitals$\}$

(Use the letters in Appendix 1, p. 433.)

$B = \{$letters with bilateral symmetry$\}$
$R = \{$letters with rotational symmetry$\}$

Draw a Venn diagram as shown
(but make it larger than this one).
Write each letter of the alphabet
in the correct part of your diagram.

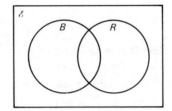

Exercise 8

1. 'Any plane shape with more than one axis of bilateral symmetry must have rotational symmetry.'

   Check the statement above. Try to find out whether it is true or false.

2. 'Any plane shape that has rotational symmetry must also have bilateral symmetry.'

   Try to find out whether the statement above is true or false.

Exercise 9

1. Cut an equilateral triangle out of paper.

2. Mark the centre of rotational symmetry on your triangle.

3. On the same triangle, draw in its three axes of bilateral symmetry. (You can find them by folding the triangle.)

4. What do you notice about your answers to questions 2 and 3?

5. (a) If C is the centre of rotational symmetry, how far is C from each of the three vertices?
   (b) What can you say about these three lengths?

6. (*a*) How far is C from each of the three sides?

(*b*) What can you say about these three lengths?

7. Compare the answers to questions 5(*a*) and 6(*a*).
Write what you notice.

Exercise 10 ━━━━━━━━━━━━━━━━━━━━━━━━━━━━ **M**

1. Copy and complete the following table:

2. Write what you notice.

3. A polygon has 24 sides. List the possible orders of rotational symmetry.

Number of sides of polygon	Possible orders of rotational symmetry
3	1, 3.
4	1, 2, 4.
5	?
6	?
7	?
8	?
9	?
10	?
11	?
12	?
13	?
14	?
15	?
16	?

4 Fractions

Exercise 1   Miscellaneous Questions

1. Draw a circle with a radius that is twice as big as the one shown below. Divide your circle into 12 equal parts. Shade $\frac{2}{3}$ of your circle.

   How many twelfths are there in $\frac{2}{3}$?

2. Draw a straight line 100 mm in length. Divide your line into eighths.

3. Simplify these fractions:

   (a) $\dfrac{14}{21}$ (b) $\dfrac{32}{40}$ (c) $\dfrac{90}{108}$ (d) $\dfrac{39}{91}$

4. Write as improper fractions:

   (a) $1\frac{2}{3}$ (b) $5\frac{1}{6}$ (c) $4\frac{7}{10}$ (d) $2\frac{11}{12}$

5. Write as mixed numbers:

   (a) $\dfrac{15}{4}$ (b) $\dfrac{36}{5}$ (c) $\dfrac{37}{8}$ (d) $\dfrac{59}{16}$

6. Copy each pair of fractions but replace each question mark by the symbol $<$ or $>$ to make the statement correct:

   (a) $\dfrac{1}{7}\ \boxed{?}\ \dfrac{1}{8}$ (c) $\dfrac{3}{5}\ \boxed{?}\ \dfrac{5}{9}$

   (b) $\dfrac{5}{6}\ \boxed{?}\ \dfrac{7}{8}$ (d) $\dfrac{11}{16}\ \boxed{?}\ \dfrac{17}{25}$

Calculations with Fractions

Exercise 2

Carry out the following calculations:

A
1. $\dfrac{2}{3} + \dfrac{1}{4}$
2. $\dfrac{4}{5} + \dfrac{1}{2}$
3. $\dfrac{5}{6} + \dfrac{3}{4}$
4. $\dfrac{3}{8} + \dfrac{2}{3}$
5. $\dfrac{7}{8} + \dfrac{9}{10}$

6. $\dfrac{4}{5} - \dfrac{3}{10}$
7. $\dfrac{2}{3} - \dfrac{1}{2}$
8. $\dfrac{5}{6} - \dfrac{5}{8}$
9. $\dfrac{9}{10} - \dfrac{1}{4}$
10. $\dfrac{5}{6} - \dfrac{3}{5}$

11. $\dfrac{4}{5} \times \dfrac{5}{8}$
12. $\dfrac{9}{10} \times \dfrac{2}{3}$
13. $\dfrac{3}{4} \times \dfrac{5}{6}$
14. $\dfrac{8}{9} \times \dfrac{3}{10}$
15. $\dfrac{2}{5} \times \dfrac{15}{16}$

16. $\dfrac{9}{16} \div \dfrac{3}{4}$
17. $\dfrac{9}{10} \div \dfrac{3}{5}$
18. $\dfrac{15}{16} \div \dfrac{5}{8}$
19. $\dfrac{5}{12} \div \dfrac{2}{3}$
20. $\dfrac{7}{9} \div \dfrac{2}{3}$

B
1. $3\frac{3}{4} + 2\frac{2}{3}$
2. $5\frac{3}{5} + 1\frac{5}{6}$
3. $2\frac{5}{8} + 3\frac{5}{6}$
4. $7\frac{7}{12} + 4\frac{7}{16}$
5. $6\frac{3}{4} + 8\frac{5}{9}$

6. $7\frac{3}{8} - 2\frac{1}{5}$
7. $6\frac{7}{10} - 4\frac{1}{4}$
8. $5\frac{7}{12} - 2\frac{3}{4}$
9. $9\frac{1}{6} - 5\frac{7}{10}$
10. $3\frac{5}{12} - 2\frac{13}{15}$

11. $\frac{9}{16} \times \frac{20}{27}$
12. $6\frac{3}{4} \times \frac{8}{15}$
13. $5\frac{3}{5} \times 3\frac{1}{8}$
14. $3\frac{3}{4} \times 2\frac{2}{5}$
15. $4\frac{7}{12} \times 1\frac{9}{15}$

16. $\frac{6}{25} \div \frac{9}{10}$
17. $\frac{15}{16} \div \frac{5}{12}$
18. $4\frac{2}{5} \div \frac{8}{15}$
19. $2\frac{9}{20} \div 2\frac{1}{10}$
20. $2\frac{1}{12} \div 4\frac{3}{8}$

C
1. $3\frac{5}{8} + 2\frac{1}{6} - 1\frac{3}{4}$
2. $5\frac{3}{10} - 4\frac{7}{12} + 2\frac{5}{8}$
3. $1\frac{1}{8} \times 4\frac{2}{3} + 3\frac{3}{5}$
4. $1\frac{1}{8} \times (4\frac{2}{3} + 3\frac{3}{5})$
5. $2\frac{2}{3} \times (5\frac{5}{8} - 3\frac{3}{10})$
6. $7\frac{3}{8} + 3\frac{1}{8} \times 2\frac{14}{15}$

7. $8\frac{1}{4} - 2\frac{4}{7} \times 2\frac{1}{10}$
8. $2\frac{11}{12} \times 2\frac{7}{10} \times 1\frac{3}{7}$
9. $1\frac{1}{15} \div 1\frac{3}{5} + 1\frac{3}{4}$
10. $2\frac{7}{10} \times 1\frac{17}{18} \div 1\frac{5}{14}$
11. $1\frac{5}{9} \div 1\frac{1}{7} \div 9\frac{1}{3}$
12. $5\frac{5}{8} \div 2\frac{6}{7} \times 5\frac{1}{3}$

Calculations involving vulgar fractions can be carried out on a calculator. If your calculator has a fraction key, normally marked $\boxed{a\frac{b}{c}}$, then such calculations are easy. If your calculator does not have a fraction key, then a method in which vulgar fractions are changed to decimals can be used.

Here are two methods of changing a vulgar fraction to a decimal:

e.g. 1 Change $5\frac{3}{4}$ to a decimal.

Method 1 $\boxed{5}\ \boxed{+}\ \boxed{3}\ \boxed{\div}\ \boxed{4}\ \boxed{=}$

Method 2 $\boxed{3}\ \boxed{\div}\ \boxed{4}\ \boxed{+}\ \boxed{5}\ \boxed{=}$

Check both methods. On some calculators method 1 will not work. (The answer should be 5.75.)

e.g. 2 Consider the calculation $5\frac{3}{4}-2\frac{4}{5}$. Here are four methods of working this out. Note that some of these methods may not work on some calculators. Try them. You should obtain the answer 2.95 $(2\frac{19}{20})$.

Method 1

$\boxed{4}\ \boxed{\div}\ \boxed{5}\ \boxed{+}\ \boxed{2}\ \boxed{\text{Min}}^{*}\ \boxed{3}\ \boxed{\div}\ \boxed{4}\ \boxed{+}\ \boxed{5}\ \boxed{-}\ \boxed{\text{MR}}\ \boxed{=}$

Method 2 $\boxed{3}\ \boxed{\div}\ \boxed{4}\ \boxed{+}\ \boxed{5}\ \boxed{-}\ \boxed{(}\ \boxed{4}\ \boxed{\div}\ \boxed{5}\ \boxed{+}\ \boxed{2}\ \boxed{)}\ \boxed{=}$

Method 3 $\boxed{5}\ \boxed{+}\ \boxed{3}\ \boxed{\div}\ \boxed{4}\ \boxed{-}\ \boxed{(}\ \boxed{2}\ \boxed{+}\ \boxed{4}\ \boxed{\div}\ \boxed{5}\ \boxed{)}\ \boxed{=}$

Method 4 $\boxed{5}\ \boxed{+}\ \boxed{3}\ \boxed{\div}\ \boxed{4}\ \boxed{-}\ \boxed{2}\ \boxed{-}\ \boxed{4}\ \boxed{\div}\ \boxed{5}\ \boxed{=}$

Exercise 3

Use a calculator to check your answers to Exercise 2.

Exercise 4   Magic Squares   **M**

Copy and complete these magic squares:

1.

$2\frac{7}{8}$		
$2\frac{1}{4}$		
$2\frac{3}{8}$	$2\frac{1}{8}$	

2.

$\frac{2}{3}$		
$1\frac{1}{3}$	$\frac{1}{6}$	1

3.

		$2\frac{7}{10}$
3	$1\frac{4}{5}$	
$\frac{9}{10}$		

*See Appendix 3, p. 437.

44

4.

	$\frac{7}{8}$	
$4\frac{3}{8}$	$6\frac{1}{8}$	
$7\frac{7}{8}$		

5.

$2\frac{1}{4}$	$1\frac{4}{5}$	
	$2\frac{7}{10}$	
	$3\frac{3}{5}$	

6.

		$4\frac{1}{6}$
	$3\frac{23}{24}$	$4\frac{3}{8}$
		$3\frac{1}{3}$

History of Fractions

Hieroglyphic notation from the Rhind Papyrus (1580 BC):

When fractions were first used, they were not written in the way we write them. The Egyptians, as shown in the Rhind Papyrus (about 1580 BC), wrote their fractions with 1 in the numerator (called *unit fractions*).

The fraction $\frac{1}{7}$ was written as ⟨glyph⟩. The only fractions that were not written in this way were $\frac{1}{2}$ and $\frac{2}{3}$.

$\frac{1}{2}$ was written as ⟨glyph⟩ or ⟨glyph⟩ and $\frac{2}{3}$ as ⟨glyph⟩.

If we wrote our fractions as unit fractions, we could write $\frac{2}{7}$ as $\frac{1}{4} + \frac{1}{28}$ (since $\frac{2}{7} = \frac{8}{28} = \frac{7}{28} + \frac{1}{28} = \frac{1}{4} + \frac{1}{28}$).

The unit fractions to be used were given in a table. The table had been produced by a scribe. He followed certain rules in producing the table. For example, consider the fraction $\frac{2}{15}$.

45

$\frac{1}{15} + \frac{1}{15}$ was not acceptable since fractions were repeated.

$\frac{1}{9} + \frac{1}{45}$ was not acceptable since the denominators were odd numbers. (Even numbers were preferred.)

$\frac{1}{10} + \frac{1}{30}$ was acceptable (written as ⌢ ⌢⌢⌢).

$\frac{1}{8} + \frac{1}{120}$ was not acceptable ($\frac{1}{8}$ was better than $\frac{1}{10}$ but $\frac{1}{120}$ was too big).

$\frac{1}{12} + \frac{1}{20}$ was a possibility, but $\frac{1}{10} + \frac{1}{30}$ was preferred.

Exercise 5

Write these fractions as the sum of different unit fractions:

e.g. $\frac{5}{9} = \frac{1}{2} + \frac{1}{18}$
(This is a better answer than $\frac{1}{3} + \frac{1}{6} + \frac{1}{18}$ since fewer fractions are used.)

1. $\frac{5}{16}$ **4.** $\frac{11}{30}$ **7.** $\frac{2}{9}$ **10.** $\frac{2}{7}$

2. $\frac{4}{15}$ **5.** $\frac{7}{24}$ **8.** $\frac{5}{18}$ **11.** $\frac{4}{5}$

3. $\frac{7}{10}$ **6.** $\frac{3}{5}$ **9.** $\frac{4}{11}$ **12.** $\frac{3}{7}$

Exercise 6   Fractions of Quantities

A   **1.** A carton contained 600 mℓ of milk. If I drank $\frac{3}{4}$ of the milk, how much did I drink?

    2. Find:
      (a) $\frac{4}{7}$ of 588   (b) $\frac{3}{7}$ of 588

    3. $\frac{3}{8}$ of 56 pupils lived within 1 mile of school. How many pupils was that?

    4. Mrs Savoy travelled $\frac{5}{6}$ of a journey of 192 km by car. How far was that?

    5. Andy spent $\frac{2}{5}$ of £18.40. How much did he spend?

6. $\frac{3}{4}$ of a fencing post is above ground. If the pole is 240 cm long, what length is under the ground?

7. $\frac{7}{10}$ of the 30 pupils were girls. How many were boys?

8. Nichola gave away $\frac{5}{12}$ of 132 sweets. How many did she have left?

B 1. 39 out of 52 pupils stay at school for lunch. What fraction is this?

2. If 120 pupils out of 800 pupils travel to school on their bicycle, what fraction is this?

3. Brynley ate 16 sweets out of a packet of 30. What fraction did he eat?

4. Out of a total of 20 h, $2\frac{1}{2}$ h was spent doing maths. What fraction of the total time was spent on maths?

5. Avril spent £2.40 out of £3.20. What fraction of the £3.20 did she spend?

6. What fraction of £4.56 is £1.71?

7. Mr Spender spent £135 out of £243. What fraction of his money did he have left?

8. Out of 315 kg of sand, 168 kg were used. What fraction is that?

Exercise 7   Miscellaneous Problems

1. Which is the most money, $\frac{3}{8}$ of £6.32 or $\frac{5}{12}$ of £5.64?

2. How many lengths of material, each $1\frac{3}{5}$ yd long, can be cut from 24 yd of material?

3. $\frac{3}{5}$ of a class were boys. If there were 12 girls in the class, how many boys were there?

4. Ray set out to walk $8\frac{1}{2}$ miles. After walking $3\frac{4}{5}$ miles, how much further did he have to walk?

5. There were 28 males at the swimming baths. If $\frac{5}{12}$ of those at the baths were female, how many females were there?

6. Add $\frac{3}{8}$ of 76 to $\frac{5}{8}$ of 76.

7. A boy ate $\frac{1}{4}$ of a cake, then gave away $\frac{5}{6}$ of the remainder. What fraction of the whole cake was left?

8. (a) If I spend $\frac{7}{12}$ of my money, what fraction have I left?
(b) If I have £2.35 left, how much did I spend?

9. A boy withdrew $\frac{1}{3}$ of the money in his savings account, then $\frac{3}{4}$ of what was left. What fraction of his savings remained in his account?

10. A girl gave away $\frac{2}{9}$ of her sweets to a friend. If she then gave $\frac{3}{4}$ of the remainder to her sister and had 7 left, how many sweets did she give to her friend?

11. In a certain school, Class 2A had 12 boys in it, and $\frac{4}{7}$ of the class were girls. Class 2B had $1\frac{1}{4}$ times as many pupils as Class 2A. If $\frac{3}{5}$ of class 2B were boys, how many girls were there in Class 2B?

12. $\frac{1}{16}$ of a mixed class containing 14 boys was absent on Monday. On Tuesday, there was full attendance because the two absentees returned to school. How many girls are there in the class?

Fractions and Formulae

Exercise 8

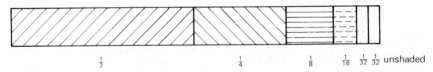

$$\frac{1}{2} \qquad \frac{1}{4} \qquad \frac{1}{8} \quad \frac{1}{16} \; \frac{1}{32} \; \frac{1}{32} \text{ unshaded}$$

The diagram above shows that:

$$\frac{1}{2} + \frac{1}{4} + \frac{1}{8} + \frac{1}{16} + \frac{1}{32} = 1 - \frac{1}{32} = \frac{32-1}{32} = \frac{31}{32}$$

We can write: $\dfrac{1}{2} + \dfrac{1}{4} + \ldots + \dfrac{1}{n} = 1 - \dfrac{1}{n} = \dfrac{n-1}{n}$

1. Test the formula for:
(a) $n = 8$ (b) $n = 32$ (c) $n = 128$ (d) $n = 512$

2. Use the formula to find:

$$\frac{1}{2} + \frac{1}{4} + \frac{1}{8} + \frac{1}{16} + \frac{1}{32} + \frac{1}{64} + \frac{1}{128} + \frac{1}{256} + \frac{1}{512} + \frac{1}{1024}$$

Exercise 9

A Here is a formula that will help you to subtract two fractions:

$$\frac{k}{l} - \frac{m}{n} = \frac{(kn - lm)}{ln}$$

1. Test the formula for these questions:

(a) $\dfrac{3}{4} - \dfrac{2}{5}$ (b) $\dfrac{4}{5} - \dfrac{1}{4}$ (c) $\dfrac{7}{10} - \dfrac{3}{8}$ (d) $\dfrac{11}{12} - \dfrac{5}{7}$

2. Test the formula using fractions of your own choice.

B Try to find a formula that will help you to add two fractions.

C The formula $\dfrac{k}{l} \div \dfrac{m}{n} = \dfrac{kn}{lm}$ helps you to divide fractions.

1. Test the formula for these questions:

(a) $\dfrac{9}{10} \div \dfrac{3}{5}$ (b) $\dfrac{5}{6} \div \dfrac{2}{3}$ (c) $\dfrac{3}{4} \div \dfrac{9}{16}$ (d) $\dfrac{5}{8} \div \dfrac{5}{12}$

2. Test the formula using fractions of your own choice.

D Try to find a formula that will help you to multiply two fractions.

E Try to use a calculator to add, subtract, multiply and divide fractions. Use the formulae. Choose your own fractions.

5 Angles, Parallels and Constructions

Miscellaneous Questions on Angles

Exercise 1

1. Write whether each angle is an acute angle, obtuse angle, reflex angle or a right-angle:

(a)

(d)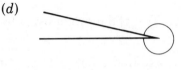

(b)

(e)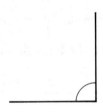

(c)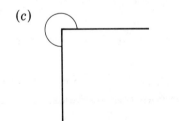

(f)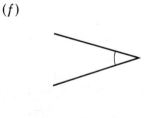

2. *Estimate* the number of degrees in each of the angles given in question 1.

3. How many degrees are there in:
   (a) $\frac{5}{8}$ turn?   (b) $\frac{4}{5}$ turn?   (c) 3 turns?

4. Calculate the angles that are labelled with Greek letters:

(a)

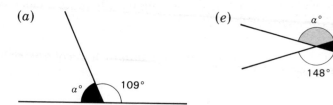

(e)

(b)

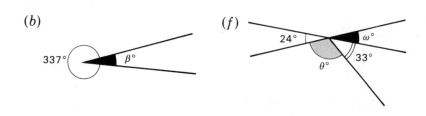

(f)

(c)

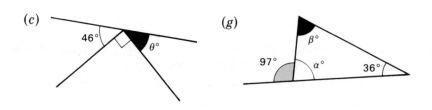

(g)

(d)

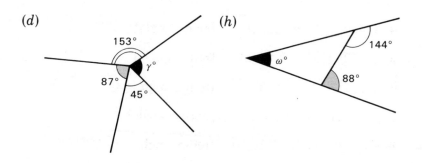

(h)

51

5. What fraction of a turn is $75°$?

6. How much time has passed when the hour hand of a clock has turned through $210°$?

7. How much time has passed when the minute hand of a clock has turned through $48°$?

8. If you point NW then turn anticlockwise to face due east, through how many degrees will you have turned?

Exercise 2

Draw a pair of axes where the
x-values range from $^-10$ to $^+10$
(that is, $^-10 \leqslant x \leqslant 10$) and the
y-values range from $^-8$ to $^+8$
(that is, $^-8 \leqslant y \leqslant 8$).

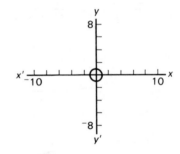

For each question, plot and join the points in the given order. Measure each angle formed (the type of angle is stated in square brackets). Use the same pair of axes for all the questions.

1. $(5, 7)$ $(8, 2)$ $(9, 7)$ [acute angle]

2. $(0, 8)$ $(4, 5)$ $(4, ^-1)$ [obtuse angle]

3. $(4, ^-7)$ $(8, ^-4)$ $(7, 0)$ [reflex angle]

4. $(^-4, 0)$ $(^-6, 7)$ $(^-8, 0)$ [acute angle]

5. $(0, ^-2)$ $(5, ^-4)$ $(^-2, ^-5)$ [reflex angle]

6. $(^-2, 7)$ $(^-4, 2)$ $(2, 3)$ [reflex angle]

7. $(^-9, ^-1)$ $(^-3, ^-2)$ $(2, 2)$ [obtuse angle]

8. $(2, ^-7)$ $(^-6, ^-7)$ $(^-8, ^-4)$ [reflex angle]

Exercise 3

Calculate the labelled angles:

1.

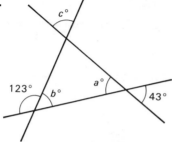

5.

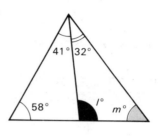

2.

$P\widehat{Q}R = \boxed{?}°$

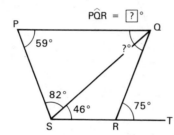

6.

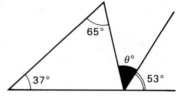

3.

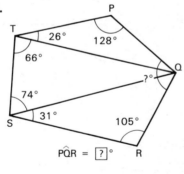

$P\widehat{Q}R = \boxed{?}°$

7.

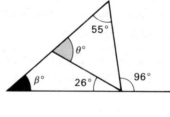

4.

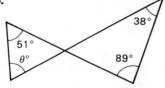

8.

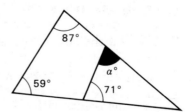

53

9.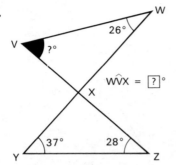

11.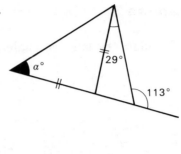

$\widehat{WVX}$ = [?]°

10.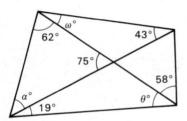

12.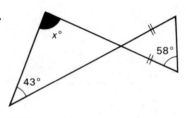

Exercise 4   Angles and Spirals

1. Draw a circle of radius 48 mm. (The diagram shown is not full size.)

2. Divide your circle into 12 equal parts (use a protractor to help you).

3. Mark a point on each radius: the first point on the first radius should be 2 mm from the centre of the circle; the second point on the next radius should be 4 mm from the centre of the circle; the third on the next radius should be 6 mm, the fourth 8 mm and so on. Continue until you reach the circumference of the circle.

4. Join the points with a smooth curve.

54

Exercise 5   Gear Wheels

Examine the gear wheels in the given diagram.

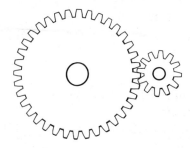

1. If the small gear wheel turns clockwise, in which direction does the large wheel turn?

2. If the large wheel has 48 teeth and the small wheel 12 teeth, work out:
  (*a*) the number of times the small wheel turns when the large wheel makes one full turn,
  (*b*) the number of degrees the small wheel turns through when the large wheel turns through 60°,
  (*c*) the number of degrees turned through by the large wheel when the small wheel turns through 60°.

3. If the large wheel has 40 teeth while the small wheel has 16 teeth:
  (*a*) How many times will the small wheel turn when the large wheel makes 4 full turns?
  (*b*) Through how many degrees will the large wheel turn when the small wheel turns through 45°?

4. If the large wheel has 30 teeth and the small wheel 18 teeth:
  (*a*) How many full turns will the large wheel make if the small wheel turns 10 times?
  (*b*) Through how many degrees will the small wheel turn when the large wheel turns through 60°?
  (*c*) Through how many degrees will the small wheel turn when the large wheel turns through 24°?
  (*d*) Through how many degrees will the large wheel turn when the small wheel turns through 60°?

Angles and Parallels

Angles that are next to each other are called *adjacent angles*. In the diagram, *a* and *c* are adjacent angles.

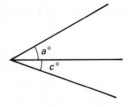

Angles that add up to 90° are called *complementary angles*.
In the diagram, $d + e = 90$, hence angles *d* and *e* are complementary angles.

We can also say that *d* is the *complement* of *e*
and *e* is the *complement of d*.

e.g. 55° and 35° are complementary angles.
55° is the complement of 35°.

Angles that add up to 180° are called *supplementary angles*.
Adjacent angles on a straight line are *supplementary*.

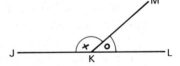

e.g. 65° and 115° are supplementary angles.
65° is the *supplement* of 115°.

A line that crosses other lines is called a *transversal*.

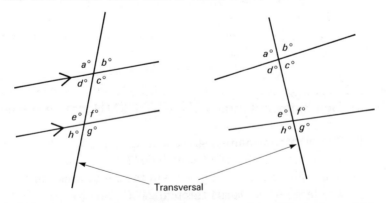

Transversal

Angles *a, b, g* and *h* are called *exterior angles* while *c, d, e* and *f* are called *interior angles*.

56

Corresponding angles are in corresponding positions with regard to the transversal and the lines it cuts. They are both on the same side of the transversal and if one lies 'above' one of the lines cut by the transversal, the other angle lies 'above' the other line.

(Both could lie 'below' instead of 'above'.) In the diagram on p. 56, corresponding angles are: *a* and *e*, *b* and *f*, *c* and *g*, *d* and *h*. Corresponding angles are sometimes called F-*angles*.

Alternate angles lie in alternate positions. One lies to the left of the transversal while the other lies to the right. One lies 'above' one of the lines cut by the transversal while the other angle lies 'below' the other line. In the diagram, *a* and *g*, *b* and *h*, *c* and *e*, and *d* and *f* are pairs of alternate angles. (*a* and *g* are called exterior alternate angles. Which others are exterior alternate angles?) Alternate angles are sometimes called Z-*angles*.

Interior angles that lie on the same side of the transversal are called *co-interior* (*or allied*) *angles*.

In the diagram on p. 56, *c* and *f*, and *d* and *e* are co-interior angles. Co-interior angles are sometimes called C-*angles* or U-*angles*.

Exercise 6

The following sentences all refer to this diagram:

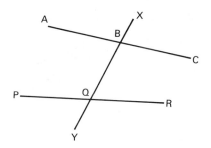

Copy and complete:

1. ∠ABX and ∠ ? are corresponding angles.

2. Angle BQP and angle ? are alternate angles.

3. One pair of co-interior angles is ∠ABQ and ∠ ? .

4. ∠XBC and ∠ ? are vertically opposite angles.

5. ∠CBQ and ∠RQY are ? angles.

57

6. Angle XBA and angle YQR are ⬚?⬚ angles.

7. Angle PQY and angle ⬚?⬚ are alternate angles.

8. Angles RQB and CBQ are ⬚?⬚ angles.

Exercise 7

Write whether each of the given pairs of angles are alternate, corresponding, co-interior or vertically opposite:

1.

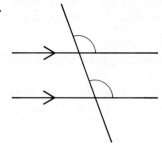

4.

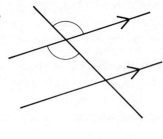

2.

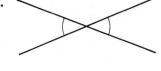

5.

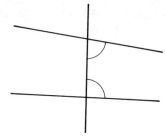

3.

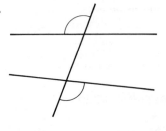

6.

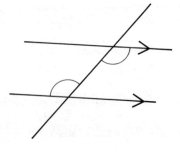

Exercise 8

1. Draw a pair of parallel lines.

2. Draw a transversal across the parallel lines.

3. (a) Measure any pair of corresponding angles.
   (b) What do you notice about the two angles?

4. (a) Measure other pairs of corresponding angles.
   (b) What do you notice about corresponding angles when lines
       are parallel?

5. (a) Measure any pair of alternate angles.
   (b) Measure other pairs of alternate angles.
   (c) What do you notice about alternate angles when lines are
       parallel?

6. (a) Measure any pair of co-interior angles.
   (b) Add them.
   (c) What do you notice?

7. (a) Measure, then add the other pair of co-interior angles.
   (b) What do you notice about co-interior angles when lines are
       parallel?

Angles and Parallels — Summary

When lines are parallel then:

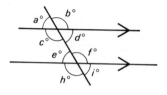

1. *Corresponding angles* are *equal.*
   $a = e, \quad b = f, \quad c = h, \quad d = i$

2. *Alternate angles* are *equal.*
   $c = f, \quad d = e, \quad a = i, \quad b = h$

3. *Co-interior* (*allied*) *angles* are *supplementary.*
   $$c° + e° = 180°$$
   $$d° + f° = 180°$$

59

Exercise 9

For each question, *calculate* the angles labelled with letters:

1.

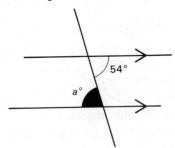

5.

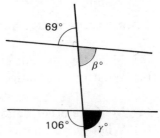

2.

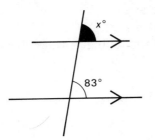

6.

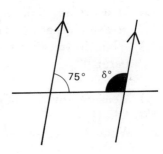

3.

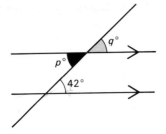

7.

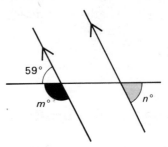

4.

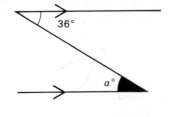

8.

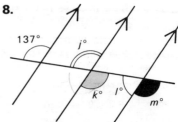

9.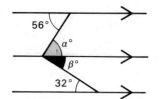

11.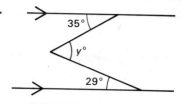

10.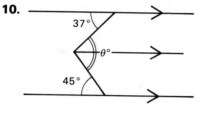

12.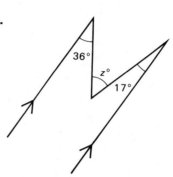

Exercise 10

For each question, write whether or not AB is parallel to CD. Give reasons for your answers.

1.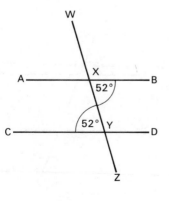

2.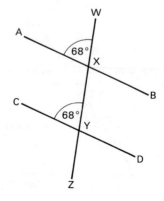

61

3.

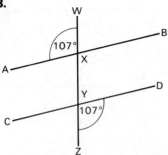

6.

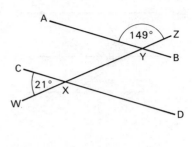

4.

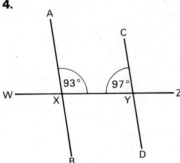

7.

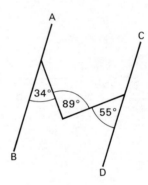

5.

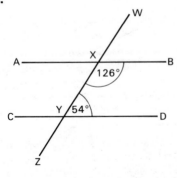

8.

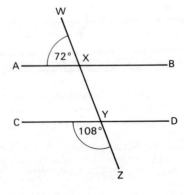

62

Copy each diagram. Fill in all the missing angles on your copies.

1.

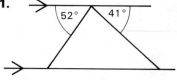

5.

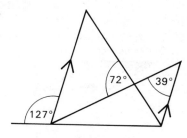

2.

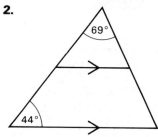

6.

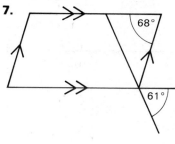

3.

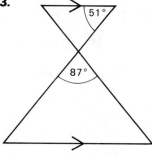

7.

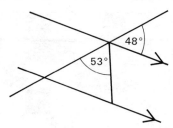

4.

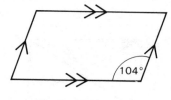

8.

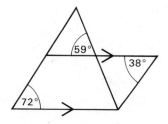

Copy and complete the crossnumber puzzle:

Across

1. The complement of 34°

3.

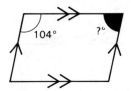

4.

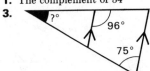

6.

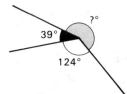

8.

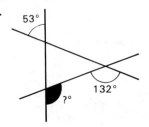

Down

2. The supplement of 119°

3.

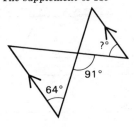

4.

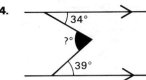

5.

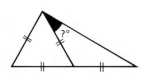

7. This angle is not wrong

8.

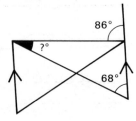

10.

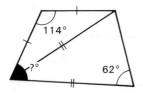

9.

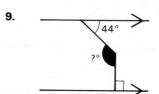

11.

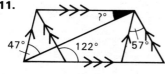

10.

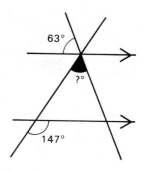

12.

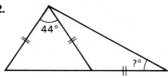

13.

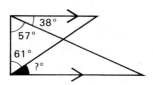

11.

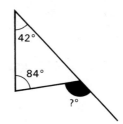

14.

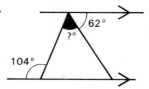

14.

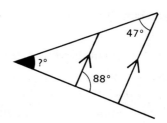

15.

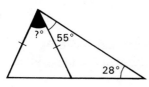

17.

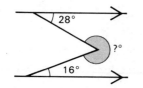

15.

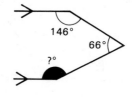

65

Across	Down

Across

18.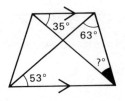

20.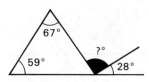

21.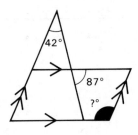

Down

16.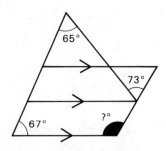

17.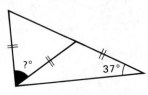

19.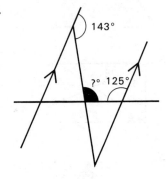

Exercise 13

Copy and complete this proof:

Given   △ABC.
To prove   The sum of the angles of a triangle is 180°.
Construction   Draw straight line DE through A and parallel to BC.

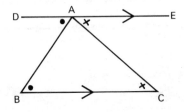

Proof ∠DAB = ∠ABC   (alternate angles, DA// ?)

  ∠EAC = ∠ ?   (alternate angles, AE// ?)

but ∠DAB + ∠BAC + ∠EAC = ?   (angles on a straight line)

hence ∠ABC + ∠BAC + ∠ACB = 180°.

Therefore the sum of the angles of a triangle = 180°.

Constructions

Exercise 14

To construct a line through a given point P and parallel to a given line AB (using a pair of compasses)

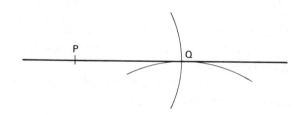

1. Draw the given line AB and mark the given point P.

2. Mark any two points, X and Y, on line AB.

3. With centre P and with radius XY, draw an arc as shown.

4. With centre Y and radius XP draw a second arc to cross the first arc. Label this new point, Q.

5. Join PQ.
   PQ is parallel to AB.

Exercise 15

To erect a perpendicular to a line from a point on the line (using a pair of compasses)

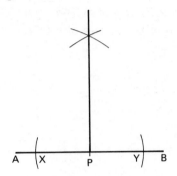

1. Let AB be the line, and P the point on it. With centre P and any convenient radius, draw arcs to cut the line AB at X and at Y (one at each side of P).

2. Now construct the perpendicular bisector of XY:
   (*a*) With centre X and radius bigger than $\frac{1}{2}$XY, draw an arc above AB.
   (*b*) With centre Y and using the *same* radius, draw an arc above AB to cross the previous one.

3. Join P to the point formed by the intersecting arcs. This line is the required perpendicular.

Exercise 16

A *To construct an angle of 60°*

1. Draw a line AB.

2. With centre A and any radius, draw a long arc (as shown) to cut AB at C.

3. With C as centre, and using the *same size* radius, draw a second arc to cut the first one at D.

4. Join AD. $\angle CAD = 60°$.

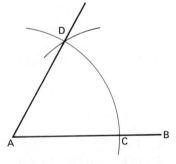

B Try to construct angles of:

    1. 120°   **3.** 150°

    2. 30°   **4.** 240°

C *To construct an angle of 90° (a right-angle) at one end of a straight line*

    1. Draw a line AB.

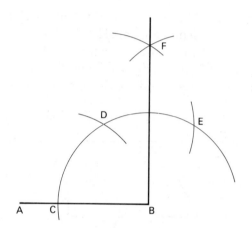

    2. To construct a right-angle at B:

      (*a*) With B as centre, and any radius, draw a long arc (almost making a semi-circle) to cut AB at C.

      (*b*) *Using the same radius throughout,* with centre C, draw an arc to cross your long arc at D.

      (*c*) With D as centre, keeping the same radius, draw two arcs, one to cross your long arc at E and the other to be directly above B and also above your long arc.

      (*d*) With centre E, keeping the same radius, draw an arc to cut your previous arc at F.

      (*e*) Join FB. ∠FBA = 90°.

D Try to construct angles of:

    1. 45°   **3.** 225°

    2. 135°   **4.** $22\frac{1}{2}$°

Exercise 17

You MUST NOT use a protractor to help with the constructions in this exercise. A protractor may only be used to measure angles after the construction has been completed.

1. Construct $\triangle$PQR where QR = 80 mm, PQ = 45 mm and PR = 50 mm. Bisect $\angle$PQR using a pair of compasses. Let the bisector meet PR at X. Measure PX.

2. Draw a straight line, AB, 70 mm long. At B, using a set square and ruler, draw a perpendicular and label it BC where BC = 38 mm. At A, using a pair of compasses, construct $\angle$BAD = 60°. Use a set square and ruler to draw DC parallel to AB. Bisect AD using a pair of compasses and let this bisector meet AB at E.

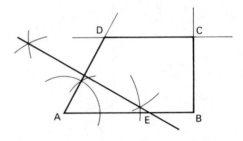

   Measure: (*a*) DC   (*b*) BE

3. Construct a rhombus where two angles measure 60° and where the sides are 50 mm long. Measure both diagonals.

4. Construct a rhombus having diagonals of lengths 80 mm and 50 mm. How long are its sides?

5. Construct the parallelogram ABCD where DC = 50 mm, AD = 30 mm and $A\widehat{D}C$ = 45°. Measure, then write the lengths of diagonals AC and BD.

6. Draw a straight line, AB, 90 mm in length. On AB, mark a point P such that AP = 50 mm. At P, construct a perpendicular to AB. Construct the angle BAQ equal to 30°, where Q lies on the perpendicular to AB drawn at P. Measure PQ.

7. Construct $\triangle$PQR where PQ = 58 mm, $P\widehat{Q}R$ = 120° and QR = 42 mm. Find the perimeter of the triangle.

8. Draw a circle of radius 28 mm. Construct a chord, AB, of length 48 mm. Now construct a chord, AC, of length 40 mm. (Find two different possible positions for C.) Join B to both points C. Write the two different lengths of BC.

Solids and Constructions

Exercise 18

1. (a) Carefully draw a face of a cube where each edge is 40 mm.

(b) If we slice through the cube as shown, cutting through vertices A, F, G, and D, the shape AFGD is called a *section* (sometimes called a *cross-section* or *plane section*). What is the shape of AFGD?

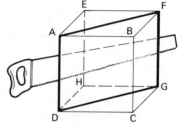

(c) Make an accurate drawing of this section. (Part (a) may help you to obtain lengths AF and DG.)

2. Another cube with edges of 40 mm is shown. X, T, and Y, are the mid-points of edges AB, BC, and CD respectively. P, U, Q, R, S, L, M, are the mid-points of edges EF, FG, GH, AE, DH, BF, CG, respectively.

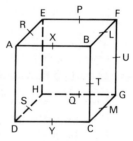

(a) Draw accurately the section that passes through X, P, Q, and Y.

(b) Make an accurate drawing of the section that passes through X, F, G, and Y.

(c) Make an accurate drawing of the section that passes through X, L, and T.

3. Is it possible to slice a cube to give the following sections? (Explain your answers.)

(a) an equilateral triangle,   (e) a parallelogram,
(b) an isosceles triangle,   (f) a trapezium,
(c) a right-angled triangle,   (g) a hexagon,
(d) a rectangle,   (h) a pentagon.

71

Exercise 19

1. Here is a cuboid of length 50 mm, breadth 35 mm, and height 20 mm.

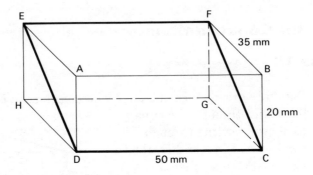

Carefully and accurately draw:

(a) face EADH,
(b) section EFCD,
(c) face ABFE,
(d) section ADGF,
(e) section AFC,
(f) section KFC where K lies on AB such that AK = 15 mm.

2. The diagram shows a square-based pyramid. Each edge of the square base is 30 mm. The slanting edges (VP, VQ, VR, and VS) are all 45 mm long.

Carefully and accurately draw:
(a) the slanting face VRQ,
(b) the vertical section VXY,
(c) the horizontal section ABCD, where A, B, C, and D are the mid-points of the edges VP, VQ, VR, and VS, respectively,
(d) the section BCSP.

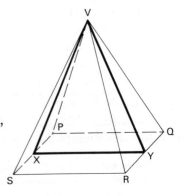

6 Decimals

Exercise 1   Miscellaneous Questions

1. Write in order of size, *smallest* first:

0.89, 0.98, 0.098, 0.809, 0.089, 0.908

2. Write as decimals:

(a) $\dfrac{7}{10}$ (b) $\dfrac{41}{100}$ (c) $\dfrac{3}{100}$ (d) $\dfrac{5}{8}$ (e) $\dfrac{3}{16}$

3. Change to vulgar fractions giving your answers in their simplest form:

(a) 0.4   (b) 0.85   (c) 0.875   (d) 0.525

4. What number is 0.001 less than 6?

5. Add one-tenth to 99.99.

6. 84.099, 84.499, 84.909, 84.0999, 84.99

(a) Which of the five numbers above is:
  (i) the smallest?   (ii) the largest?

(b) List the numbers given above that are bigger than $84\frac{1}{2}$.

Approximations

Exercise 2   Decimal Places

A Write these decimals correct to the nearest whole number:

1. 8.9   **7.** 203.80

2. 5.4   **8.** 41.099

3. 8.26   **9.** 599.52

4. 71.6   **10.** 129.75

5. 60.81   **11.** 118.602

6. 39.09   **12.** 35.499

B Round these decimals to the number of decimal places stated:

1. 8.67 to 1 d.p.
2. 40.732 to 2 d.p.
3. 61.549 to 2 d.p.
4. 0.8601 to 2 d.p.
5. 0.5532 to 1 d.p.
6. 0.9618 to 3 d.p.
7. 6.839 to 1 d.p.
8. 32.76 to 1 d.p.
9. 11.084 to 2 d.p.
10. 7.0658 to 3 d.p.
11. 9.0271 to 2 d.p.
12. 447.09 to 1 d.p.
13. 86.949 to 2 d.p.
14. 0.99 to 1 d.p.
15. 12.96 to 1 d.p.
16. 4.8977 to 2 d.p.

Significant Figures

$$1.57 \text{ m} = 157 \text{ cm} = 1570 \text{ mm} = 0.001\,57 \text{ km}$$

Each of the above gives the same length, so all of these measurements must be to the same degree of accuracy.

The three figures, 1, 5 and 7 occur in all four numbers and are called *significant figures.*

The four numbers have been written correct to three significant figures (sometimes written as 3 s.f. or possibly 3 sig. figs.).

Note in particular that 0.001 57 has only 3 s.f.

Exercise 3

How many significant figures are there in each of the following numbers?

e.g. 1   46.31 has 4 s.f.

e.g. 2   7.06 has 3 s.f.

e.g. 3   0.0602 has 3 s.f.

e.g. 4   5.270 has 4 s.f.

e.g. 5   0.007 035 0 has 5 s.f.

1. 7.618
2. 39.621
3. 40.7
4. 29.08
5. 0.83
6. 0.09
7. 9836
8. 700.25
9. 2017.4
10. 3.70
11. 9.200
12. 64.030
13. 1.010
14. 741.0807
15. 19.4501
16. 0.06
17. 0.606
18. 0.060 60

Exercise 4

Write the following numbers correct to the number of significant figures given in the brackets:

1. 6.175	(3)	**7.** 5.0702	(3)	**13.** 12.09	(2)
2. 71.84	(2)	**8.** 0.4063	(2)	**14.** 765.18	(3)
3. 93.74	(3)	**9.** 0.0233	(2)	**15.** 51.76	(1)
4. 17.295	(4)	**10.** 0.7803	(3)	**16.** 0.0873	(1)
5. 0.6327	(1)	**11.** 6.0025	(4)	**17.** 2.399	(3)
6. 0.846	(2)	**12.** 9.0018	(3)	**18.** 14.098	(4)

Estimating

To *estimate* an answer to a question, the numbers in the question should be rounded to create a calculation that can be worked out in your head. (Usually, we work with one significant figure.)

Exercise 5

Estimate the answers to these. Work with one significant figure.

1. 6.9×5

2. 7.84×2.17

3. 9.05×4.18

4. $8.75 \div 2.84$

5. 564×728.1

6. $59.41 \div 1.91$

7. 6.66×82.5

8. 708×5.99

9. $827 \div 38.6$

10. $49.06 \div 2.09$

11. 0.63×0.876

12. 5.02×0.502

13. 0.033×0.77

14. $69.04 \div 3.76$

15. 19.57×0.603

16. 983×0.0545

17. 0.285×0.0644

18. $0.381 \div 0.018$

19. 0.0765×0.03

20. $0.0093 \div 0.459$

21. $\dfrac{8.96 \times 7.84}{5.72}$

22. $\dfrac{87.3}{4.6 \times 3.1}$

23. $\dfrac{43 \times 19.6}{5.1 \times 7.9}$

24. $\dfrac{65.7 + 83.1}{27.65}$

25. $\dfrac{286.3}{26.8 + 9.73}$

26. $\dfrac{76.5 \times 92.4}{8.83 - 2.91}$

27. $\dfrac{61.2 \times 80.7}{4.12 + 7.61}$

29. $\dfrac{88.2 + 57.6}{0.61 \times 0.482}$

28. $\dfrac{94.5 - 27.6}{1.75 \times 6.15}$

30. $\dfrac{23.7 + 46.8}{7.841 - 2.806}$

Calculations

Exercise 6

Work out the following. Give each answer correct to three significant figures.

1. $71.26 + 1.94 + 3.72$

2. $407.82 - 127.35$

3. $47.003 - 19.644$

4. 15.7×5.6

5. 204.1×9.2

6. $134.848 \div 5.6$

7. $51.82 + 63.09 + 76$

8. $16.2243 \div 8.1$

9. $0.489\,65 \div 0.07$

10. 17.61×80.5

11. $\dfrac{8.7 \times 2.34}{3.6}$

12. $\dfrac{48 \times 64.7}{16.9}$

13. $\dfrac{35.8 + 49.1}{1.25}$

14. $\dfrac{91.8 \times 76.8}{0.47}$

15. $\dfrac{0.051 \times 4.602}{7.2}$

16. $\dfrac{98.37 - 35.89}{0.29}$

17. $\dfrac{62.93}{3.16 \times 4.07}$

18. $\dfrac{0.87 \times 42}{7.91 - 6.35}$

19. $\dfrac{4.69 \times 34.8}{0.17 \times 0.802}$

20. $\dfrac{35.47 + 19.63}{9.72 - 6.851}$

21. $\dfrac{4.02 + 9.64}{3.5 \times 0.21}$

22. $\dfrac{91.7 - 28.2}{14.7 \times 0.961}$

23. $\dfrac{4.701 - 3.82}{5.9 \times 4.7}$

24. $\dfrac{35.1 \times 46}{1.83 + 5.27}$

25. $\dfrac{0.071 \times 0.85}{5.13 - 4.99}$

Exercise 7

1. When any number is multiplied by any other number that is *bigger than 1*, will the answer be 'always bigger', 'always smaller' or 'sometimes bigger and sometimes smaller', than the number started with?

2. Repeat question 1 using *less than 1* instead of bigger than 1.

3. Answer question 1 for division instead of multiplication.

4. Answer question 2 for division instead of multiplication.

Exercise 8   Density

Given that: $\text{Density} = \dfrac{\text{mass}}{\text{volume}}$

$\text{Volume} = \dfrac{\text{mass}}{\text{density}}$

$\text{Mass} = \text{volume} \times \text{density}$

1. Calculate the density of silver, in grams per cubic centimetre (g per cm^3), if 7 cm^3 has a mass of 73.5 g.

2. Calculate the density, in kilograms per cubic metre (kg per m^3), of aluminium, if 4 m^3 has a mass of 10 800 kg.

3. Calculate the density of copper, in grams per cubic centimetre (g per cm^3), if 12 cm^3 has a mass of 107.16 g.

4. The density of lead is 11.4 g per cm^3. Calculate the mass of 8 cm^3 of lead.

5. Calculate the volume of ebony which has a mass of 64.8 g, given that the density of ebony is 1.2 g per cm^3.

6. The density of magnesium is 1740 kg per m^3. Calculate the mass of 2.4 m^3 of magnesium.

7. Brass has a density of 8400 kg per m^3. Calculate the volume of brass that has a mass of 12 600 kg.

8. 6000 cm³ of agate has a mass of 15.69 kg. Calculate the density of agate in grams per cubic centimetre (g per cm³).

9. The mass of 3 m³ of pine is 1 440 000 g. Calculate the density of pine in kilograms per cubic metre (kg per m³).

10. An article made of brass (density = 8.4 g per cm³) has a mass of 126 g. What would its mass be if it was made of copper (density = 8.93 g per cm³)?

11. A bottle holds 500 cm³ of milk when full, its total mass then being 860 g. When empty, its mass is only 145 g. Calculate the density of milk.

12. A bottle of mass 152 g contains paraffin (density = 0.895 g per cm³). If the bottle will hold 800 cm³ of paraffin, what is the total mass of the bottle and the paraffin?

Exercise 9

1. A piece of sheet metal is 0.38 mm thick. Find the total thickness of a pile of 18 sheets.

2. The *pitch* of the thread of a bolt is the distance a nut moves along the bolt when it is given one full turn.

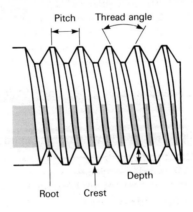

If a bolt thread has a pitch of 1.42 mm, how far will the nut move when it makes 13 full turns?

3. If some wire has a resistance of 1.34 ohms per centimetre of length, calculate the total resistance of a 48 cm length of this wire.

4. Copper tubing expands by 0.008 35 mm for each degree centigrade rise in temperature. If the temperature of the tubing is increased from 18 °C to 64 °C, find its expansion.

5. The circumference of a circle is about 3.14 times the diameter of a circle:
(*a*) Calculate the circumference when the diameter is 3.45 cm.
(*b*) Calculate the diameter when the circumference is 21.69 cm.
(Give your answer correct to 3 s.f.)

6. A rectangular garden is 19.6 m long and 9.5 m wide. Calculate its perimeter.

7. Mrs Osborne needed two lengths of rope, one measuring 6.64 m and the other 4.87 m:
(*a*) What is the total length needed?
(*b*) If the two pieces of rope were cut from a piece measuring 13.5 m, what length was left?

8. 12.55 ℓ of paraffin is poured into seven containers. If all seven containers contain the same amount, find, correct to three significant figures, the number of litres in each.

Money

Earning Money

People work to earn money. The weekly earnings (*wages*) are often worked out as an amount paid per hour, called the *basic hourly rate* (or *basic rate*, or *hourly rate*).

Wage = hours worked × hourly rate

Exercise 10

A Copy and complete the table:

	Hours worked	Hourly rate	Wage
1.	30	£6	?
2.	25	£3.50	?
3.	35	£1.80	?
4.	40	£3.90	?
5.	36	£4.75	?
6.	28	£5.35	?
7.	32	£2.76	?
8.	38	£7.30	?
9.	37	£4.29	?
10.	34	£5.42	?

B Copy and complete the table:

	Wage	Hours worked	Hourly rate
1.	£160	40	?
2.	£112	32	?
3.	£198	?	£5.50
4.	£ 95.20	34	?
5.	£ 41.80	?	£1.90
6.	£217	?	£6.20
7.	£357.75	27	?
8.	£175.50	39	?
9.	£128.82	38	?
10.	£173.16	?	£4.68

The wages that are earned in a week are called the *gross weekly wages* (or *gross wages* or *gross pay*). Take-home pay is less than the gross pay because of the *deductions* made by an employer. For each employee, an employer must deduct income tax and National Insurance from the gross pay. (Other deductions may also need to be made.) The amount left, the take-home pay, is called the *net weekly wages* (or *net pay*).

Net pay = gross pay − deductions

Copy and complete the table:

	Gross pay	Deductions	Net pay
1.	£178	£ 63.20	?
2.	£199.50	£ 71.75	?
3.	£225.42	?	£145.82
4.	£116.25	?	£ 79.55
5.	?	£ 49.30	£ 96.85
6.	?	£ 92.89	£163.89
7.	£ 87.75	£ 24.86	?
8.	?	£ 59.85	£116.85
9.	£124.02	?	£ 86.53
10.	£288.55	£103.72	?

Spending Money

Exercise 12

1. A pack of three video tapes that normally costs £11.25 is sold for £10.47. How much discount is that?

2. A washing machine costing £299.95 was sold for £259.99. How much discount was that?

3. A bicycle costing £178.50 was sold at a discount of £26.78, what was the selling price?

4. Caradog bought a personal stereo for £37.20, then sold it for £28.90. How much did he lose on the sale?

5. A lawn mower costing £247 was sold at a loss, the loss being £53.65. How much was it sold for?

6. Mr Fitzpatrick bought a Portagym for £259.99, then sold it for £293.45. How much profit did he make?

7. Mrs Quayle made seven payments of £8.56 towards a music centre. How much was that?

8. Alison bought a tennis racket from a catalogue for £27.40. She paid 20 equal instalments. How much was each instalment?

Hire-Purchase

Cash price
The cash price is the price paid for goods at the time of buying. Note that the payment need not be cash. The cash price may be paid by cheque or by credit card*.

Buying on credit (easy terms)
This is a way of buying goods over a period of time (payments are usually made weekly or monthly).

Hire-purchase (HP)
HP is one way of buying on credit. Goods do not belong to you (and are only on hire) until the last payment has been made.

Credit sales
This is another way of buying on credit. The goods belong to you as soon as the first payment is made.

Deposit
The amount that is paid straight away when agreement is made to buy on credit is called the deposit.

*See the glossary, p. 444.

Balance (amount outstanding)
The balance is the amount that is owed at a particular time.

Instalments
These are the payments that are made at regular intervals when buying on credit.

Interest charges (interest or credit charge)
The extra charge made for buying on credit.

> HP price = deposit + balance
> HP price − cash price = credit charge

Exercise 13

1. A television costs £259.95. After a deposit of £51.99, find the balance.

2. A fridge-freezer cost £359.95 cash. If the HP price was £434.50, find the credit charge.

3. A snooker table cost £219.90 cash. It could be bought for a deposit of £45 followed by 12 monthly payments of £19.70.

   (a) Find the total of the 12 monthly payments.
   (b) Calculate the total HP cost of the snooker table.
   (c) How much extra is paid on HP than by paying cash?

4. Some bedroom furniture can be bought for a deposit of £149 followed by 24 equal payments of £33.75. Calculate the total cost.

5. Mr Silvester paid a deposit followed by 24 payments of £9.85 for a dishwasher:
(a) What did the 24 payments total?
(b) If the total HP price was £299.99, how much was the deposit?

6. A sewing machine cost £223.50 on HP. If the deposit was £44.70 and the balance was paid in 12 equal instalments, find each instalment.

7. A keyboard can be bought on HP for a deposit of £66.65 followed by 12 monthly payments of £15.78. Its cash price is £199.99. How much more is paid on HP than by paying cash?

8. A computer costs £691.90 cash. It can be bought for a deposit of £150 followed by 24 equal payments of £31.15. Calculate the credit charge.

Exercise 14   Invoices   M

Copy and complete these invoices:

1.

Quantity	Item	Unit cost	Cost £	p
12	aster	@ £1.15	?	?
5	iris	@ £1.38	?	?
4	phlox	@ £1.09	?	?
6	lupin	@ 99 p	?	?
2	hosta	@ £3.42	?	?
		Total cost	?	?

2.

Quantity	Item	Unit cost	Cost £	p
4	biscuit cutter	@ 38 p	?	?
2	cake tin	@ £1.96	?	?
3	flan dish	@ £3.79	?	?
1	egg dish	@ £6.75	?	?
4	cooling tray	@ £2.71	?	?
5	measuring spoon	@ £1.53	?	?
		Total cost	?	?

Recurring Decimals

The decimal 2.623 762 376 237 623 7 and so on is called a *recurring decimal*. The pattern of digits is repeated for ever. Some people call them *repeating decimals* and others *circulating decimals*.

The decimal above would usually be written as 2.6̇237̇ (in some countries it would be written as 2.6237). The dots above the 6 and 7 mean that all the digits from 6 to 7 inclusive should be repeated.

0.3̇52̇ stands for 0.352 352 352 and so on,
0.352̇ stands for 0.352 222 2 and so on (since the dot is only above the 2, only the digit 2 is repeated),
0.35̇2̇ stands for 0.352 525 252 and so on.

Exercise 15

1. Using a calculator, try to find some recurring decimals. (Key in a common fraction and see if it gives a recurring decimal.) Note the denominators that give recurring decimals.

e.g. $\frac{2}{3}$ is 0.6666 and so on ($\frac{2}{3} = 0.\dot{6}$)

Note that $0.666\,666\,66 = 0.666\,666\,7$ correct to seven decimal places. Your calculator probably gives $\frac{2}{3}$ as $0.666\,666\,7$. Key in $\boxed{2}\,\boxed{\div}\,\boxed{3}\,\boxed{=}$ to check this.

2. Make out a table of denominators up to and including 30. The table should show which denominators give recurring decimals when the numerator is 1.

Non-recurring	Recurring
2	3
4	and so on
and so on	

Exercise 16

A Change the following fractions into recurring (circulating) decimals. Set out your work carefully. Keep the decimal points in a straight line. Each digit should be written directly under another.

1. (a) $\frac{1}{7} = 0.14\,\boxed{?}\,\boxed{?}\,\boxed{?}\,\boxed{?}$
   (b) $\frac{3}{7} = 0.$
   (c) $\frac{2}{7} = 0.$
   (d) $\frac{6}{7} =$
   (e) $\frac{4}{7} =$
   (f) $\frac{5}{7} =$

2. Look carefully at the pattern in the digits of the decimals in question 1. What do you notice?

3. Try to work out how to write down the fractions in the correct order to create a pattern.

4. (a) Copy this circle.

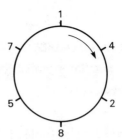

(b) Compare the decimal for $\frac{1}{7}$ with the numbers on the circle.

(c) Compare the decimals for $\frac{3}{7}$, $\frac{2}{7}$, $\frac{6}{7}$, $\frac{4}{7}$ and $\frac{5}{7}$ with the numbers on the circle.

(d) Try to work out why the fractions in part (c) are listed in that order.

5. (a) On your circle, join the numbers that are diametrically opposite.

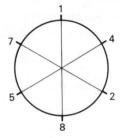

(b) Add them.

(c) Write what you notice.

6. $\frac{1}{7} = 0.142\,857$
$\phantom{\frac{1}{7} = 0.}\underline{857}$

(a) Copy the decimal for $\frac{1}{7}$.

(b) Write the second half of the decimal under the first as shown above.

(c) Add the two digits in each column.

(d) Write what you notice.

B Answer the questions in part A for the thirteenths. (List the fractions in an order that will give a pattern. Note that you may need to make two lists for the thirteenths. Only one list was needed for the sevenths.)

Exercise 17

Using a calculator, write $\frac{5}{17}$ as a recurring decimal. Explain your method.

7 Ratio and Proportion

Ratios of Two Quantities

Exercise 1

For each question, write how many times as big the first quantity or line is than the second:

A
1. £9, £3
2. 36 min, 9 min
3. 24 cm, 4 cm
4. 15 in, 3 in
5. 48 km, 3 km
6. 84, 7
7. 65 p, 5 p
8. 102 miles, 17 miles
9. 171 days, 9 days
10. 360°, 72°
11. ──────────────────────────
   ────
12. ──────────────────────────────────
   ──────

B
1. £6, 50 p
2. £9, 25 p
3. 2 m, 10 cm
4. 3 m, 15 cm
5. 4 kg, 200 g
6. 500 mm, 2.5 cm
7. 12 min, 45 s
8. 6 yd, 2 ft
   (3 ft = 1 yd)
9. 4 ℓ, 250 mℓ
10. 9 weeks, 7 days
11. 5 days, 8 h
12. 4 years, 8 months
13. 540 min, 3 h
14. £7.20, 80 p
15. 3.5 m, 70 cm
16. 6 ft, 9 in
   (12 in = 1 ft)

Simplifying Ratios

Exercise 2

Write these ratios in their simplest form:

1. 12:4
2. 15:5
3. 5:15
4. 8:20
5. 18:6
6. 20:4
7. 20:6
8. 24:18

9. 45:36
10. 28:98
11. 69:46
12. 18:18
13. 48:60
14. 0.6:0.3
15. 1.6:0.4
16. 1.2:0.8

17. 0.4:2.4
18. 18:0.9
19. 2.4:3.6
20. $1\frac{1}{2}:\frac{3}{4}$
21. $6\frac{1}{4}:25$
22. $7\frac{1}{2}:5$
23. 56:42
24. 85:51

Exercise 3

Write the following as ratios in their simplest form:

1. 21 cm to 7 cm
2. 32 p to 8 p
3. 4 kg to 14 kg
4. £90 to £60
5. £90 to £75
6. 39 km to 52 km
7. 3 cm to 24 mm
8. 8400 cm to 7.2 m
9. 24 lb to 16 lb
10. 800 m to 4 km
11. 420 g to 2.8 kg
12. 0.3 kg to 0.45 kg
13. 9 months to 2 years
14. £1.32 to £1.54
15. 3 days to 20 h

16. 270 mg to 1.8 g
17. £1.44 to 84 p
18. 6.5 kg to 5.2 kg
19. 7.6 m to 5.7 m
20. 135° to 360°
21. $1\frac{1}{4}$ t to 1 t
22. 2 km to $1\frac{3}{5}$ km
23. 0.8 kg to 0.32 kg
24. $2\frac{1}{4}$ ℓ to 3 ℓ
25. $9\frac{3}{4}$ yd to $6\frac{1}{2}$ yd
26. 9.6 ℓ to 12 ℓ
27. 8.4 kg to 4.8 kg
28. $4\frac{1}{2}$ m to $4\frac{4}{5}$ m
29. $8\frac{1}{4}$ ft to $5\frac{3}{5}$ ft
30. $2\frac{2}{3}$ mℓ to $3\frac{1}{5}$ mℓ

Exercise 4   Ratio of Three Quantities

Write the following ratios in their simplest form:

1. 4:6:8
2. 15:35:20
3. 8:4:12

4. 9:12:6
5. $7\frac{1}{2}:20:10$
6. 30:18:24

7. $5:3.5:4$

8. $54:36:30$

9. $4.2:1.4:2.1$

10. $63:18:45$

11. $32:48:56$

12. $1\frac{1}{2}:2\frac{1}{2}:2$

13. $0.25:0.05:0.3$

14. $9.1:2.6:7.8$

15. $5.25:4.5:6$

16. $3\frac{3}{4}:\frac{5}{6}:1\frac{2}{3}$

Exercise 5   Finding Ratios

1. There were 14 women in a shop together with 8 men. Find in its simplest form:
   (a) the ratio of the number of women to the number of men,
   (b) the ratio of the number of men to the number of women,
   (c) the ratio of the number of women to the total number of people in the shop.

2. A firm's production costs came to £15 000 last year and £21 000 this year. Find, in its simplest form, the ratio of this year's to last year's production costs.

3. A sheet of paper is 300 mm long and 210 mm wide. Find, in its simplest form, the ratio of the length to the width.

4. Two squares have sides of length 6 cm and 8 cm. Find, in their simplest form, the following ratios for the larger to the smaller square:
   (a) lengths of sides,
   (b) perimeters,
   (c) areas.

5.

   By measuring and calculating find, for the line above, the following ratios in their simplest form:
   (a) PQ:QR   (b) RQ:QP   (c) PR:PQ   (d) QR:PR

6.

   If $AB:BC = 3:2$, find $AC:AB$. (The line has not been drawn to scale.)

91

7. Some goods were bought for £162 then sold for £216. Find, in its simplest form:
   (a) the ratio of the cost price (CP) to the profit,
   (b) the ratio of the profit to the selling price (SP),
   (c) the ratio of the SP to the CP.

8. Some shares, at today's price, are 126 p each. Their lowest price was 96 p and their highest price was 240 p each. Find, in its simplest form:
   (a) the ratio of the highest to the lowest price,
   (b) the ratio of today's price to the highest price,
   (c) the ratio of the lowest price to today's price.

Finding Missing Quantities

Exercise 6

A Find the missing values that make the ratios the same:

1. $10:6 = 5:\boxed{?}$

2. $12:9 = \boxed{?}:3$

3. $8:12 = \boxed{?}:3$

4. $15:\boxed{?} = 3:2$

5. $16:\boxed{?} = 2:5$

6. $0.9:0.6 = \boxed{?}:2$

7. $9.8:\boxed{?} = 7:4$

8. $4\frac{1}{2}:7\frac{1}{2} = \boxed{?}:5$

9. $\boxed{?}:1.8 = 3:2$

10. $4:1\frac{1}{2} = 8:\boxed{?}$

B Find the missing quantities that make the ratios correct:

1. £20 to $\boxed{?} = 5:4$

2. 54 mm to $\boxed{?} = 6:5$

3. $\boxed{?}$ to 56 km $= 5:8$

4. 48 lb to $\boxed{?} = 3:4$

5. $\boxed{?}$ to 18 days $= 7:2$

6. 2.1 kg to $\boxed{?} = 3:2$

7. $\boxed{?}$ to 0.8 cm $= 1:4$

8. 8.7 m to $\boxed{?} = 29:9$

9. $\boxed{?}$ to 84 p $= 8:7$

10. 7.8 ℓ to $\boxed{?} = 13:6$

92

1. In the following table, the ratio of each top number to the number directly below it is always the same. Copy and complete the table.

4	6	12	?	26	1	?	5	?	?
10	?	?	20	?	?	35	?	25	$7\frac{1}{2}$

2. Here are the ingredients for *Scampi provençale* to serve five people. Rewrite the ingredients for three.

    25 g butter   150 mℓ dry white wine
    1 onion   juice of $\frac{1}{2}$ lemon
    1 clove of garlic   salt
    100 g mushrooms   freshly ground black pepper
    $\frac{1}{2}$ kg tomatoes $\frac{1}{2}$ kg peeled scampi
    10 mℓ tomato purée   seasoned flour
    5 mℓ dried mixed herbs   30 mℓ corn oil
    10 mℓ cornflour

3. A nurse diluted a drug with water in the ratio 1:5. If she used 80 mℓ of the drug:
    (a) How much water did she use?
    (b) How much solution was made up altogether?

4. A builder, to do some pointing, used sand and cement in the ratio 2:1. If he used 180 kg of sand, how much cement did he use?

5. A photographer diluted some developer with water in the ratio 1:10. If he used 300 mℓ of water:
    (a) How much developer did he use?
    (b) How much solution was made up altogether?

6. Donna and Toby shared some money in the ratio 3:5. If Donna received £72 of the money:
    (a) How much did Toby receive?
    (b) How much was shared altogether?

7. An orange drink was diluted with water in the ratio 1:4.

    (a) If $\frac{1}{2}$ ℓ of orange was used:

        (i) How much water was used?

        (ii) How many litres were made up altogether?

    (b) If 1.2 ℓ of water was used:

        (i) How many millilitres of orange were used?

        (ii) How many litres were made up altogether?

8. A model ship is built to a scale of 1:200. If the model is 0.75 m long, what is the length of the real ship?

Ratios in the Form 1:*m* or *m*:1

Exercise 8

A *e.g.* $56:32 = \dfrac{56}{32}:\dfrac{32}{32}$ (dividing both values by 32)

$$= \underline{\underline{1.75:1}}$$

The ratio 56:32 has been written in the form *m*:1. Write the following ratios in the form *m*:1.

1. 13:4	**4.** 14:40	**7.** 0.63:0.7	**10.** 10.41:2.4
2. 19:8	**5.** 0.7:5	**8.** 29:40	**11.** 0.93:0.2
3. 7:10	**6.** 1.5:1.2	**9.** 6.3:1.25	**12.** 0.063:2.4

B Write these ratios in the form 1:*m*.

1. 9:72	**4.** 12:417	**7.** 3.6:171	**10.** 0.75:3
2. 8:51	**5.** 15:291	**8.** 0.16:2	**11.** 2.8:2.1
3. 7:203	**6.** 20:43	**9.** 14:0.49	**12.** 14.4:8.1

Exercise 9   Value for Money

Work out which is the better value for money:

1.	500 g for 90 p	or	300 g for 57 p?
2.	3 kg for £2.52	or	4 kg for £3.32?
3.	15 ℓ for £3	or	24 ℓ for £5?
4.	£5 for 8 m	or	£7 for 9.8 m?
5.	19 m for 76 p	or	25 m for 95 p?
6.	£3.06 for 18 in	or	£5.88 for 35 in?

7. $12\frac{1}{2}$ ft for £7.80   or $7\frac{1}{2}$ ft for £4.80?
8. 29 cm for £3.40   or   42 cm for £2.80?
9. 13.5 t for £182.20   or   8.5 t for £114.75?
10. £8.70 for 3.8 m   or   £12.15 for 5.3 m?

Exercise 10   Heat Lost by Animals ▧ **M**

The amount of heat lost by an animal depends on the surface area of
its body. An animal that can keep its body heat for longer periods of
time can live in colder regions. So animals with smaller surface areas
compared with their body mass (or volume) can live more easily in
colder regions. The ratio of surface area to volume depends on the
size of the animal. We can see how this ratio changes by calculating
surface areas and volumes of cubes.

1. Copy and complete the table:

Edge of cube (cm)	Surface area of cube (cm²)	Volume of cube (cm³)	Surface area / Volume
1	6	1	6
2	24	?	?
3	54	27	2
4	?	?	1.5
5	?	?	?
6	?	216	?
7	?	?	?
8	?	?	?
10	?	?	?
12	864	?	?
15	?	?	0.4
20	2400	?	?

95

2. Which size of animal (larger or smaller) is more likely to be found in polar regions?

3. (a) A man weighing 68 kg has a surface area of 1.87 m². Find his surface area to mass ratio in the form $m:1$.
   (b) A baby has a mass of 6 kg and a surface area of 0.39 m². Find the surface area to mass ratio in the form $m:1$.
   (c) Explain why babies feel the cold more than adults.

4. A female white rat has a mass of 0.276 kg and a surface area of 0.072 m². Find the surface area to mass ratio in the form $m:1$.

5. A one-day old baby rat has a mass of 0.0052 kg and a surface area of 0.0043 m². Find the surface area to mass ratio in the form $m:1$.

Exercise 11   Route Factors   M

Geographers calculate the *route factors* for different towns and cities. The route factor is the ratio of the road distance to the direct distance. The smaller the route factor, the more direct is the road distance between the two places.

Road Distances in Kilometres

London

256	Sheffield				
595	363	Edinburgh			
339	250	512	Aberystwyth		
97	355	704	405	Eastbourne	
395	520	848	485	439	Truro

Direct Distances in Kilometres

London

227	Sheffield				
531	303	Edinburgh			
288	203	396	Aberystwyth		
89	313	618	351	Eastbourne	
371	420	638	245	379	Truro

1. Copy and complete the route factors table, on the page opposite. (Give each route factor in the form $m:1$ and correct to two decimal places.) Use the two tables above to help you.

e.g. The road distance from Sheffield to Aberystwyth is 250 km.
The direct distance from Sheffield to Aberystwyth is 203 km.

$$\text{The route factor} = \frac{250}{203} = 1.23 \text{ (to 2 d.p.)}$$

Route Factors

London

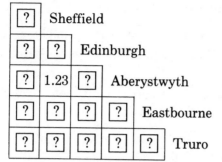

?	Sheffield
?	?	Edinburgh
?	1.23	?	Aberystwyth
?	?	?	?	Eastbourne
?	?	?	?	?	Truro

2. Which place in the table tends to have the smallest route factors?

3. (*a*) What is the highest route factor in the table?
(*b*) Explain why the route factor in part (*a*) is so high.

Exercise 12

1. Draw several squares.

2. For each square, measure the length of:
(*a*) its sides,
(*b*) its diagonals.

3. (*a*) For each square calculate the ratio,

length of diagonal : length of side.

(Give this ratio in the form $m:1$.)
(*b*) What do you notice about the ratios?

4. Find $\sqrt{2}$ on your calculator.

5. Write about your findings.

Exercise 13

1. Scientists say that density is mass per unit volume (that is, the ratio of mass to volume written in the form $m:1$). Calculate:
   (a) the density of silver, in grams per cubic centimetre, if 9 cm³ have a mass of 94.5 g,
   (b) the density of aluminium, in kilograms per cubic metre, if 1.5 m³ have a mass of 4050 kg.

2. Using Ohm's law we can write that the resistance (in ohms) in an electrical circuit is the ratio of the voltage to the current (in amperes).

   An electric kettle works at 240 V. It carries a current of 7.5 A. Find its resistance.

3. The ratio of load to effort gives the mechanical advantage of a machine. If an effort of 18 N lifts a load of 81 N, find the mechanical advantage. (N stands for newtons.)

4. The teacher/pupil ratio is calculated for schools. Calculate the ratios in the form $1:n$ for these schools:
   (a) 54 teachers and 972 pupils,
   (b) 792 pupils and 45 teachers.

5. A 60 g bar of chocolate contains about 315 calories. Calculate the number of calories in:
   (a) 80 g of chocolate,   (b) 112 g of chocolate.

Rates

'We are travelling at a speed of 40 miles' is a meaningless statement. (Only one quantity has been given.)

'We are travelling at a speed of 40 miles per hour' makes sense. (Two quantities have been given.)

When both quantities are given, we have what is called a *rate*. Miles per hour (m.p.h.), pence per metre etc. are rates.

The second quantity in a rate is usually given as one unit, so we have:

the number of miles travelled in *one* hour (m.p.h.)
the number of pence for *one* metre (pence per metre)

A rate of £4 per kilogram can also be written as £4/kg.

Exercise 14

1. (a) A car travelled 141 miles in 3 h. Calculate the ratio of the number of miles travelled to the number of hours taken (m.p.h.).

   (b) A car travelled at a steady 39 m.p.h. How far did it travel in 3 h?

2. A car travelled 200 km in $2\frac{1}{2}$ h. Calculate the ratio of distance travelled to time taken (km/h).

3. A car used 19 ℓ of petrol in travelling 266 km. Find the ratio of the number of kilometres travelled to the number of litres used, giving your answer in the form $n:1$ (km/ℓ).

4. A wheel made 390 full turns (revolutions or revs) in $\frac{1}{2}$ h. Find the number of revs made in 1 min (r.p.m. or revs/min).

5. If a carpet costs £9.95 per square metre (£9.95/m²), what would 15 m² cost?

6. If 12 ℓ of milk cost £5.52, find the cost per litre.

7. A box of a dozen pencils costs £2.76, find the cost per pencil.

8. The exchange rate between French francs and pounds sterling* is 9.96 francs to one pound, at the present time. How many francs would you get for £23?

Proportional Division

Exercise 15

1. Divide £125 into two parts in the ratio 3:2.

2. Divide 240 schillings in the ratio 5:1.

3. Share 420 francs in the ratio 25:3.

4. Share 750 jelly babies in the ratio 6:4.

5. Divide 10.2 m into two parts in the ratio 9:8.

*See the glossary, p. 447.

6. Share £5.07 in the ratio 6:7.

7. (a) Share 3200 cm in the ratio 9:7.
   (b) Share 3200 cm in the ratio 7:9.

8. (a) Share 3200 cm in the ratio 9:3.
   (b) Share £120 in the ratio 14:21.

9. £84 was shared between Conall and Shari in the ratio 4:3. How much did each receive?

10. 1.2 ℓ of lemonade was shared between Ifan and April in the ratio 3:5. How much did each receive?

11. £144 was divided between Oxfam and the RSPCA in the ratio 7:2. How much did each receive?

12. Brass is an alloy made up of copper (Cu) and zinc (Zn) in the ratio 3:2. If there is 1.9 kg of brass, find:
   (a) how much copper it contains,
   (b) how much zinc it contains.

Exercise 16

1. If Susan received £36, when some money was shared between John and herself in the ratio 3:4, how much money was shared?

2. The sum of the ages of David and Ann is 44 years. In four years time the ratio of David's age to Ann's age will be 6:7. Find their present ages.

3. £95 is to be shared between Jack and Jill such that Jill should receive $\frac{2}{3}$ of the amount received by Jack. How much do they each receive?

4. Helen and Joanne share some money in the ratio 8:5. If Joanne receives £40, how much money was being shared?

5. In a test, Mark got $\frac{2}{3}$ of the total possible mark. The ratio of Jennifer's mark to Mark's mark was 3:4. If Jennifer got 45 marks, what was the total possible mark?

6. Ian and Stuart share some marbles in the ratio 7:4. If Ian received 12 more marbles than Stuart, how many did Stuart receive?

Proportion (Direct Proportion)

If you earn £3 an hour you should be paid £6 for working 2 h, £9 for working 3 h, £12 for working 4 h, and so on.

Your earnings depend on the number of hours worked.

$$\text{More hours} \longrightarrow \text{more pay}$$
$$\text{Less hours} \longrightarrow \text{less pay}$$

Hours worked and earnings are said to be in *direct proportion.*

The proportional relationship between the two quantities can be seen from a table.

Hours worked	1	2	3	4	5	6	7	8
Earnings (£)	3	6	9	12	15	18	21	24

$$\tfrac{1}{3} = \tfrac{2}{6} = \tfrac{3}{9} = \tfrac{4}{12} = \tfrac{5}{15} = \tfrac{6}{18} = \tfrac{7}{21} = \tfrac{8}{24}$$

Note   If you double the hours worked you double the earnings; in fact, whatever number the hours worked are multiplied by, the earnings are multiplied by the same number.

Exercise 17

Draw a pair of axes as shown.
Plot and draw a graph using the table given above.

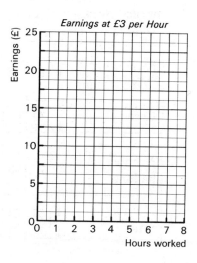

Earnings at £3 per Hour

Note   The graph obtained is the sort of graph you will always obtain when illustrating two quantities that are in direct proportion.

Exercise 18

For each of the following, write whether it is 'TRUE' or 'FALSE':

1. 3 cartons of milk cost £1.17 so 6 cartons of the same size cost £2.34.

2. When 2 people watch a TV programme, it lasts $1\frac{1}{2}$ h. If 4 people watch the same programme, it will last 3 h.

3. When 4 people listen to a record, it lasts 3 min. If 20 people listen to that same record, it will last 15 min.

4. At the age of 30 years, Ben can jump a height of 2 m. When he is 90 years old he will be able to jump a height of 6 m.

5. 2 ℓ of orange can fill 6 identical glasses, so 3 ℓ of orange will be able to fill 9 glasses of the same size as before.

6. A 14-year-old boy takes size 7 in shoes. When he is 28 years old he will take size 14.

7. From the top of a cliff 1 person can see 9 miles, so 4 people will be able to see 36 miles.

8. Maniksha is 12 year's old and is 5 ft tall. When she is 24 year's old she will be 10 ft tall.

Exercise 19   **M**

The tables give sets of numbers that are in direct proportion. Copy and complete them.

1.

Number of items bought	1	2	3	6	8	10	12	15	20
Cost (£)	?	?	21	?	56	?	?	?	?

2.

Number of gallons	1	3	4	5	?	9	?	?	16
Number of miles	?	?	148	?	259	?	444	555	?

3.	Number of packs	3	?	?	15	21	27	?	48	57
	Total mass (kg)	?	8	12	?	28	?	48	?	?

4.	Number of cookies made	?	8	20	28	?	?	48	52	?
	Quantity of sugar (g)	15	?	75	?	120	135	?	?	315

Here are three different methods of solving the same proportion problem. (You need not learn all three.)

Problem   4 pens cost £32. Find the cost of 6 pens, if they all cost the same.

Method 1   (Making a table)

Number of pens	4	2	6
Cost (£)	32	16	48

So 6 pens cost £48.

Method 2   (Unitary method)
    4 pens cost £32
so   1 pen costs £8 $(32 \div 4)$
∴   6 pens cost £48 (6×8)

Method 3   (Ratio method)
    4 pens cost £32
so   6 pens cost $\dfrac{6}{4} \times 32$ pounds $= £48$

The reasoning for method 3 is:
We can multiply by $\frac{4}{6}$ or $\frac{6}{4}$ (the ratio of the numbers of pens); since *more* pens cost *more* money, it is necessary to multiply by $\frac{6}{4}$ (it gives a bigger answer).

Exercise 20

1. If 2 books cost £14, what would 4 books at the same price cost?

2. If 3 bars of chocolate cost £1.56, what would be the cost of 12 bars of the same sort and size?

3. I require 1200 mm of wood to frame 2 photographs of the same size. What length of wood do I need to be able to frame 6 photographs of the same size as the first two?

4. If it takes 15 m of material to make 5 pairs of curtains a certain size, how many pairs of curtains of the same size can I make with 45 m of material?

5. A building is 10 storeys high and the number of steps between each floor is always the same. If there are 114 steps in 6 flights, how many steps will I climb up if I climb only 2 flights?

6. A shop sells packets of foreign stamps, where each packet costs the same. If 2 packets cost 56 p, what would 3 packets cost?

7. If it takes me 4 h to walk 20 km, how long will it take, at the same speed, to walk 35 km?

8. 5 theatre tickets cost £20. What would 3 tickets cost for the same-priced seats?

9. 4 pencils cost 84 p, what would 6 pencils of the same type cost?

10. 3 bars of chocolate weigh 750 g. What would 7 similar-sized bars weigh?

11. Travelling at a steady speed, I travel 96 km in 2 h. How far would I travel in $2\frac{1}{2}$ h, travelling at the same speed?

12. 4 identical books cost £15.80, what would 10 of the same sort of book cost?

Revision Exercises
I to VII

Revision Exercise I

1. $M = \{$months of the year that contain a letter A$\}$
   List set M.

2. Describe the set $\{25, 30, 35, 40, 45, 50, 55, 60\}$ in words.

3. $9 \boxed{?} \{$divisors of 2835$\}$. What is the missing symbol, $\notin$ or $\in$?

4. The set of even numbers that are factors of $95 = \emptyset$.
   Is the above statement true or false?

5. $\mathscr{E} = \{$natural numbers that are less than 16$\}$ $F = \{$factors of 15$\}$
   (a) Show the above sets on a Venn diagram.
   (b) List F'.

6. Are the sets $\{$m, y, t, h, i, c, a, l$\}$ and $\{$y, i, t, e, m, c, h, l$\}$ equal sets?

7. Combine each pair of sets as instructed. Re-arrange the letters of each answer to form a word. Carry out the instruction given by the seven words.
   (a) $A = \{$w, h, i, t, e, r$\}$ $B = \{$t, w, i, r, l, e, d$\}$ Find $A \cap B$.
   (b) $C = \{$o, t, h, e, r$\}$ $D = \{$t, h, e, m$\}$ Find $C \cap D$.
   (c) $F = \{$t, e, a, s$\}$ $G = \{$s, e, n, t$\}$ Find $F \cap G$.
   (d) $H = \{$o, f, t, e, n$\}$ $J = \{$l, o, a, f$\}$ Find $H \cap J$.
   (e) $K = \{$c, a, r, t, s$\}$ $L = \{$s, o, f, a$\}$ Find $K \cup L$.
   (f) $M = \{$f, o, r, g, e$\}$ $N = \{$f, o, n, d$\}$ Find $M \cap N$.
   (g) $P = \{$f, r, y$\}$ $Q = \{$r, o, t$\}$ Find $P \cup Q$.

8. (a) Copy the diagram and shade $A \cup B$.
   (b) On another copy of the Venn diagram, shade $A' \cup B$.

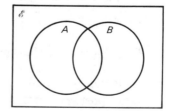

9. In a survey, it was discovered that 28 people had either a pen or a pencil or both with them. 6 had a pencil but no pen, 23 did not have a pencil and 8 had neither a pencil nor a pen.
   (a) Draw a Venn diagram to show the above information.
   (b) How many had both a pencil and a pen?
   (c) How many had a pen but no pencil?
   (d) What was the total number of people questioned?

Revision Exercise II

1. There were 1068 people at a concert:
   (a) Write the number in words.
   (b) Round the number correct to the nearest hundred.

2. There were 27 600 people at the match correct to the nearest hundred. Find:
   (a) the largest number of people before rounding,
   (b) the smallest number of people before rounding.

3. Mr Tudor earned £287 for 38 h work. Working with one significant figure, estimate the amount earned per hour.

4. Find the missing digits:

$$
\begin{array}{r}
\boxed{?}\ 3\ \boxed{?}\ 2 \\
-\ 5\ \boxed{?}\ 4\ 9 \\
\hline
2\ 4\ 6\ \boxed{?} \\
\hline
\end{array}
$$

5. Work out by a quick method, without using a calculator:
   $693 + 572 + 207$

6. Copy and complete:
   (a) $793 + 254 = 800 + \boxed{?}$
   (b) $619 - 225 = \boxed{?} - 200$

7. Find the sum of the numbers from 1 to 200 inclusive.

8. Eight lampposts, along a straight stretch of road, are positioned 50 m apart. How far is it between the two end ones?

Revision Exercise III

1. For each shape, write the number of lines of bilateral symmetry:

   (a) 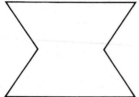 (b)

2. On a copy of the given shape, draw the line of bilateral symmetry.

3. What is the order of rotational symmetry of the given shape?

4. Name the type of triangle that has the given number of axes of bilateral symmetry. If no such triangle exists, say so.

   (a) 0   (b) 1   (c) 2   (d) 3

5. A plane shape has exactly two axes of bilateral symmetry. Must the two axes be perpendicular? Investigate this.

Revision Exercise IV

1. (a) Draw a rectangle of length 9 cm and breadth 3 cm.
   (b) Divide the length into 6 equal parts and the breadth into 4 equal parts then, by drawing straight lines, divide the rectangle up into 24 small rectangles.
   (c) Shade $\frac{3}{8}$ of the original rectangle.
   (d) How many small rectangles should you have shaded?

2. Work out:

(a) $3\frac{5}{8} + 2\frac{1}{5}$ (b) $4\frac{3}{8} - 2\frac{5}{6}$ (c) $2\frac{2}{5} \times 2\frac{3}{16}$ (d) $3\frac{1}{3} \div 1\frac{1}{6}$

3. Work out: $2\frac{7}{10} \times (1\frac{1}{2} + 2\frac{2}{3})$

4. Write $\frac{4}{15}$ as the sum of two different fractions having unit numerators. Try to find three different solutions.

5. Crystal spent $\frac{3}{8}$ of her brother's money. If her brother had £45.60, how much of her brother's money did Crystal spend?

6. Mrs Farmer sold 162 kg out of 270 kg of potatoes. What fraction was that?

7. There were two fields. One field had an area of $1\frac{1}{2}$ acres and the other an area of $1\frac{2}{3}$ acres. Find the total area of the two fields.

8. Work out: $12 \times \frac{5}{12}$ of £3.42

Revision Exercise V

1. Calculate the labelled angles:

(a)

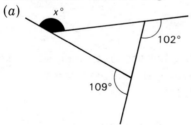

(b)

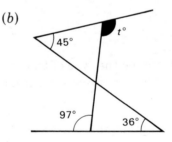

2. (a) What is the supplement of 39°?
(b) What is the complement of 82°?

3. Calculate the labelled angles:

(a)

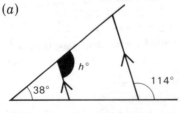

(b)

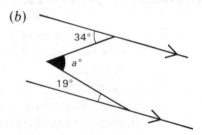

4. (*a*) Sketch the diagram. On your copy, fill in all the missing angles.

(*b*) What sort of triangle is:
  (i) △BCD?
  (ii) △ACD?

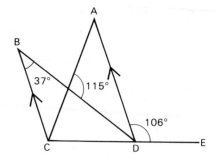

5. Construct quadrilateral ABCD using the information given in the diagram below (you are not allowed to use a protractor). Measure both diagonals.

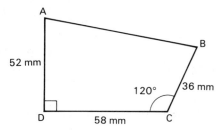

6. The diagram is of a regular tetrahedron. Each of the four faces is an equilateral triangle. If each edge measures 45 mm:

(*a*) Make an accurate drawing of face ABC.

(*b*) Make an accurate drawing of section ADE, where E is the mid-point of BC.

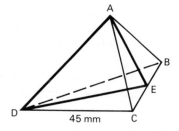

Revision Exercise VI ━━━━━━━━━━━━━━ **M**

1. Write these decimals correct to the nearest whole number:
  (*a*) 3.56   (*b*) 7.495   (*c*) 301.802   (*d*) 39.96

2. (*a*) Round 7.8659 correct to two decimal places.
  (*b*) Round 42.7995 correct to three decimal places.

3. How many significant figures are there in:
  (*a*) 7.024?   (*b*) 0.006 15?   (*c*) 30.031?   (*d*) 0.057 00?

4. (a) Round 0.930 64 correct to two significant figures.
   (b) Round 36.095 correct to four significant figures.
   (c) Round 0.0487 10 correct to three significant figures.

5. Estimate the answers to these. Work with one significant figure.
   (a) 9.87×62.3

   (b) 0.0804×3.71

   (c) $6.358 \div 0.294$

   (d) $\dfrac{4.86 \times 9.187}{5.702}$

   (e) $\dfrac{56.91 + 83.2}{6.74}$

6. Work out the following, giving each answer correct to three significant figures:
   (a) 8.76×0.95

   (b) $27.2616 \div 3.7$

   (c) $4.29 \div 0.74$

   (d) $\dfrac{7.8 \times 1.77}{5.24}$

   (e) $\dfrac{64.9 - 38.7}{1.4 \times 0.46}$

7. Brass has a density of 8.4 g per cm^3. Calculate the mass of 6.7 cm^3 of brass.

8. An 8.3 cm length of wire has a resistance of 10.707 ohms. Calculate the resistance of 1 cm of the wire.

9. Anna worked 32 h a week and earned £2.48 per hour. Calculate her weekly earnings.

10. If you were paid £4.16 an hour, for how many hours would you need to work to earn £162.24?

11. Mr Gould earned £297.48 in a week (gross). Deductions totalled £108.72. Calculate his net pay.

12. A dress, priced at £39.95, was sold for £32.99 in a sale. How much discount was that?

13. Some furniture cost £799.99 cash. It could be bought on HP for a deposit of £160 followed by 24 equal payments of £38.67.
    (a) Calculate the hire-purchase price.
    (b) How much could be saved by paying cash?

14. Copy and complete the invoice:

Quantity	Item	Unit cost	Cost	
			£	p
1	fishing rod	@ £29.95		
1	reel	@ £7.80		
3	nylon line	@ £2.49		
4	packet of hooks	@ 87 p		
3	float	@ £1.15		
1	bait box	@ £1.90		
		Total cost		

15. If $\dfrac{1}{n}$ gives a recurring decimal, write ten possible values of n.

Revision Exercise VII

1. How many times as big as 16 m is 80 m?

2. Write these ratios in their simplest form:
(a) 12:15   (b) 1.5:0.9   (c) $4\frac{2}{3}:5\frac{5}{6}$

3. Write as ratios in their simplest form:
(a) 3 cm to 18 mm
(b) £1.80 to £75 p
(c) $3\frac{3}{4}$ yd to $4\frac{1}{6}$ yd

4. If $42:63 = 2:\boxed{?}$, what is the missing number?

5. If $\boxed{?}$ to 24 kg = 7:3, what is the missing quantity?

6. Write, in its simplest form, the ratio 24:32:16.

7. For the given triangle find, in its simplest form:
   (a) the ratio of the largest to the smallest side,
   (b) the ratio of the smallest side to the perimeter.

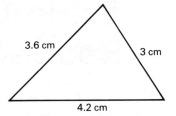

8. A lemon drink is diluted with water in the ratio $1:3$. If 1.5 ℓ of water is used:
   (a) How much lemon is used?
   (b) How many litres are made up altogether?

9. Write the ratio $8:5$ in the form:
   (a) $1:m$ (b) $m:1$

10. Which is the better value for money, 4 kg for £3.10 or 3.5 kg for £2.80?

11. Density is the ratio of mass to volume (written in the form $m:1$). Calculate, to three decimal places, the density of cast iron in grams per cubic centimetre, if 481 cm^3 of cast iron has a mass of 3.448 kg.

12. Mr Fairbank saved £45 from his £200 earnings, while Mrs Hughes saved £55 from her earnings of £250:
    (a) Who saved more money?
    (b) Calculate their savings to earnings ratios. Give your answers in the form $n:1$.
    (c) Who has the higher savings to earnings ratio?

13. £82.50 was shared between two people in the ratio $4:7$. Calculate the larger share.

14. 75 g sugar is used in making 24 nut cookies:
    (a) How much sugar is needed in making:
        (i) 48 nut cookies? (ii) 16 nut cookies?
    (b) How many nut cookies can be made using:
        (i) 300 g sugar? (ii) 100 kg sugar?

8 Scale Drawings and Bearings

The Idea of a Scale

Exercise 1

Look at the scale of the map below. Measure each distance between the points marked. What is the distance in kilometres from:

1. Shell Cove to South-East Point?
2. Sun River to Reed Lake?
3. Moonlight Mountains to Copper Cliffs?
4. Reed Lake to Golden Lagoon?
5. South-East Point to Sun River?
6. Copper Cliffs to Shell Cove?
7. Periwinkle Bay to Moody River?
8. Spyglass Hill to Swaying Palms?
9. Ruby River to Paradise Bay?
10. Moonlight Mountains to Shell Cove?

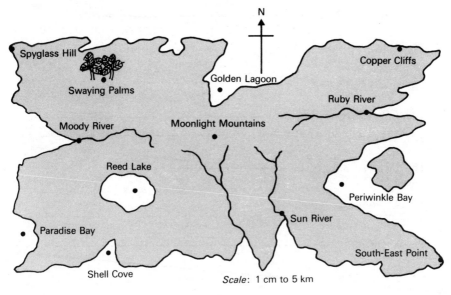

Scale: 1 cm to 5 km

113

Exercise 2

Each line has been drawn to the given scale. Find its true length.

1. 1 cm to ? m —————————————————————

? ? to 8 m —————————————

? m to 4 cm ——————————————————

4. (a) 1 cm to 0.5 m —————————————————
(b) 10 cm to 5 m ————————————————

5. 1 cm represents 6 m ————————————

6. 1 cm represents 12 km ———————

7. 1:5 ——————————————————————————

8. 1:20 ——————————————————————

9. 1:40 —————————————————————

10. 1:100 ——————————

11. 1 mm to 3 cm ————————————————————

12. 1 cm represents 30 cm ————————

13. 1 cm represents 25 km ———————————————

14. (a) 1 mm to 8 mm —————————————————————
(b) 1 cm to 8 cm ——————————————————————

15. 1 cm to 2.5 km ——————————————————

16. 1:1000

——————————————————————————————

17. 1:100 000 ———————————————————————

18. 1:2 000 000 ———————————————

1. Here is a plan of a bungalow. It is drawn to a scale of 1:100.

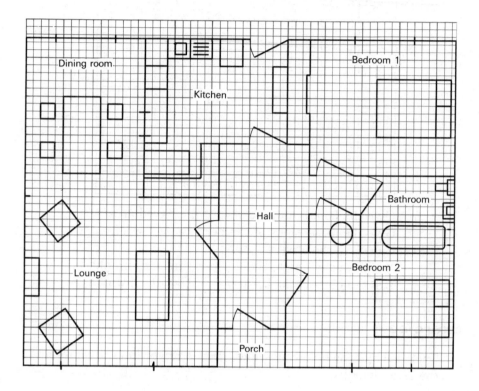

(a) Give the length and breadth of:
   (i) bedroom 2,
   (ii) the bathroom.
(b) Give the dimensions of the porch.
(c) Give the dimensions of the cylinder cupboard (next to the bathroom)
(d) Give the dimensions of bedroom 1 (do not include the wardrobe space).
(e) If the lounge and dining room were separate give the dimensions of:
   (i) the lounge,
   (ii) the dining room.
(f) Give the largest length and breadth of the kitchen.
(g) Give the overall dimensions of the bungalow.

2. Here is a plan of a garden:

Scale 1:250

(*a*) Give the length and breadth of the paved area.
(*b*) Give the dimensions of the herbaceous border.
(*c*) Calculate the area of:
    (i) the paved area,   (iii) the shrubbery,
    (ii) the herbaceous border,   (iv) the lawn.

Exercise 4

Using each of the following scales, draw straight lines to represent the given lengths:

A 1 cm represents 4 m
    1. 12 m   **2.** 40 m   **3.** 26 m   **4.** 34 m   **5.** 15 m

B 1 cm to 5 km
    1. 40 km   **2.** 15 km   **3.** 55 km   **4.** $22\frac{1}{2}$ km   **5.** 36 km

C 1:200
    1. 10 m   **2.** 16 m   **3.** 19 m   **4.** 3 m   **5.** 7.6 m

D 1:600
    1. 24 m   **2.** 54 m   **3.** 63 m   **4.** 21 m   **5.** 69 m

E 1 cm represents 300 m
    1. 2100 m   **2.** 1.2 km   **3.** 3 km   **4.** 750 m   **5.** 1.92 km

F

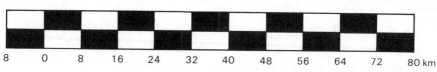

8   0   8   16   24   32   40   48   56   64   72   80 km

1. 40 km   **2.** 96 km   **3.** 52 km   **4.** 34 km   **5.** 74.4 km

G 1:400 000
1. 40 km   **2.** 48 km   **3.** 16 km   **4.** 22 km   **5.** 31 km

H 1:5 000 000
1. 100 km   **2.** 450 km   **3.** 175 km   **4.** 205 km   **5.** 330 km

Exercise 5   M

Trace the elephant. Next to it, try to draw yourself. (Use the same scale.)

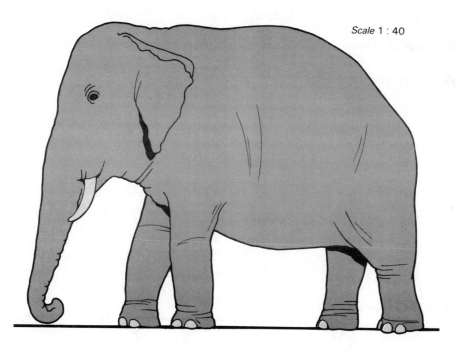

Scale 1 : 40

Bearings

The diagram shows the positions of two ships, one at P and the other at Q. Q is at a *bearing* of 065° from P. The bearing is the angle measured clockwise from *North*.

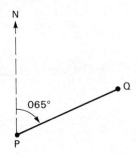

Note that if a bearing is measured *from* P, the angle itself must be at P. The bearing can have any value up to 360° and must be written using three figures. Such bearings are called *three-figure bearings* (or *circular bearings* or *absolute bearings*).

Note   To write that Q is at a bearing of 65° from P (for the diagram above) is incorrect. Three digits *must* be used.

Exercise 6

A For each diagram, give the bearing of Q from P:

1.
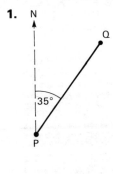

2.
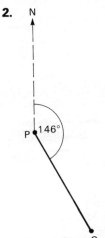

3.
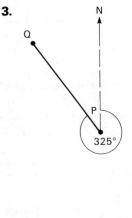

118

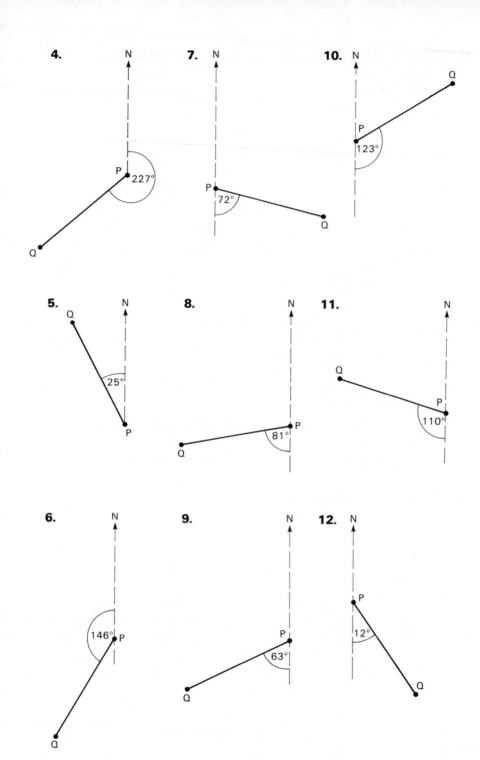

4.

5.

6.

7.

8.

9.

10.

11.

12.

119

B **1.** What is the bearing of:
     (a) Y from X?
     (b) Z from X?

3. What is the bearing of:
     (a) M from P?
     (b) K from P?

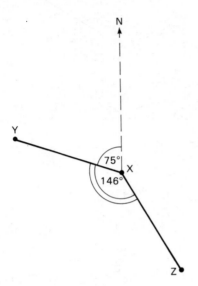

2. What is the bearing of:
     (a) B from A?
     (b) C from A?

4. What is the bearing of:
     (a) F from Q?
     (b) G from Q?

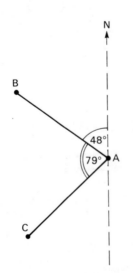

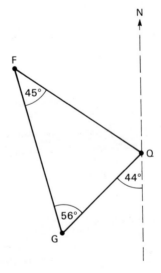

Bearings and Scale Drawings

Exercise 7

1. Mark a point P near the centre of your page (you need at least 4 cm in each direction from the point). Draw a North line.

Using a scale of 1:40000 plot these points:
(a) A, which is 2 km from P at a bearing of 045°,
(b) B, which is 1.6 km from P at a bearing of 215°,
(c) C, which is 1.4 km from P at a bearing of 153°,
(d) D, which is 800 m from P at a bearing of 296°.

2. Cambridge is 42 km at a bearing of 080° from Bedford, while Melton Mowbray is 75 km at a bearing of 338° from Bedford. Using a scale of 1 cm to 10 km, make a scale drawing to show the positions of the three places.

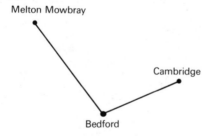

By measuring, find:
(a) the distance of Melton Mowbray from Cambridge,
(b) the bearing of Melton Mowbray from Cambridge,
(c) the bearing of Cambridge from Melton Mowbray.

Exercise 8 **M**

You need a copy of the map given on the next page.

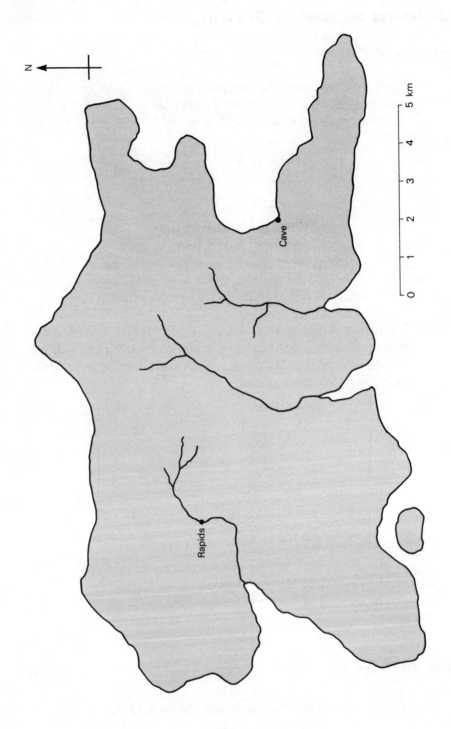

A On your copy of the map, mark the following places:

1. The Wreck, which is 7 km on a bearing of 054° from the Rapids.

2. The Palm Tree, which is 4 km from the Rapids and 6 km from the Cave (show two positions).

3. The Creek, which is 5 km from the Rapids and 8.5 km from the Cave.

4. Death Forest, which is 7.9 km on a bearing of 116° from the Rapids.

5. Paradise Mountains at 4.7 km on a bearing of 295° from the Cave.

B 1. On your copy of the map, follow the given instructions to find the treasure. Mark an X on the map where the treasure lies.

Start at the cave then travel:
   3 km at 330°,
   1 km due west,
   2.5 km at 205°,
   2.3 km at 318°,
   then 5.8 km at 218°.

2. If you followed the instructions in question 1, but in a different order, would the treasure be in the same place?

Angles of Elevation and Depression

The *angle of elevation* is the angle measured *upwards* from the horizontal to an object. The angle of elevation of the top of the building from the man is 10°.

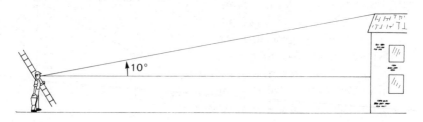

The *angle of depression* is the angle measured *downwards* from the horizontal to an object. The angle of depression of the boat from the girl is 20°.

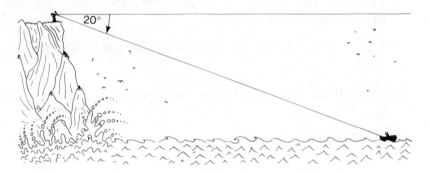

Remember that both of these angles are measured from the horizontal.

'Elevate' means 'to raise or lift';
'the angle of elevation' is 'the turn upwards'.

'Depress' means 'to push down or lower';
'the angle of depression' is 'the turn downwards'.

Exercise 9   Further Scale Drawings

1. The angle of elevation of the top of an Ash tree from a point on the ground, 40 m from the foot of the tree, is 23°.
   Make a scale drawing using a scale of 1 cm to 5 m. Find the height of the tree.

   23°
   40 m

2. From the top of a building, 20 m high, the angle of depression of a point on the ground is 29°.
   Make a scale drawing using a scale of 1 cm to 4 m and use it to find the distance of the point from the foot of the building.

   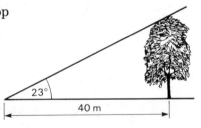

   29°
   20 m
   ?

124

3. P, Q and R are trees on each side of a river as shown. QR = 55 m, PQ = 50 m and PR = 40 m. Find, by making a scale drawing, the width of the river. (Use a scale of 1 cm to 5 m.)

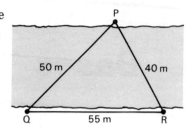

4. A ladder leans against a wall and makes an angle of 70° with the ground. The foot of the ladder is 1.6 m from the bottom of the wall.

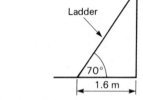

(*a*) Make a scale drawing. Use a scale of 1:50.

(*b*) How long is the ladder?

(*c*) How high up the wall does the ladder reach?

(*d*) If the foot of the ladder is now moved until it is 2.5 m from the bottom of the wall:

    (i) Make a scale drawing to show the new position of the ladder.

    (ii) How far up the wall does the ladder now reach?

    (iii) What angle does the ladder now make with the ground?

5. The triangle has been drawn to a scale of 1:60. Draw it to a scale of 1:15.

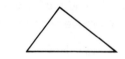

6. The drawing shows a plan of a tennis court. The dimensions are given in feet.

Draw a plan of the tennis court. (If you have a ruler marked in inches, use a scale of 1 in to 20 ft; otherwise, choose your own scale.)

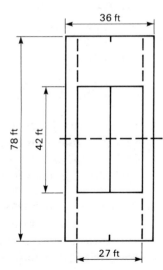

9 Bases

There are 20 crosses in the diagram.
There are 3 groups of six.
There are 2 crosses left over.
There are 32_6 crosses.

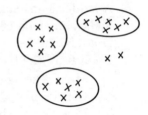

Note In 32_6, the six means we are grouping in sixes. We say there are 32 crosses in base 6. The small number 6, called the *subscript,* tells you which base it is.

Exercise 1

Throughout this exercise, if the base is not stated, you should presume that the number is in base ten.

A 1. (*a*) How many crosses are shown?
  (*b*) Draw around groups of five.
  (*c*) How many groups of five are there?
  (*d*) How many crosses are left over?
  (*e*) Write, in base 5, the number of crosses shown.

2. If there are 20 crosses:
  (*a*) How many groups of eight could there be?
  (*b*) How many crosses would be left over?
  (*c*) Write, in base 8, the number 20.

3. If there are 13 crosses:
  (*a*) How many groups of four could there be?
  (*b*) How many crosses would be left over?
  (*c*) Write 13 in base 4.

4. If there are 32 crosses:

(*a*) How many groups of six could there be?

(*b*) How many crosses would be left over?

(*c*) Write 32 in base 6.

B Tins of beans are packed in boxes of 8:

1. How many tins are there in 4 boxes?

2. How many tins are there if there are 3 boxes and 7 tins left over?

3. How many boxes are needed to hold 56 tins?

4. If there are 62 tins, how many boxes are needed and how many tins will be left over?

5. How many tins are there if there are 7 boxes and 3 tins left over?

Exercise 2

A Copy the following but write the correct number in place of each question mark:

e.g. 63_8 = $\boxed{?}$ eights + $\boxed{?}$ units = $\boxed{?}_{ten}$

63_8 = 6 eights + 3 units = 51_{ten}

1. 41_5 = $\boxed{?}$ fives + $\boxed{?}$ units = $\boxed{?}_{ten}$

2. 12_4 = $\boxed{?}$ fours + $\boxed{?}$ units = $\boxed{?}_{ten}$

3. 37_9 = $\boxed{?}$ nines + $\boxed{?}$ units = $\boxed{?}_{ten}$

4. 11_2 = $\boxed{?}$ twos + $\boxed{?}$ units = $\boxed{?}_{ten}$

5. 62_7 = $\boxed{?}$ sevens + $\boxed{?}$ units = $\boxed{?}_{ten}$

6. 59_{12} = $\boxed{?}$ twelves + $\boxed{?}$ units = $\boxed{?}_{ten}$

B Convert the following numbers from their given base into base ten:

1. 23_6	**5.** 24_5	**9.** 44_5	**13.** 43_8	**17.** 50_{16}
2. 41_8	**6.** 46_9	**10.** 21_3	**14.** 33_5	**18.** 18_{12}
3. 17_9	**7.** 32_7	**11.** 32_4	**15.** 78_9	**19.** 45_{12}
4. 35_8	**8.** 23_4	**12.** 40_6	**16.** 77_8	**20.** 39_{16}

Exercise 3

Convert the following numbers from base ten into the given base:

1. 9_{ten} to base 4
2. 25_{ten} to base 8
3. 38_{ten} to base 9
4. 12_{ten} to base 4
5. 27_{ten} to base 6

6. 40_{ten} to base 8
7. 17_{ten} to base 5
8. 8_{ten} to base 3
9. 26_{ten} to base 7
10. 58_{ten} to base 8

11. 66_{ten} to base 9
12. 45_{ten} to base 9
13. 28_{ten} to base 6
14. 61_{ten} to base 12
15. 72_{ten} to base 16

Exercise 4

Eggs are packed into cartons of 6.
6 cartons of 6 eggs then fill a box.

1. How many eggs does each box hold?

2. How many eggs have I got if I have:
   (a) 5 cartons?
   (b) 3 cartons and 4 eggs?
   (c) 4 boxes?
   (d) 2 boxes and 4 eggs?
   (e) 1 box and 5 cartons?
   (f) 2 boxes, 1 carton and 4 eggs?
   (g) 4 boxes, 5 cartons and 1 egg?
   (h) 5 boxes, 2 cartons and 3 eggs?

3. Write the number of boxes and cartons needed and the number of eggs left over when the given numbers of eggs are packed:
   (a) 29   (c) 54   (e) 90   (g) 119
   (b) 39   (d) 75   (f) 85   (h) 190

Exercise 5

A Copy the following, but write the correct number in place of each question mark:

1. $314_6 = \boxed{?}$ thirty-sixes, $\boxed{?}$ sixes and $\boxed{?}$ units $= \boxed{?}_{ten}$

2. $231_5 = \boxed{?}$ twenty-fives, $\boxed{?}$ fives and $\boxed{?}$ units $= \boxed{?}_{ten}$

3. $140_8 = \boxed{?}$ sixty-fours, $\boxed{?}$ eights and $\boxed{?}$ units $= \boxed{?}_{\text{ten}}$

4. $101_2 = \boxed{?}$ fours, $\boxed{?}$ twos and $\boxed{?}$ units $= \boxed{?}_{\text{ten}}$

5. $323_4 = \boxed{?}$ sixteens, $\boxed{?}$ fours and $\boxed{?}$ units $= \boxed{?}_{\text{ten}}$

6. $627_9 = \boxed{?}$ eighty-ones, $\boxed{?}$ nines and $\boxed{?}$ units $= \boxed{?}_{\text{ten}}$

B Change the following numbers from the given base into base ten:

1. 312_4	**6.** 110_7	**11.** 123_4
2. 212_3	**7.** 220_3	**12.** 204_6
3. 203_5	**8.** 320_4	**13.** 453_7
4. 110_3	**9.** 122_4	**14.** 216_9
5. 110_4	**10.** 213_5	**15.** 157_{12}

C Convert the following numbers from the given base into base ten:

1. 1101_2	**5.** 1423_5	**9.** 2012_3
2. 1201_3	**6.** 10110_2	**10.** 1032_5
3. 1110_2	**7.** 110101_2	**11.** 4006_8
4. 3102_4	**8.** 110201_3	**12.** 1101110_2

Exercise 6

Convert these from base ten to the given base:

A

1. 46 to base 8		**7.** 99 to base 6
2. 21 to base 5		**8.** 86 to base 5
3. 74 to base 9		**9.** 150 to base 7
4. 47 to base 7		**10.** 256 to base 9
5. 58 to base 4		**11.** 101 to base 6
6. 25 to base 3		**12.** 356 to base 12

B

1. 41 to base 2		**5.** 231 to base 4
2. 100 to base 4		**6.** 317 to base 5
3. 65 to base 3		**7.** 86 to base 2
4. 236 to base 8		**8.** 182 to base 3

Using a Calculator

Exercise 7

e.g. 1 Change 2314_5 from base 5 to base ten.

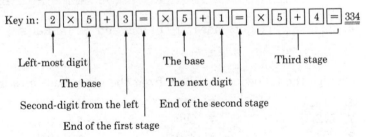

Key in: 2 × 5 + 3 = × 5 + 1 = × 5 + 4 = 334

Left-most digit
The base
Second-digit from the left
End of the first stage
The base
The next digit
End of the second stage
Third stage

The third stage is a repeat of the second stage but using the next digit from the left.
The second stage is repeated for each digit that remains.

e.g. 2 Convert 120102_3 to base ten.

Key in: 1 × 3 + 2 = × 3 + 0 =

× 3 + 1 = × 3 + 0 = × 3 + 2 = 416

You could save time by missing out the steps + 0
Now try some of the questions in Exercise 5 using a calculator.

Exercise 8

A Convert 710_{ten} to base 4.

1. Find and write the base 4 headings. These can be found by keying:

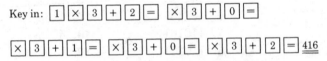

1 × 4 × 4 × 4 × 4 and so on.

Stop as soon as you reach a number that is bigger than the number in the question (710 in this case).
The required headings are: 256 64 16 4 1

2. Clear the display.

3. Key in the given number ([7] [1] [0]).   710

4. Subtract the left-most heading

  ([−] [2] [5] [6] [=]).   454

Repeat the subtraction until the display is
less than the heading (<256).   198

Note how many subtractions were carried out
(in this case, 2). That number should be
written under the heading that was being
subtracted.

    256   64   16   4   1
     2

5. Move to the first heading to the right that is   134
less than the display. (In this case the next,   70
the number 64.) Subtract that heading as   6
many times as necessary until the display is
smaller than it. The number of subtraction (3
in this case) should be written under the
heading being subtracted:

    256   64   16   4   1
     2   3

6. Repeat step 5 as many times as necessary   (−4)
until the display is zero. Zero should be written   2
under any heading that does not have a digit   (−1)
under it (16 in this case).   1

    256   64   16   4   1   (−1)
     2   3   0   1   2   0

B **1.** Test the method on questions in Exercise 6.

    2. Try to work out a method of your own that uses a calculator.

Exercise 9

List the numbers from 1 to 40. Next to each number, list the binary numbers that have the same value.

Some of the entries in your list should be:

$$1 = 1$$
$$2 = 10$$
$$3 = 11$$
$$\cdot \qquad \cdot$$
$$\cdot \qquad \cdot$$
$$\cdot \qquad \cdot$$
$$9 = 1001$$
$$10 = 1010$$
$$\cdot \qquad \cdot$$
$$\cdot \qquad \cdot$$
$$\cdot \qquad \cdot$$
$$23 = 10111$$
$$\cdot \qquad \cdot$$
$$\cdot \qquad \cdot$$
$$31 =$$
$$\cdot \qquad \cdot$$
$$\cdot \qquad \cdot$$
$$\cdot \qquad \cdot$$
$$\cdot \qquad \cdot$$
$$\cdot \qquad \cdot$$
$$40 =$$

ASCII CODE

When a key is depressed on a computer keyboard, a signal is sent to the computer. This signal is in the form of a binary code. The most commonly used code is ASCII*. The ASCII code for A is 1000001 which has 7 *bits* (binary digits). A is called an *upper case* letter (a capital letter) while small letters, such as a, are called *lower case*. The ASCII codes for various letters and numbers are shown opposite.

Note   If the first 2 bits are 1 1 the character is a lower case letter; if the first 2 bits are 1 0 the character is an upper case letter; if the first 3 bits are 0 1 1 the character is a number.

*See the glossary, p. 443.

Lower case	Binary	ASCII	Upper case	Binary	ASCII	Number	Binary	ASCII
a	1	1100001	A	1	1000001	1	1	0110001
b	10	1100010	B	10	1000010	2	10	0110010
c	11	1100011	C	11	1000011	3	11	0110011
d	100	1100100	D	100	1000100	4	100	0110100
e	101	1100101	E	101	1000101	5	101	0110101
f	110	1100110	F	110	1000110	6	110	0110110
g	111	1100111	G	111	1000111	7	111	0110111
h	1000	1101000	H	1000	1001000	8	1000	0111000
i	1001	1101001	I	1001	1001001	9	1001	0111001

Code for lower case letters — Binary for letter position — Code for upper case letters — Binary for letter position — Code for numbers — Binary for the numbers

Exercise 10

A In each question, the ASCII code for letters and/or numbers has been given. Find what has been written.

1. 1010000
1000101
1000111

2. 1010011
1101111
1110101
1110100
1101000

3. 0110110
0110011
0110000

4. 1000010
1100001
1110011
1100101
1110011

5. 1110100
1101000
1100101

6. 1010000
1101111
1110010
0111001
0110010
0110100

B Write the following in ASCII code:

1. CHORD
2. East
3. 5178
4. metric
5. Percentage
6. eight

133

Hexadecimal

Exercise 11

In base ten, ten different symbols are used for the digits:

    0, 1, 2, 3, 4, 5, 6, 7, 8 and 9

How many different symbols are needed for the digits in the following?

1. base 2.   **2.** base 8.   **3.** base 5.   **4.** base 16.

Base 16 is called *hexadecimal* (*hex* for short). Sixteen different symbols are needed for the digits (0 to 9 plus six others). Hex and octal are both used in computing (for data, instructions and addressing).

Long strings of binary digits can be shortened and become easier for a programmer to handle if they are written in hex or octal.

In some computers, when a program is being loaded into the computer from tape, the number of the block being loaded at that instant is shown on the screen. The numbering is probably in hex. The six extra symbols used are usually the first six letters of the alphabet. Here are some numbers in base ten and in hex.

Base ten	Hex	Base ten	Hex
1	1	9	9
2	2	10	A
3	3	11	B
4	4	12	C
5	5	13	D
6	6	14	E
7	7	15	F
8	8	16	10

Base ten	Hex	Base ten	Hex
17 (16 + 1)	11	25 (16 + 9)	19
18 (16 + 2)	12	26 (16 + 10)	1A
19	13	27 (16 + 11)	1B
20 (16 + 4)	14	28	1C
21	15	29	1D
22	16	30 (16 + 14)	1E
23	17	31	1F
24 (16 + 8)	18	32	20

Exercise 12

A Convert the following numbers from hexadecimal to base ten:

e.g. 1 $43_{hex} = 4 \times 16 + 3 \; = 64 + 3 \; = \underline{\underline{67_{ten}}}$

e.g. 2 $3E_{hex} = 3 \times 16 + 14 = 48 + 14 = \underline{\underline{62_{ten}}}$

1. 19_{hex} **5.** $5F_{hex}$

2. 28_{hex} **6.** $6A_{hex}$

3. $2B_{hex}$ **7.** $8C_{hex}$

4. $4D_{hex}$ **8.** AB_{hex}

B Convert the following numbers from base ten to hexadecimal:

e.g. $91_{ten} = 5B_{hex}$ (since $5 \times 16 + 11 = 91$)

1. 46_{ten} **5.** 79_{ten}

2. 49_{ten} **6.** 135_{ten}

3. 60_{ten} **7.** 160_{ten}

4. 88_{ten} **8.** 122_{ten}

1. Copy and complete the following table:

	Base ten	Base 2	Base 3	Base 4	Base 5	Base 6	Base 7	Base 8
Odd	1	1	1	1	?	?	?	1
Even	2	10	2	2	?	?	?	?
Odd	3	11	10	?	3	?	3	?
Even	4	?	11	10	?	4	?	?
Odd	5	101	12	?	?	?	?	5
Even	6	?	?	?	11	?	?	?
Odd	7	?	?	?	?	?	?	?
Even	8	?	?	?	?	12	?	?
Odd	9	?	?	21	?	?	?	11
Even	10	?	?	?	?	?	13	?
Odd	11	?	102	?	?	?	?	?
Even	12	1100	?	?	22	?	?	?
Odd	13	?	?	?	?	?	?	?
Even	14	?	?	?	?	?	?	?

2. How would you recognise an even number in base:

   (a) 10?

   (b) 2?

   (c) 4?

   (d) 8?

   (e) 6?

   (f) 5?

   (g) 3?

   (h) 7?

Exercise 14

1. Which binary number follows 10111_2?

2. Which binary number comes immediately before 11010?

3. Which base 8 number comes immediately before 560_8?

4. Which of these are even numbers:
    421_4, 302_5, 110010_2, 326_8, 21012_3?

5. What is the smallest number that ends in 0 when written in both bases 3 and 5?

6. Write these binary numbers in order of size from largest to smallest:
    101101_2, 1000101_2, 100101_2, 110101_2,
    1000111_2, 1001001_2

Two-state Systems

Exercise 15   Railway Sidings

The drawing shows some railway sidings.
Every 100 m there is a set of points at which the line splits into two lines.

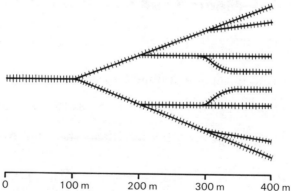

Find the missing numbers:

1. At 100 m the line splits into [?] lines.

2. At 200 m the line splits into [?] lines.

3. At 300 m the line splits into $\boxed{?}$ lines.

4. At 400 m the line splits into $\boxed{?}$ lines.

5. At 500 m the line splits into $\boxed{?}$ lines.

6. At 600 m the line splits into $\boxed{?}$ lines.

Exercise 16   A Family Tree

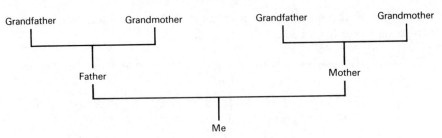

If the family tree was continued to show earlier generations, how many of the following would there be?

1. parents,

2. grandparents,

3. great grandparents,

4. great great grandparents,

5. great great great grandparents,

6. great great great great grandparents.

Exercise 17   Magic Cards   M

Either use the given set of six magic cards opposite or make your own set.

A 1. Ask a friend to think of a number between 1 and 63.

2. Ask that person to show you which cards the number is on.

3. You can then quickly tell your friend the number he or she thought of.

To do this, add the numbers in the top left-hand corners of the cards your friend shows you. This total is the required number.

B 1. Look at the numbers in the top left-hand corner of each card. Which base do the numbers suggest?

2. Try to work out why the method works.

Hint Write down the numbers from 1 to 63 in base 2.

1	3	5	7	9	11	13	15
17	19	21	23	25	27	29	31
33	35	37	39	41	43	45	47
49	51	53	55	57	59	61	63

2	3	6	7	10	11	14	15
18	19	22	23	26	27	30	31
34	35	38	39	42	43	46	47
50	51	54	55	58	59	62	63

4	5	6	7	12	13	14	15
20	21	22	23	28	29	30	31
36	37	38	39	44	45	46	47
52	53	54	55	60	61	62	63

8	9	10	11	12	13	14	15
24	25	26	27	28	29	30	31
40	41	42	43	44	45	46	47
56	57	58	59	60	61	62	63

16	17	18	19	20	21	22	23
24	25	26	27	28	29	30	31
48	49	50	51	52	53	54	55
56	57	58	59	60	61	62	63

32	33	34	35	36	37	38	39
40	41	42	43	44	45	46	47
48	49	50	51	52	53	54	55
56	57	58	59	60	61	62	63

Make a set of 15 cards like the card shown below. (The holes should be in the same position on each card.)

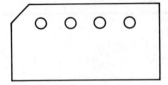
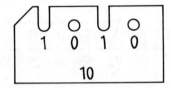

Number the cards from 1 to 15. (Number 10 is shown above.)

Cut out slots on each card using the binary system. A hole stands for 0 and a slot for 1. In the example, 10 is 1010 in binary, so slots are cut out from the left-hand hole and the third from left.

Now shuffle the cards.

Base ten	Base 2
1	0001
2	0010
3	0011
4	0100
5	0101
6	0110
7	0111
8	1000
9	1001
10	1010
11	1011
12	1100
13	1101
14	1110
15	1111

Push a needle through the right-hand holes in the cards. Lift the needle. (The cards with slots in this position will be left behind.) Place the set of cards picked up with the needle at the front of the pack. Now push the needle through the second hole from the right. The cards lifted out should again be placed at the front.

Repeat this for the third hole from the right and then the fourth hole (the left-hand hole).

The cards should now be sorted into order from 1 to 15.

Cut out of paper some rectangles to stand for masses. You can make the three shown.

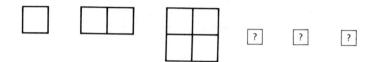

To weigh 1 oz, a shopkeeper can use a 1 oz mass.
To weigh 2 oz, a shopkeeper can use a 2 oz mass.
To weigh 3 oz, a 2 oz and a 1 oz mass can be used.
To weigh 4 oz, a 4 oz mass can be used.
For 5 oz, a 4 oz and a 1 oz mass can be used, and so on.

Try to find out what the next three masses must be so that the shopkeeper can weigh up to 63 oz. Record your answers in a table:

Use a 1 for a mass that is used and 0 for a mass that is not used.

Make out the table to weigh up to 40 oz.

Amount to be weighed	Masses needed					
	[?]	[?]	[?]	4 oz	2 oz	1 oz
1 oz	0	0	0	0	0	1
2 oz	0	0	0	0	1	0
3 oz	0	0	0	0	1	1
4 oz	0	0	0	1	0	0
5 oz	0	0	0	1	0	1
6 oz	0	0	0	1	1	0
⋮						
38 oz	[?]	[?]	[?]	1	[?]	0
39 oz	[?]	[?]	[?]	[?]	[?]	[?]
40 oz	[?]	[?]	[?]	[?]	[?]	[?]

Exercise 20

A Using scales, masses are normally placed all on the same pan. Suppose the masses are placed on either or on both pans, and that we have five masses, 1 oz, 3 oz, 9 oz and two unknown masses:

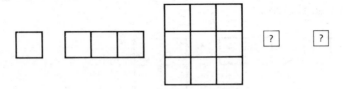

To weigh 11 oz, put the 9 oz mass with the 3 oz mass on one pan (12 oz total). With 1 oz on the other pan, an 11 oz mass is needed to balance the scales.

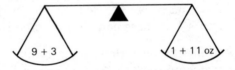

1. Find the two missing masses mentioned above that will allow the heaviest possible mass to be weighed and yet still allow all possible whole numbers of ounces up to that heaviest mass to be weighed.

2. Explain with a diagram how to weigh 43 oz using any of the five masses above and using both pans of a pair of scales.

B 1. Using masses of 1 oz, 4 oz, 9 oz and 16 oz, which masses up to 30 oz cannot be weighed using these four masses, if they can be used on either or on both pans?

2. Which two masses up to 33 oz cannot be weighed using the masses 1 oz, 3 oz, 11 oz and 18 oz, if they can be used on either or both pans?

3. Which masses up to 45 oz cannot be weighed using the masses 2 oz, 5 oz, 9 oz and 29 oz, if they can be used on either or both pans?

142

10 Time, Timetables and the Calendar

Time

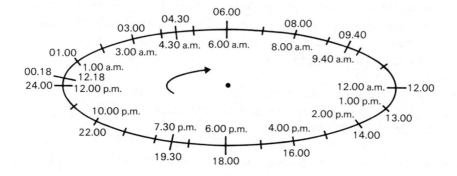

Exercise 1

1. How many seconds are there in:
   (a) 1 min?   (b) 8 min?   (c) 15 min?   (d) 42 min?

2. How many minutes are there in:
   (a) 3 h?   (b) 7 h?   (c) 9 h?   (d) 19 h

3. How many seconds are there in:
   (a) 3 min 19 s?   (b) 7 m 43 s?   (c) 14 min 56 s?

4. How many hours are there in:
   (a) 300 min?   (b) 480 min?   (c) 660 min?   (d) 1080 min?

5. A runner ran 12 laps of a track at 63 s per lap. How long did that take in minutes and seconds?

6. A 4 × 400 m relay was run in 2 min 58 s. The first three legs were run in 44.32 s, 44.95 s and 44.76 s. How fast was the last leg?

7. How many days are there in:
   (a) 96 h?   (b) 39 weeks?   (c) 48 weeks?

8. How many weeks are there in:

(a) 56 days?   (b) 98 days?   (c) 189 days?

Exercise 2

A How long is a minute? Try this:

With a friend's help, try to estimate 1 min. Your friend should use a stopwatch or an ordinary watch that shows seconds. When he or she tells you to start, try to estimate 1 min. Tell your friend when you think exactly 1 min has passed. Note the actual time measured. By how many seconds were you wrong?

Now time your friend.

B Use a stopwatch to help you to find the number of beats your pulse makes in 30 s. (It may be easier if a friend helps you.)

How many beats would that be per minute?

C **1.** Type the following program into a computer (it should work on most computers):

```
1Ø   REM***TIMING***
2Ø   LET I = Ø
3Ø   PRINT "START"
4Ø   FOR N = 1 TO 1ØØ
5Ø      LET I = I + 1
6Ø   NEXT N
7Ø   PRINT "STOP"
8Ø   END
```

2. Have a stopwatch ready and run the program. When START is printed, start the stopwatch. When STOP is printed, stop the stopwatch. Note the time taken for the program to run.

3. Change line 4Ø of the program as follows then repeat step 2 above:

(a) 4Ø   FOR N = 1 TO 5ØØ
(b) 4Ø   FOR N = 1 TO 1ØØØ
(c) 4Ø   FOR N = 1 TO 5ØØØ
(d) 4Ø   FOR N = 1 TO 1ØØØØ
(e) 4Ø   FOR N = 1 TO 5ØØØØ

4. What is the program making the computer do after printing START and before printing STOP?

144

5. Compare the times you have noted.
    (a) Is the time for 10000 (in line 40, question 3(d)) double the time for 5000 (in 3(c))?
    (b) Is the time for 50000 five times the time for 10000?

6. If possible, run the program on different makes of computer. Find out which computer is fastest in running this program.

D A drug manufacturer is not only interested in the product formed by a reaction but also in how fast the reaction is (the *rate of reaction*). A product that is formed quickly is likely to be cheaper to manufacture. You may have carried out this experiment in science:

1. Measure 50 cm^3 of 0.2 M sodium thiosulphate solution into a conical flask.

2. Put 5 cm^3 of 2 M hydrochloric acid into a measuring cylinder.

3. Mark a cross on a piece of filter paper.

4. Place the conical flask over the cross.

5. Pour the acid into the sodium thiosulphate solution, start a stopwatch and shake the flask gently. Put the flask back on top of the cross.

6. Look at the cross on the filter paper through the solution (look from above). Stop the watch when the cross just disappears.

7. Rinse the flask immediately.

8. Note the time taken.

9. Repeat the above steps with 50 cm^3 of diluted solution, using:
    (a) 40 cm^3 of 0.2 M sodium thiosulphate solution and 10 cm^3 of water,
    (b) 30 cm^3 of 0.2 M sodium thiosulphate solution and 20 cm^3 of water,
    (c) 20 cm^3 of 0.2 M sodium thiosulphate solution and 30 cm^3 of water,
    (d) 10 cm^3 of 0.2 M sodium thiosulphate solution and 40 cm^3 of water.

10. How does the time change as the solution gets weaker?

Exercise 3

A Write these times using the 24-hour clock notation:

1. half-past four in the morning,

2. twenty past seven in the evening,

3. quarter-past two in the afternoon,

4. twenty minutes to ten in the evening,

5. quarter to seven in the morning,

6. twenty-three minutes past ten in the morning,

7. fourteen minutes to four in the afternoon,

8. nine minutes past midnight,

9. six minutes to nine in the morning,

10. eighteen minutes to one in the afternoon.

B Write the times in part A using the 12-hour clock notation.

C Write these times in words (do not forget to state whether the time is in the morning, afternoon or evening):

1. 01.15	**5.** 13.35	**9.** 18.56	**13.** 2.51 a.m.
2. 4.25 p.m.	**6.** 10.40 a.m.	**10.** 9.17 a.m.	**14.** 23.43
3. 17.05	**7.** 11.50	**11.** 07.32	**15.** 03.26
4. 20.18	**8.** 12.30 p.m.	**12.** 22.59	**16.** 5.54 p.m.

D Write these times using the 24-hour clock notation:

1. 8.15 a.m.	**4.** 9.50 a.m.	**7.** 11.40 p.m.	**10.** 8.03 p.m.
2. 6.20 p.m.	**5.** 10.10 a.m.	**8.** 4.58 a.m.	**11.** 1.16 p.m.
3. 9.45 p.m.	**6.** 10.21 p.m.	**9.** 2.47 p.m.	**12.** 12.25 a.m.

E Write these times using the 12-hour clock notation:

1. 03.10	**4.** 01.55	**7.** 15.12	**10.** 12.36
2. 17.25	**5.** 16.48	**8.** 21.57	**11.** 00.50
3. 19.35	**6.** 23.05	**9.** 02.18	**12.** 14.45

Intervals of Time

Exercise 4

1. How many hours are there from 7 o'clock in the morning until 9 o'clock in the evening?

2. How many hours are there from 16.25 until 09.25 on the following day?

3. How many hours are there from 20.15 on Thursday until 07.15 on the following Tuesday?

4. A concert started at 19.45 and finished at 22.10. How long did it last?

5. A train left at 11.14 and arrived at its destination 3 h 55 min later. What was its time of arrival?

6. A radio broadcast started at 21.25 and lasted 1 h 18 min. At what time did it finish?

7. A coach left London at 08.47 and arrived in Edinburgh at 17.14. How long did the journey take?

8. My train was 37 min late when it arrived in York at 13.16. At what time should it have arrived?

9. Mr Chopra arrived at his destination at 13.12 after travelling for $2\frac{1}{2}$ h. At what time had he set off?

10. A coach set off at 09.22 and was already 28 min late. The journey took the same length of time as usual. If the bus was due to arrive at its destination at 15.06, at what time did it actually arrive?

11. A train arrived at its destination at 19.25, the journey having taken 37 min longer than usual. If it had set off at its correct time of 13.54, at what time should it have arrived?

12. A coach arrived at its destination 13 min late at 12.05. It had left its point of departure at the scheduled time of 09.17. How long should the journey normally take?

Exercise 5 Using a Timetable

Hereford → Worcester

Mondays to Fridays

								D		E					
								◇		◇					
								125		**125**					
Miles								∅		∅					
0	Hereford	d	09 31	....	....	11 50	....	13 48	....	15 33	16 46	17 39	....	18 47	19 30	21 25
14	Ledbury	d	10 48	..	..	12 10$_e$	..	14 06	..	15 50	17 03	17 58	..	19 05	19 51$_p$	21 45$_q$
18	Colwall	d	09 56	....	....	12 18	....	14 14	....	15 58	17 11	18 06	....	19 13	19 59	21 53
21	Great Malvern	d	10 02	10 31	10 59	12 27$_e$	13 14	14 20	14 50	16 03	17 19	18 15	18 58	19 19	20 04	22 03$_q$
22	Malvern Link	d	10 06	10 34	11 02	12 30	13 17	14 23	14 53	16 07	17 22	18 18	19 01	19 22	20 07	22 06
28¾	Worcester Foregate St.	d	10 17	10 45	11 13	12 41	13 26	14 33	15 02	16 17	17 33	18 29	19 12	19 33	20 18	22 20$_q$
29½	Worcester Shrub Hill	a	....	10 47	11 15	12 43	13 28	14 36	15 04	....	17 35	18 31	19 14	19 35	20 20	22 22

Worcester → Hereford

Mondays to Fridays

													BHX	◇	
													◇	G	
													⬭	⬭	
Worcester Shrub Hill	d	06 25	07 05	08 12	....	10 48	12 46	15 48	16 30	....	17 51	18 34	19 20	20 22	22 03
Worcester Foregate St.	d	06 28	07 08	08 15	10 25	10 51	12 49	15 51	16 33	17 28	17 54	18 37	19 24	20 25	22 06
Malvern Link	d	06 37	07 17	08 25	10 36	11 00	12 58	16 01	16 42	17 39	18 03	18 46	19 34	20 35	22 15
Great Malvern	d	06 40a	07 23	08 30	10 40	11 04	13 05j	16 05	16 46	17 44	18 07	18 50	19 37	20 40	22 19
Colwall	d	....	07 30	08 39	10 47	11 10	13 11	16 11	16 52	17 50	18 13	18 56	19 43	20 45	22 25
Ledbury	d	..	07 40	08 46	10 53	11 17	13 20	16 18	17 04n	17 58	18 20	19 06c	19 50	20 53	22 32
Hereford	a	....	07 58	09 03	11 10	11 35	13 38	16 37	17 22	18 16	18 38	19 24	20 07	21 10	22 50

◇	Seats may be reserved	a	Arrival time
125	Train formed of Inter City 125 stock	d	Departure time
∅	Hot dishes available to order	e	Arr. Ledbury 12 06, Great Malvern 12 23
1	Also conveys first class accommodation	e	Arr. 19 46
BHX	Does not run on Bank Holidays	q	Arr. Ledbury 21 41, Great Malvern 21 58
⬭	Buffet car of trolley service		Worcester Foregate Street 22 15
D	Cotswold and Malvern Express	j	Arr. 13 02
E	Cheltenham Spa Express	n	Arr. 16 59
G	Cathedrals' Express	c	Arr. 19 02

Use the above timetable to answer the following:

1. If I leave Hereford at 17.39, at what time should I arrive at Worcester Shrub Hill?

2. If I leave Malvern Link at eleven o'clock in the morning, at what time should I arrive in Hereford?

3. Give the time, in minutes, of the journey from Colwall to Worcester Shrub Hill on the 12.18 train from Colwall.

4. If I miss the 17.54 train from Worcester Foregate St. by 4 min, how long must I wait for the next train?

5. I want to travel from Great Malvern to Hereford, leaving Great Malvern between 7 o'clock and 8 o'clock in the evening. Which train should I catch?

6. If I arrived in Worcester, at Foregate St. station, at 14.33, at what time must I have left Ledbury?

7. Travelling from Colwall to Worcester Foregate St., I wish to arrive at Worcester Foregate St. before half-past eight in the evening. At what time should I leave Colwall?

8. At what time must I have left Malvern Link to arrive in Ledbury at 16.59?

9. For how many minutes does the 12.46 from Worcester Shrub Hill stop at Great Malvern?

10. If I arrived in Hereford at 21.10, what was the name of the train I travelled on?

11. Draw the symbol used when there is a buffet car.

12. A train arrives in Ledbury at 21.41, at what time should it arrive at Great Malvern?

13. At what time does the Cheltenham Spa Express leave Malvern Link?

14. A girl from Ledbury has an interview in Hereford at 14.30. The place where the interview is to be held is 15 min from the station. Which train should the girl catch?

15. Give one way of travelling from Hereford to Worcester Shrub Hill on the train to arrive at Worcester Shrub Hill before 11 o'clock in the morning.

149

A Copy and complete the time card below:

Day	In	Out	In	Out	Total time

Employer: Mint Brothers

Department: Accounts

Name: E.B. IDLE

Employee's Ref. No.: 09165

Week ending: 16 March

Day	In	Out	In	Out	Total time
Mon	08.45	12.00	13.00	17.00	? h ? min
Tue	08.50	11.45	13.15	16.30	? h ? min
Wed	08.30	12.10	13.05	?	8 h 05 min
Thur	08.45	?	12.55	16.45	7 h 00 min
Fri	08.55	12.15	?	17.00	6 h 40 min
Sat	?	12.40	—	—	4 h 05 min
				Total time for the week	? h ? min

B Some people work *flexitime*. That means they can vary the times they work each day.

Make out a time card for Mrs F. Sharp-Major. She needs to work 33 h 45 min during the week. She does not work on Saturday or Sunday. She must start in the morning between 08.00 and 09.45 and finish at any time between 16.00 and 18.00. Lunch can be taken between 11.45 and 14.15.

The Calendar

Many different calendars have been used in various parts of the world. Our calendar is based on the Roman calendar. The oldest Roman calendar is probably due to Romulus, the first King of Rome (753–715 BC). The year was 304 days long and was divided into ten months, the first month being Martius (March).

Numa Pompilius, the second king (715–672 BC) is said to have added the two months Januarius and Februarius.

The months were:

(1) Martius	(5) Quintilis	(9) Novembris
(2) Aprilis	(6) Sextilis	(10) Decembris
(3) Maius	(7) Septembris	(11) Januarius
(4) Junius	(8) Octobris	(12) Februarius

When Julius Caesar ruled Rome he decided to make the calendar astronomically correct. He decreed that the year 46 BC would have 445 days, and following that year, each year would have 365 days, with an extra day every fourth year. He decreed that the year should begin with Januarius. Quintilis, the month in which he was born, was changed to Julius. The month of Sextilis was later named after the Emperor Augustus.

The Julian calendar was used until AD 1582 when it was changed slightly by Pope Gregory XIII. It was calculated that a year was not $365\frac{1}{4}$ days long but was 365 days, 5 h, 49 min and 12 s long. In the countries that accepted this new-style calendar, the day after 4 October 1582 became 15 October. The Gregorian calendar was not adopted in Great Britain until 1752 when 11 days were 'lost'.

In the Julian calendar a year is a leap year if it divides exactly by 4 (just divide the last two digits). This is also true of the Gregorian calendar except when the last two digits of a year are both zeros. Then, the first two digits must also divide exactly by 4 (that is, the year must divide by 400). So in the Julian calendar the first year in each new century was a leap year, while in the Gregorian calendar only one in four was a leap year.

e.g. 1 1964 was a leap year (64 divides exactly by 4).

e.g. 2 1938 was not a leap year.

e.g. 3 2200 will not be a leap year (22 does not divide exactly by 4).

151

Other calendars have since been suggested. In 1931, two schemes were put forward, one was for 13 months of 28 days and the other was as follows:

Jan 31 days	Apr 31 days	July 31 days	Oct 31 days
Feb 30 days	May 30 days	Aug 30 days	Nov 30 days
Mar 30 days	June 30 days	Sept 30 days	Dec 30 days

In both schemes an extra day at the end of each year would be needed. Leap years would be as in the Gregorian calendar. Neither scheme was accepted.

Exercise 7

1. Which of the following years were leap years?
   1924, 1930, 1941, 1944, 1950, 1956, 1966, 1976

2. How many days are there in September?

3. How many days were there in:
   (a) February 1928? (b) February 1962?

4. How many days were there from:
   (a) 16.30 on 17 March 1974 to 16.30 on 15 April 1974?
   (b) noon on 13 February 1980 to noon on 8 April 1980?

5. A cinema was closed from 21 December until 4 January inclusive. How many days was that?

6. Hayley set off on holiday on 24 July and returned on 6 August. For how many nights was she away?

7. Find the number of days from midnight on 23 May 1970 until midnight on 14 September 1974.

8. What is the date 75 days after 14 February 1984?

9. If 23 April is a Friday, on what day is 30 May of the same year?

10. If today is 13 March, what will be the date in exactly 6 weeks' time?

11. If 19 January was a Thursday, what will be the date of the first Thursday in March if it is a leap year?

12. 27 November is a Tuesday. What was the date of the last Tuesday in May of the same year?

13. 16 August is a Saturday. What was the date of the first Monday in March of the same year?

14. Mr Worthington was 65 years old on 16 October 1986. In which year was he born?

15. How many leap years were there from 1871 to 1987 inclusive?

16. Give the reason why the year 1900 was not a leap year, but the year 2000 will be, even though both numbers are exactly divisible by 4.

Time Zones

Since the Sun appears to rise in the east, places east of Greenwich have noon before it is noon at Greenwich (noon GMT), while places to the west have their noon later.

In 24 h, the Earth rotates through 360°.
In 1 h, the Earth rotates 15°.

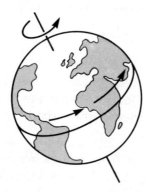

The world is divided into 24 *time zones*. The time zones approximately follow the lines of longitude. (Places to the east are ahead in time by about 1 h for every 15° E. Places to the west are behind by about 1 h for every 15° W.)

Exercise 8   A Holiday in Corfu

You can fly to Corfu from:
Gatwick 3 h 25 min
Luton 3 h 30 min
Bristol 3 h 35 min
Cardiff 3 h 40 min
Birmingham 3 h 35 min
East Midlands 3 h 40 min
Manchester 3 h 45 min
Teesside 3 h 45 min
Newcastle 3 h 50 min
Glasgow 3 h 55 min
Edinburgh 3 h 55 min

The time in Corfu is
2 h ahead of the time
in the UK.

The Suppl. column shows
the flight supplements.

Departure Airport and Day	No. of Nights	First Departure	Last Departure	Take-off Time	Home Landing	Flight Code	Suppl. (£)
GATWICK (Mon)	7/14	2 May	24 Oct/17 Oct	17.45	16.45	5209	18
LUTON (Thur)	7/14	5 May	20 Oct/13 Oct	07.30	00.45 (Fri)	5210	0
BRISTOL (Mon)	7/14	2 May	24 Oct/17 Oct	09.15	01.30 (Tue)	5211	16
CARDIFF (Mon)	14	2 May	17 Oct	17.45	16.45	5212*	26
BIRMINGHAM (Thur)	7/14	5 May	20 Oct/13 Oct	07.30	15.15	5213	19
E. MIDLANDS (Mon)	14	9 May	10 Oct	17.45	16.45	5214*	27
MANCHESTER (Mon)	7/14	2 May	24 Oct/17 Oct	08.45	01.45 (Tue)	5215	20
MANCHESTER (Mon)	10	2 May	17 Oct	08.45	16.45 (Thur)	5215	0
MANCHESTER (Thur)	7/14	5 May	20 Oct/13 Oct	07.00	16.45	5216	24
MANCHESTER (Thur)	11	5 May	20 Oct	07.00	01.45 (Tue)	5216	0
TEESSIDE (Thur)	14	12 May	13 Oct	17.00	15.15	5220*	34
NEWCASTLE (Thur)	7/14	5 May	20 Oct/13 Oct	08.30	15.15	5217	33
GLASGOW (Mon)	14	2 May	17 Oct	06.30	01.15 (Tue)	5218*	36
EDINBURGH (Thur)	14	5 May	6 Oct	16.45	15.45	5219	45

Please Quote: Flight Code, Hotel Code and Number of Nights required

All flights weekly except those marked *fortnightly.

REMEMBER TO ADD: AIRPORT CHARGES £10.30, INSURANCE 7 nts £6.50, 10/11 nts £7.20, 14 nts £7.80

Use the information above to help you to answer these questions:

1. Mr and Mrs Bainbridge flew from East Midlands Airport to Corfu on 17 August:
   (a) At what time did they take off?
   (b) What was the time in Corfu when they landed?
   (c) On the return journey, what was the time in Corfu when they took off from Corfu Airport?

2. Mr and Mrs Mackay flew from Edinburgh to Corfu on 6 June:
   (a) How many nights' holiday did they have?
   (b) On what day did they take off?
   (c) What was the time in Corfu when they landed?
   (d) What was the time in Corfu when they took off from:
       (i) Edinburgh?
       (ii) Corfu?

3. For each departure airport given, work out the time in Corfu when:

(a) the aeroplane lands in Corfu,

(b) the aeroplane takes off from Corfu.

Exercise 9 Miscellaneous Questions

Note The values given throughout this exercise are from *The Astronomical Almanac.*

A 1. A lunar month has, on average, 29.530 589 days. Use a calculator to find the length of a lunar month in days, hours, minutes and seconds, correct to the nearest second.

2. A sidereal month is 27.321 662 days long. Find its length in days, hours, minutes and seconds, correct to the nearest second.

3. A tropical year is 365.242 191 days long. Find its length in days, hours, minutes and seconds correct to the nearest second.

4. A sidereal year is 365.256 63 days long. Find its length in days, hours, minutes and seconds correct to the nearest second.

B For the months and years given in part A, find and write dictionary or encyclopedia definitions. For each one, if a different decimal value is given, change it to days, hours, minutes and seconds; then find the difference in seconds between the value given in part A and the value found.

11 Area

Rectangular Areas

Exercise 1

1. Calculate the area of a rectangle of length 12 cm by 8 cm.

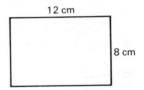

2. A rectangular mirror is 42.5 cm long and 32 cm wide. Calculate its area.

3. The floor of a classroom is 9.3 m long and 7.4 m wide. Calculate its area.

4. There are two bedrooms in a house. One is 5.3 m long and 3.8 m wide, while the other is 4.5 m square. Which has the larger area?

5. A painting measures 0.92 m by 0.64 m. Calculate its area.

6. How many 15 cm square tiles are needed to tile a rectangular area of wall measuring 2.55 m by 1.95 m?

7. Mrs Astley has four full boxes of 6 in square wall tiles with three dozen tiles in each box. If she uses them to tile two areas of wall, one measuring 6 ft 6 in by 2 ft 6 in and the other 4 ft by 4 ft 6 in, without wasting any of the tiles, how many tiles will be left? (12 in = 1 ft)

8. A carpet measuring 6 m by 4 m is cut to fit a room 5.6 m long and 3.8 m wide. What area of carpet is wasted?

9. (a) Calculate the area of the room shown here.
   (b) If carpet costs £9.70 per square metre and underlay costs a further £3 per square metre, calculate the total cost of carpet and underlay for this room.

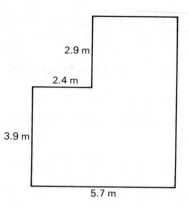

10. A carpet measuring 3.5 m by 2.5 m is placed on the floor of a room that is 5 m long and 4 m wide. What area of floor is not covered by the carpet?

11. A rectangular lawn is 57 ft long and 28 ft wide. A square flower bed with sides measuring $6\frac{1}{2}$ ft is cut out of the lawn. What area of lawn remains?

12. A rectangular garden, 27 m long, is fenced on three sides except for a 1.8 m gap in one of the long sides. 37 panels of fencing are used, each 1.8 m wide. Calculate the area of the garden.

Exercise 2   To Calculate a Length when an Area is Given

1. Calculate the missing dimension in each rectangle:
   (a)   (b)

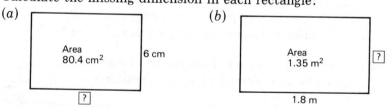

2. A rectangle is 14 cm long. If it has an area of 126 cm², calculate its width.

3. A rectangle of length 20 cm has a perimeter of 50 cm:
   (a) Calculate its area.
   (b) Find the length of side of a square that has the same area as the rectangle.

4. A square has an area of 81 cm^2:

    (*a*) Find the perimeter of the square.

    (*b*) A rectangle having the same-sized perimeter as the square is 11 cm long. Calculate the area of the rectangle.

5. A rectangular piece of paper has an area of 62 400 mm^2. If its width is 210 mm, calculate its length correct to three significant figures.

6. A rectangular kitchen floor is 4.05 m long. It is tiled using 513, 15 cm square tiles. What is the width of the kitchen?

Change of Units

Exercise 3

1. (*a*) Draw a 6 cm square.

    (*b*) Find the area of a 6 cm square.

    (*c*) Draw a rectangle with an area of 6 cm^2.

    (*d*) Is a 6 cm square the same size as 6 cm^2?

2. Is a 5 cm square the same size as 5 cm^2?

3. Must an area of 25 cm^2 be a square?

Exercise 4

1. (*a*) How many millimetres are there in 1 cm?

    (*b*) How many square millimetres are there in 1 cm^2?

2. (*a*) What is the area of the square in Fig. 1? (Give your answer in square centimetres.)

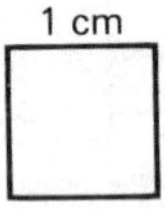

    1 cm

    Fig. 1

    (*b*) What is the area of the square in Fig. 2? (Give your answer in square millimetres.)

    10 mm

    Fig. 2

    (*c*) Since both squares are the same size, how many square millimetres are there in 1 cm^2?

3. (a) Draw a sketch of a square with sides of length 1 m. What is the area of this square (give your answer in square metres)?
   (b) Now draw a sketch of another square with sides that are also 1 m in length, but this time label the length of each side in centimetres. What is the area of this second square (give your answer in square centimetres)?
   (c) Since the squares in parts (a) and (b) have the same area, how many square centimetres are there in 1 m²?

4. 12 in = 1 ft
   How many square inches are there in 1 ft²? (A sketch may help.)

5. How many square feet are there in 1 yd²? (3 ft = 1 yd)

6. How many square yards are there in 1 mile²?
   (1760 yd = 1 mile)

Exercise 5

1. Cut out of paper, rectangles of sizes 9 cm by 2 cm, 7 cm by 2 cm, 6 cm by 3 cm, 6 cm by 1 cm, 5 cm by 4 cm, 5 cm by 3 cm, 5 cm by 2 cm, 5 cm by 1 cm, 4 cm by 3 cm, 4 cm by 1 cm, 3 cm by 3 cm, 3 cm by 2 cm, 3 cm by 1 cm and 2 cm by 2 cm.

2. (a) Can the 14 rectangles of question 1 be placed together to form a square?
   (b) If a square can be made, draw it and give the length of its side.

Exercise 6   Surface Area of a Cuboid

1. For the cuboid shown:
   (a) Sketch its net.
   (b) Calculate its surface area.

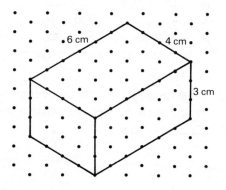

6 cm   4 cm   3 cm

159

2. A cuboid measures 11 cm by 6 cm by 5 cm. Calculate its surface area.

3. Each edge of a cube measures 6 cm. Calculate its total surface area.

4. A room is 4 m long, 3.8 m wide and 2.4 m high. Calculate the total area of all four walls, ignoring doors and windows.

5. A room is 5.2 m long, 4.1 m wide and 2.5 m high. Calculate:
   (a) the area of the ceiling,
   (b) the total area of all four walls ignoring any doors and windows.

Areas of Parallelograms and Triangles

Exercise 7

A Find the areas of parallelograms which have bases and perpendicular heights of the following sizes. (Give answers to three significant figures.)

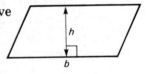

	Base	Perpendicular height		Base	Perpendicular height
1.	4.68 m	3.57 m	**6.**	8.173 m	9.604 m
2.	6.17 cm	5.23 cm	**7.**	12.56 m	9.348 m
3.	18.7 cm	12.4 cm	**8.**	76.18 m	39.32 m
4.	472 mm	385 mm	**9.**	21.5 cm	32 cm
5.	73.9 cm	93.4 cm	**10.**	14.9 cm	19.7 cm

B Find the areas of the following triangles giving each answer correct to three significant figures.

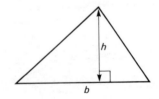

	Base	Perpendicular height			Base	Perpendicular height
1.	7.68 m	5.41 m	**6.**		4.082 m	3.792 m
2.	1.93 m	2.54 m	**7.**		86.4 cm	102.6 cm
3.	9.4 cm	7.6 cm	**8.**		415 mm	363 mm
4.	2.06 m	1.95 m	**9.**		3.907 m	1.099 m
5.	12.8 cm	14.7 cm	**10.**		17.6 cm	12.8 cm

Exercise 8 Transformation of Formulae

1. (a) $2x = 8$ Find x.
   (b) $2x = b$ Find x in terms of b.
   (c) $ax = b$ Find x in terms of a and b.

2. (a) $3t = 15$ Find t.
   (b) $et = 15$ Find t in terms of e.
   (c) $et = c$ Find t in terms of e and c.

3. $mp = h$ Find: (a) p in terms of h and m,
                              (b) m in terms of h and p.

4. $n = df$ Find: (a) d in terms of n and f,
                              (b) f in terms of n and d.

5. $A = lb$ Find: (a) l in terms of A and b,
                              (b) b in terms of A and l.

6. $A = bh$ Find: (a) b in terms of A and h,
                              (b) h in terms of A and b.

7. Find z if:

   (a) $\dfrac{z}{2} = 6$ (b) $\dfrac{z}{a} = 6$ (c) $\dfrac{z}{a} = y$

8. Find t if:

   (a) $\dfrac{t}{5} = 4$ (b) $\dfrac{t}{5} = l$ (c) $\dfrac{t}{k} = l$

9. Find A if $\dfrac{A}{b} = h$.

10. Find r if:

    (a) $\frac{1}{2}r = 5$ (b) $\frac{1}{2}r = s$

11. Copy and complete:

    (a) $\frac{1}{2}ab = 8$ (b) $\frac{1}{2}ab = c$ (c) $\frac{1}{2}ab = c$

          $ab = \boxed{?}$ $ab = \boxed{?}$ $ab = \boxed{?}$

           $a = \boxed{?}$ $a = \boxed{?}$ $b = \boxed{?}$

12. If $\frac{1}{3}Ah = V$, find h in terms of V and A.

13. If $m = \frac{1}{3}ng$:

    (a) Find n in terms of g and m.

    (b) Find g in terms of n and m.

14. If $A = \frac{1}{2}bh$:

    (a) Find b in terms of A and h.

    (b) Find h in terms of A and b.

Finding a Length when an Area is Given

Exercise 9   Parallelograms

A Calculate the area of each parallelogram:

1.

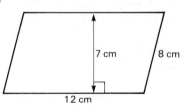

7 cm   8 cm   12 cm

3.

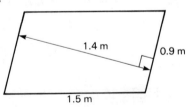

1.4 m   0.9 m   1.5 m

2.

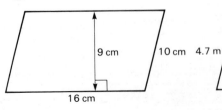

9 cm   10 cm   16 cm

4.

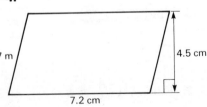

4.7 m   4.5 cm   7.2 cm

B Calculate the perpendicular height of each parallelogram:

1. Area = 63 cm²

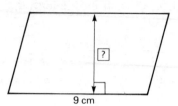

9 cm

3. Area = 1.24 m²

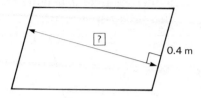

0.4 m

2. Area = 84 cm²

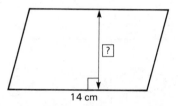

14 cm

4. Area = 20.8 m²

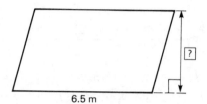

6.5 m

C Calculate the base of each parallelogram:

1. Area = 120 cm²

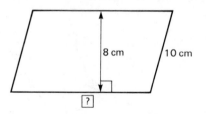

8 cm   10 cm

3. Area = 7.8 m²

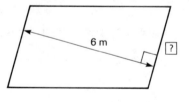

6 m

2. Area = 132 m²

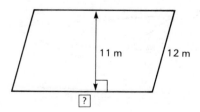

11 m   12 m

4. Area = 21.28 cm²

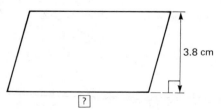

3.8 cm

D Calculate:
  (*a*) the area of each parallelogram,
  (*b*) the perpendicular height, labelled *h*, of each parallelogram.

1.

3.

2.

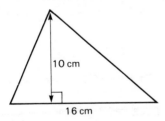

4.

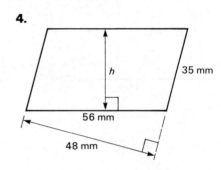

Exercise 10 Triangles

A Calculate the area of each triangle:

1.

3.

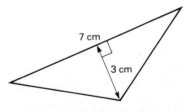

2.

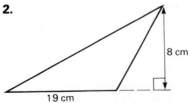

4.

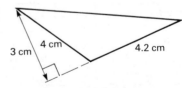

B Calculate the perpendicular height of each triangle:

1. Area = 28 cm²

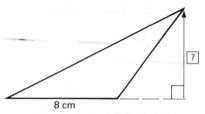

8 cm

3. Area = 1.35 cm²

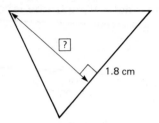

1.8 cm

2. Area = 78 cm²

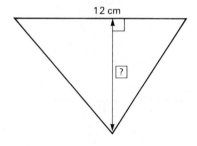

12 cm

4. Area = 252 cm²

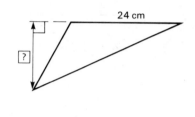

24 cm

C Calculate the base of each triangle:

1. Area = 45 m²

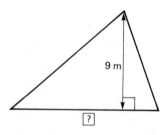

9 m

3. Area = 15.2 cm²

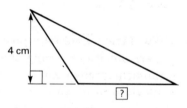

4 cm

2. Area = 105 cm²

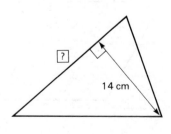

14 cm

4. Area = 26.68 cm²

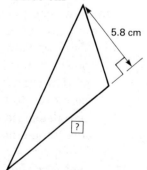

5.8 cm

165

D Calculate:
(a) the area of each triangle,
(b) the length of each side labelled b.

1.

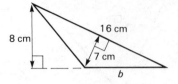

3.

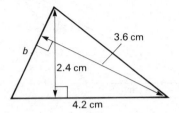

2.

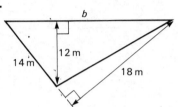

4.

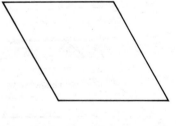

Area of Trapezia, Rhombuses and Kites

Exercise 11

1. Draw a trapezium on a piece of paper. Cut it out. Using one straight cut, cut your trapezium into two pieces so that the two pieces can be moved to form a parallelogram.

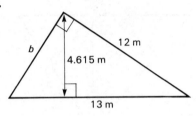

2. Draw two copies of a rhombus on a piece of paper. Cut them out.

(a) Using *one* straight cut, cut one rhombus into two pieces so that the two pieces can be moved to form a parallelogram that is neither a rectangle nor a rhombus.

(b) Using two straight cuts, cut the other rhombus into three pieces so that the pieces can be moved to form a rectangle.

Exercise 12

Copy and complete:

1. (*a*)

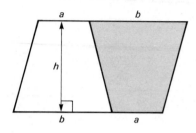

(*b*)

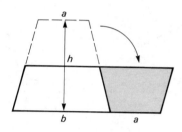

Area of a trapezium = ?

2.

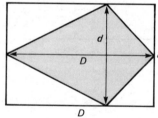

Length of long diagonal $= D$ units
Length of short diagonal $= d$ units
Area of a kite $= \boxed{?}$

3.

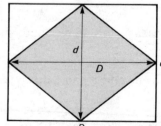

Length of long diagonal $= D$ units
Length of short diagonal $= d$ units
Area of a rhombus $= \boxed{?}$

Exercise 13

A Calculate the area of each of the following trapezia:

1.

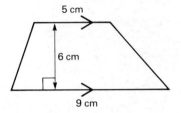

5 cm

6 cm

9 cm

4.

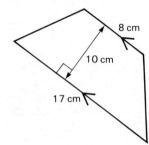

8 cm

10 cm

17 cm

2.

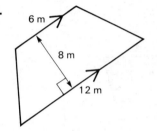

6 m

8 m

12 m

5.

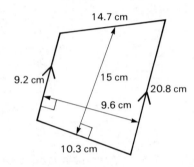

14.7 cm

9.2 cm

15 cm

20.8 cm

9.6 cm

10.3 cm

3.

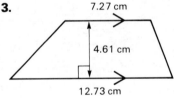

7.27 cm

4.61 cm

12.73 cm

6.

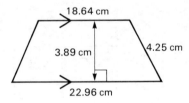

18.64 cm

3.89 cm

4.25 cm

22.96 cm

B Calculate the area of each of the following:

1. A kite with long diagonal measuring 8 cm and short diagonal measuring 6 cm.

2. A rhombus with long diagonal measuring 12 cm and short diagonal measuring 7 cm.

3. A kite with a long diagonal of 16.5 cm and a short diagonal of 10.4 cm.

4. A rhombus with diagonals measuring 7.83 m and 11.8 m.

168

5. A kite with diagonals measuring 54 mm and 32 mm.

6. A square where each diagonal measures 9 cm.

Exercise 14

Here is a plan showing the plots of land that are being sold for the building of six houses:

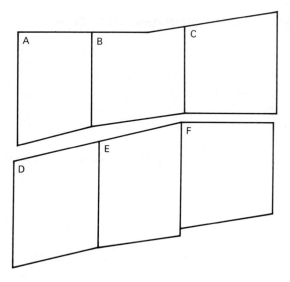

It has been drawn to a scale of 1:1000.

1. Calculate the area of each plot.

2. Give the plots in order of sizes of area from largest to smallest.

Measurements Necessary to Calculate Areas

Exercise 15   Constructions and Area

1. Construct $\triangle ABC$ where $BC = 80$ mm, $A\widehat{B}C = 60°$ and where $AB = 55$ mm:
   (*a*) How long is AC?
   (*b*) By measuring and calculating, find the area of $\triangle ABC$.

2. Construct parallelogram PQRS where PQ = 70 mm and QR = 40 mm, and where angle QPS = 45°:
   (a) How long is PR?
   (b) By measuring and calculating, find the area of this parallelogram.

3. Construct a rhombus having sides that are 50 mm long and where the obtuse angle between two of the sides is 120°:
   (a) How long are each of the diagonals?
   (b) Calculate the area of the rhombus.

Exercise 16 Co-ordinates and Area

Draw a pair of axes as shown. Use a scale of 1 cm to 1 unit on both axes. For each question, plot the points and join them in the given order using straight lines. (Use the one pair of axes throughout.) Calculate the area of each shape.

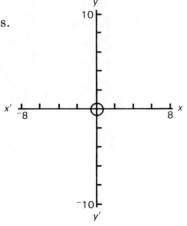

1. (0, ⁻8) (⁻5, ⁻8) (⁻7, ⁻10) (⁻2, ⁻10) (0, ⁻8)

2. (1, 7) (4, 9) (7, 7) (4, 5) (1, 7)

3. (⁻6, 3) (⁻8, 8) (⁻6, 10) (⁻4, 8) (⁻6, 3)

4. (5, ⁻2) (5, 4) (8, 3) (8, ⁻1) (5, ⁻2)

5. (⁻1, 2) (0, ⁻1) (⁻7, 2) (⁻1, 2)

6. (⁻8, 0) (⁻8, ⁻3) (⁻3, ⁻6) (⁻3, ⁻3) (⁻8, 0)

7. (0, ⁻7) (6, ⁻5) (4, ⁻9) (0, ⁻7)

8. (⁻2, ⁻1) (1, ⁻5) (4, ⁻3) (⁻2, ⁻1)

12 Percentages

1. For each square, write what percentage has been shaded:
   (a)   (b)    (c)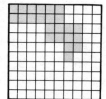

2. On squared paper, using a 10 by 10 square as shown for each question, shade the given percentages:

   (a) 60%   (b) 25%   (c) 84%   (d) 8%

3. Write each percentage as a common fraction:
   (a) 37%   (b) 51%   (c) 13%   (d) 9%   (e) 97%

4. Write each common fraction as a percentage:
   (a) $\dfrac{63}{100}$ (b) $\dfrac{81}{100}$ (c) $\dfrac{39}{100}$ (d) $\dfrac{7}{100}$ (e) $\dfrac{3}{100}$

5. Write each percentage as a decimal:
   (a) 19%   (b) 46%   (c) 66%   (d) 30%   (e) 2%

6. Write each decimal as a percentage:
   (a) 0.92   (b) 0.87   (c) 0.4   (d) 0.6   (e) 0.01

7. For each square, write what percentage has been shaded:

(a) 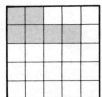   (b) 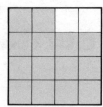   (c)

Exercise 2

A Write each percentage as a common fraction in its simplest terms:

1. 20%	**6.** 12%	**11.** 98%	**16.** 72%	**21.** $18\frac{1}{2}\%$
2. 25%	**7.** 27%	**12.** 35%	**17.** 84%	**22.** $67\frac{1}{2}\%$
3. 45%	**8.** 82%	**13.** 68%	**18.** 94%	**23.** $12\frac{1}{2}\%$
4. 95%	**9.** 48%	**14.** 22%	**19.** $8\frac{1}{2}\%$	**24.** $22\frac{1}{2}\%$
5. 65%	**10.** 32%	**15.** 16%	**20.** $77\frac{1}{2}\%$	**25.** $33\frac{1}{3}\%$

B Write as percentages:

1. $\dfrac{9}{10}$	**5.** $\dfrac{3}{4}$	**9.** $\dfrac{39}{50}$	**13.** $\dfrac{5}{8}$	**17.** $\dfrac{13}{16}$
2. $\dfrac{2}{5}$	**6.** $\dfrac{3}{20}$	**10.** $\dfrac{17}{50}$	**14.** $\dfrac{21}{40}$	**18.** $\dfrac{25}{32}$
3. $\dfrac{1}{2}$	**7.** $\dfrac{17}{20}$	**11.** $\dfrac{11}{25}$	**15.** $\dfrac{43}{80}$	**19.** $\dfrac{9}{32}$
4. $\dfrac{1}{10}$	**8.** $\dfrac{11}{20}$	**12.** $\dfrac{19}{25}$	**16.** $\dfrac{3}{16}$	**20.** $\dfrac{2}{3}$

Exercise 3

1. Here are the marks out of 25 in a test. Find the percentage mark for each person. List the names in order from highest mark to lowest. Write the percentage obtained beside each name.

M.T. Vann	$\dfrac{12}{25}$	B. Quick	$\dfrac{16}{25}$	S. Topp	$\dfrac{6}{25}$
B.E. Wright	$\dfrac{7}{25}$	S.O. Long	$\dfrac{23}{25}$	H.I. Street	$\dfrac{9}{25}$
I. Ball	$\dfrac{22}{25}$	E.S. Short	$\dfrac{20}{25}$	E.B. Last	$\dfrac{24}{25}$

2. Here are the marks out of 32 in a test. Find the percentage mark for each person giving the percentage correct to the nearest whole number. List the names in order from highest mark to lowest. Write the percentage obtained beside each name.

L.O. Marks $\dfrac{27}{32}$ D. Light $\dfrac{30}{32}$ C. Sawyer $\dfrac{16}{32}$

L. Lowe $\dfrac{29}{32}$ A. Winner $\dfrac{7}{32}$ T. Potts $\dfrac{13}{32}$

C. Ling $\dfrac{15}{32}$ W. Ince $\dfrac{8}{32}$ M.I. Way $\dfrac{11}{32}$

3. Sheila got 29 out of 40 in a test. What percentage was that?

4. Anne got 60% in a test. What was her mark out of 20?

5. Bharat got 85% in a test. What was his mark out of 40?

6. My percentage mark was 52%. What was my mark out of 50?

Finding a Percentage of a Quantity

Exercise 4

1. Find 10% of:
   (a) 40 kg   (b) 300 g   (c) £45   (d) 120 m

2. Find 50% of:
   (a) £38   (b) £11   (c) 86 kg   (d) $23

3. Find 20% of:
   (a) £70   (b) 350 people   (c) 4.5 cm   (d) 890 g

4. Find 25% of:
   (a) £56   (b) 18 kg   (c) 140 lb   (d) 22 ℓ

5. Find 40% of:
   (a) £60   (b) 3.5 m   (c) 145 g   (d) 57 cm

6. Find 75% of:
   (a) 360 g   (b) £2984   (c) 3 m   (d) 7.92 km

7. Find 7% of:
   (a) £1800   (b) 250 g   (c) 390 ℓ   (d) 41 m

8. Find 5% of:
  (*a*) £260   (*b*) £3480   (*c*) 4 ℓ   (*d*) 5.8 km

9. Find $2\frac{1}{2}$% of:
  (*a*) £5000   (*b*) 24 ℓ   (*c*) 720 g   (*d*) £536

10. Find $12\frac{1}{2}$% of:
  (*a*) 144 ft   (*b*) 96 m   (*c*) £52   (*d*) £37.20

---

e.g. Use a calculator to find 27% of £45.
Here is one method:

Key in: $\boxed{\cdot}\ \boxed{2}\ \boxed{7}\ \boxed{\times}\ \boxed{4}\ \boxed{5}\ \boxed{=}$

　　　　　　　27%　　　of　　　£45　　　=

To use the above method, you need to change a percentage to a decimal in your head.

Note $16\frac{1}{2}$% = 0.165 and $3\frac{1}{2}$% = 0.035

Exercise 5

A Use a calculator to check your answers to Exercise 4.

B Use a calculator to find:

1. 35% of £460
2. 62% of 15 ℓ
3. 13% of 78 francs
4. 87% of 6.2 kg
5. 56% of 95 m
6. 74% of 59 kg

7. 6% of £98
8. 3% of 5 ℓ
9. $7\frac{1}{2}$% of 45 t
10. $10\frac{1}{2}$% of 8.4 m
11. $22\frac{1}{2}$% of £36.40
12. $4\frac{1}{2}$% of £84

Exercise 6   Discount

1. A video costing £490 was sold at 10% discount. Find:
  (*a*) the discount,   (*b*) the selling price.

2. A shop reduced its prices by 20%. Find the discount on goods that cost:
  (*a*) £50   (*b*) £95   (*c*) £6.80   (*d*) £17.20

3. Find, to the nearest penny, the discount at 25% on an article costing £49.95.

4. A drill costing £37.99 was sold at a discount of 15%. Find, to the nearest penny:
(*a*) the amount of discount,
(*b*) the selling price of the drill.

5. Some furniture cost £950 less $12\frac{1}{2}$% discount:
(*a*) How much discount was that?
(*b*) What was the price after discount?

6. Some luggage costing £87.95 was sold at a discount of 5%:
(*a*) Calculate the discount giving the amount correct to the nearest penny.
(*b*) Find, to the nearest penny, the selling price.

7. Everything in a sale was sold at 12% discount. Calculate the amount of discount on goods that cost:
(*a*) £415   (*b*) £64.50   (*c*) £19.50

8. A firm advertised a sale in which they gave a discount of 35% off their recommended retail price (RRP):
(*a*) Calculate the discount off goods at £187.
(*b*) What would be the price after discount of goods that cost £187?

Miscellaneous Questions

Exercise 7

1. I received 6% interest on £1950. How much interest was that?

2. A clock cost £32 plus 15% VAT. Work out:
(*a*) the VAT,   (*b*) the price including VAT.

3. Mr Soyler earned £185 per week. If he was given a 4% rise, calculate:

(a) the amount of his rise per week,

(b) his weekly earnings after the rise.

4. A car valued at £8260 last year is now worth 20% less. Calculate:

(a) how much the car has decreased in value,

(b) how much the car is worth now.

5. Mrs Aitken has to pay income tax on £3100. If the rate of tax is 25% p.a.,* how much must she pay?

6. A credit card* company charged 2% interest per month. Find the monthly interest on £186.

7. 8% of 850 pupils were absent. How many was that?

8. Mrs Yeatman saved 32% of her earnings. How much did she save out of £298?

9. Mr Moretto bought a bracelet for £134 then sold it to make 28% profit. Find the selling price.

10. 11% of 4900 microchips were faulty. How many were not faulty?

11. Due to inflation a firm increased its prices by 4%. Find the increase on goods that cost £498.

12. Some solder is made up of 60% lead, 35% tin and 5% bismuth. If there is 180 g of solder, calculate the mass of:

(a) the lead,

(b) the tin,

(c) the bismuth.

13. In measuring a line of length 450 mm, my error was 4%. Find:

(a) the smallest possible measurement made,

(b) the largest possible measurement made.

14. A firm made 117 680 cassettes last year. This year, production increased by $17\frac{1}{2}\%$. Calculate the number made this year.

15. A salesperson received $12\frac{1}{2}\%$ commission on sales totalling £1352. Calculate the commission.

*See the glossary, pp. 447 and 444.

16. A camera costs £384.99 cash. It was bought on hire-purchase for a deposit of $33\frac{1}{3}\%$ followed by 12 equal payments of £25.89.
(*a*) Calculate the cost on hire-purchase.
(*b*) Calculate the amount saved by paying cash.

Exercise 8

1. Change the following percentages to decimals:
(*a*) 123%   (*b*) 165%   (*c*) 116%   (*d*) 108%

2. Write as common fractions:
(*a*) 125%   (*b*) 140%   (*c*) 115%   (*d*) $112\frac{1}{2}\%$

3. (*a*) Find 15% of £29.
(*b*) Find 100% of £29.
(*c*) Find 100% of £29 + 15% of £29.
(*d*) Find 115% of £29.
(*e*) Write what you notice about the answers to parts (*c*) and (*d*).

4. (*a*) Find 24% of £175.
(*b*) Find 100% of £175.
(*c*) Find 100% of £175 + 24% of £175.
(*d*) Find 124% of £175.
(*e*) Write what you notice about the answers to parts (*c*) and (*d*).

Exercise 9

The River Wyre in Lancashire contains approximately:

Trout	60%
Migratory trout	20%
Salmon	15%
Coarse fish	5%

Draw a pie chart to show the fish in the River Wyre.

13 Directed Numbers

Directed Numbers in Practical Situations

Exercise 1

1. Write the temperatures shown on the given thermometers:

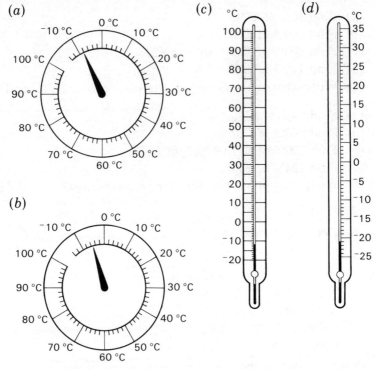

(a)

(c)

(d)

(b)

2. The temperature fell from 2 °C to ⁻4 °C. Through how many degrees had it fallen?

3. The temperature was ⁻1 °C. If it then fell by 6 °C, what would the new temperature be?

4. Consider the temperatures:

   3 °C, ⁻2 °C, 4 °C, ⁻6 °C, ⁻3.5 °C, ⁻1.8 °C, 2.7 °C, ⁻4.6 °C

   (a) Which of the temperatures are less than ⁻3 °C?

   (b) Write the temperatures in order giving the coldest first.

   (c) Which is the third highest temperature?

5. If the daytime temperature on Mercury is 350 °C and the night-time temperature is ⁻170 °C, find the difference between the two temperatures.

6. If the temperature on the surface of Venus is 480 °C while the temperature at the cloud tops is ⁻33 °C, find the difference between the two temperatures.

Exercise 2

Show the following as directed numbers and simplify each result:

e.g.   A lift goes up 4 floors then down 6 floors.

   $^{+}4 + {^{-}6} = {^{-}2}$

   This is the same as going down 2 floors.

1. A lift goes up 2 floors then down 7 floors.

2. I travel 8 km due north then 15 km due south.

3. I travel 19 km due north then 13 km due south.

4. The aeroplane gained 415 m in height then descended 190 m.

5. The aeroplane descended by 620 ft then climbed 475 ft.

6. The aeroplane descended 285 m then descended a further 340 m.

7. Mr Backhouse deposited £46 in his bank account, then later withdrew £74.

8. Mrs Arnold made a loss of £143 then a profit of £89.

9. 23 people got off a bus at one stop while 14 people got on. At the next stop, 7 got off while 9 got on.

10. A car used 14 ℓ of petrol. 26 ℓ were then put into the tank; then it used 19 ℓ and a further 8 ℓ.

179

Addition and Subtraction of Directed Numbers

Exercise 3

Find the value of:

A
1. $4 - 7$
2. $2 - 9$
3. $11 - 5$
4. $5 - 11$
5. $3 - 6$
6. $12 + 3 - 9$
7. $7 - 6 - 4$
8. $3 - 9 + 8$
9. $0 - 4 + 2$
10. $5 - 12 + 3$
11. $2 + 3 - 16$
12. $4 - 7 + 9 - 6$
13. $2 - 13 - 12 + 10$
14. $41 - 29 - 19 - 32$
15. $16 - 51 + 13 - 7$

B
1. $10 + {}^-6$
2. $5 + {}^-11$
3. ${}^-2 + 8$
4. ${}^-8 + 6$
5. ${}^-7 - 5$
6. $3 - {}^-10$
7. $9 - {}^-1$
8. ${}^-4 + {}^-8$
9. ${}^-5 - {}^-11$
10. ${}^-7 - {}^-3$
11. ${}^-12 - {}^-6$
12. ${}^-9 + {}^-3$
13. $4 + {}^-7 + {}^-2$
14. ${}^-2 - 5 + {}^-4$
15. $9 - {}^-3 + 8$
16. $2 - {}^-9 - 15$
17. ${}^-1 - {}^-1 - {}^-2$
18. ${}^-6 + {}^-3 - {}^-5$
19. $13 - {}^-13 + {}^-10$
20. $1 - {}^-14 + {}^-19$
21. $3 - 7 - {}^-4 + 8$
22. ${}^-2 - 8 + {}^-3 - {}^-9$
23. ${}^-12 + 2 - 9 - {}^-1$
24. $0 - {}^-4 - {}^-3 - {}^-8$
25. ${}^-13 - {}^-4 - 6 + {}^-2$
26. $21 + {}^-13 - {}^-3 - 15$
27. ${}^-2 - {}^-2 - {}^-2 - {}^-2$
28. ${}^-5 + {}^-5 - 5 - {}^-5$
29. $17 - {}^-6 + {}^-8 - {}^-7$
30. ${}^-14 + {}^-8 - {}^-10 - 13$

C
1. $6 + (-7)$
2. $10 + (-2)$
3. $(-1) - (-5)$
4. $10 - (-3)$
5. $(-9) - (-2)$
6. $(-6) + 5$
7. $(-1) + (-4)$
8. $(-3) + 9$
9. $11 - (-4)$
10. $2 - (-10)$
11. $(-5) + (-8)$
12. $(-4) + (-2)$
13. $5 - (-3) + (-1)$
14. $(-7) - (-5) - (-2)$
15. $(-1) - (-4) + 8$
16. $(-3) + (-9) - (-2)$
17. $(-4) - (-10) - 7$
18. $(-9) + 9 - 11$
19. $13 - (-6) + (-10)$
20. $(-8) + 9 - (-3)$
21. $(-7) - (-4) + (-2)$
22. $3 - (-6) - (-1)$
23. $1 - 8 + (-7)$
24. $0 - (-4) - 5$
25. $(-5) + (-3) - (-8)$
26. $(-8) - 7 - (-2)$
27. $(-12) + 3 + (-6)$
28. $5 + (-9) - (-4)$
29. $(-7) - (-7) - (-6)$
30. $(-9) + (-10) - (-3)$

Exercise 4

Find the missing numbers that will make the statements correct:

1. $\boxed{?} + {}^-1 = 5$
2. $\boxed{?} - 5 = {}^-3$
3. $\boxed{?} - {}^-8 = 11$
4. $9 + \boxed{?} = {}^-2$
5. ${}^-8 - \boxed{?} = {}^-12$
6. $\boxed{?} + {}^-4 = {}^-9$
7. $\boxed{?} - {}^-6 = 8$
8. $\boxed{?} - {}^-5 = {}^-1$
9. ${}^-6 - \boxed{?} = 0$
10. $\boxed{?} + {}^-6 = 1$

11. $\boxed{?} - {}^-6 = 6$
12. $\boxed{?} - {}^-8 = 16$
13. $\boxed{?} + {}^-8 = {}^-10$
14. ${}^-9 + \boxed{?} = {}^-4$
15. $1 - \boxed{?} = 10$
16. $\boxed{?} - 7 = {}^-6$
17. ${}^-13 - \boxed{?} = {}^-12$
18. ${}^-8 + \boxed{?} = {}^-12$
19. $\boxed{?} + 2 = {}^-8$
20. $12 - \boxed{?} = 19$

Like Terms

Exercise 5

Simplify where possible:

1. $4n - 7n + 2n + 6n$
2. $8c + c - 6c - 2c$
3. $g - 8g - 2g + 3g$
4. $6m + 2m - 3m - 9m$
5. $3j + 4j - 5j - 2j$
6. $9p + 2y - 6p + 3y$
7. $5b - 3v + v - 2b$
8. $7s - 8s + 2t - 3s$
9. $5 + l - 2 + 8l$
10. $e - 6z - 4e + 9z$

11. $3a - 4f + 5a - f$
12. $2k - w - 3w + k - 7w$
13. $4q - 6 + 9 - 5q - 6q$
14. $7 - 6d + 1 - 3d + 7d - 5$
15. $8n - 9n - 8d + 4n + 5d$
16. $4t - z + 2w - 9w + 3z - t$
17. $6h + 17y - 3y - 11h - 9h + y$
18. $5x - 7 - 14 - 14x + 2x - 4$
19. $9r - 2r - 3s + t - 2s + 5r$
20. $2u + 3a - 15c + 9c - 7a + 4u$

Exercise 6

Where possible, simplify the following expressions:

1. $4ad - 2ad + 3da - ad$
2. $3cad + 2dca - dac - 2cda$
3. $5vw - 2wv - wv + 3vw$
4. $mt - 5mt - 2tm - 3mt$
5. $8 - us + 7 + 4su - 5$
6. $3ab + 4ac - 2bc - 2ca$

181

7. $9xy - 2yz + 7xz$

8. $3del - 4led + 6de - 3el$

9. $4pqr - 3qrp + 8rqp + 2qp$

10. $8ud - 3bu - 3du + 4bd$

11. $9sam - 8ams + 2mas - ma$

12. $4y + 3by - 2b - 7yb + y$

13. $7jet - 2te + 6et - 6ejt$

14. $5act - 2cat - 8act + 7cta$

15. $3m - 2pm + 6 + 4mp - 5p$

16. $8 - 3jd + 2 + 2dj - 4jd$

Exercise 7

Where possible, simplify the following expressions:

1. $t^2 + 5t - 2t + 8$

2. $m^2 - 6m + 3m - 5$

3. $a^2 - 4m - 7m + 1$

4. $3h^2 + 2h - 9h - 2$

5. $6p^2 + 4p - 2p^2 - 3p$

6. $5v - 2v^2 + 2v - v^2$

7. $4ij + 6i - ji + 3j$

8. $2y^2z - 4yz^2 + 2zy^2$

9. $b^2 - 8b - 3b^2 + 10b$

10. $4u - u^2 + 3u^2 - 9u$

11. $3c^2 - 9 + c + 2c^2 + 3$

12. $4mn^2 - 2nm^2 + 3m^2n$

13. $7rq - 3r^2q - 4qr + 2qr^2$

14. $9 - a + 4a - 3 + 2a^2$

15. $5d^2 - 3d + 4d^2 - 6d^2 - d^2$

16. $3k^2l - kl^2 + 2lk^2 - lk + l^2k$

17. $8su^2t + 2us^2t - 4tus^2 - u^2st$

18. $4ef^2g - f^2eg + gef^2 - 3e^2gf$

19. $8wx^2 - 4w^2x^2 + 2x^2w - 9w^2x$

20. $t^2e - te^2 + 4e^2t + et^2 - 7e^2t$

Multiplication and Division of Directed Numbers

Exercise 8

Copy these. By finding a pattern, fill in the missing answers:

1.
$$^+4 \times {}^+3 = {}^+12$$
$$^+4 \times {}^+2 = {}^+8$$
$$^+4 \times {}^+1 = \boxed{?}$$
$$^+4 \times \ 0 = 0$$
$$^+4 \times {}^-1 = \boxed{?}$$
$$^+4 \times {}^-2 = \boxed{?}$$
$$^+4 \times {}^-3 = \boxed{?}$$
$$^+4 \times {}^-4 = \boxed{?}$$

2.
$$^-4 \times {}^+4 = {}^-16$$
$$^-4 \times {}^+3 = \boxed{?}$$
$$^-4 \times {}^+2 = \boxed{?}$$
$$^-4 \times {}^+1 = \boxed{?}$$
$$^-4 \times \ 0 = 0$$
$$^-4 \times {}^-1 = \boxed{?}$$
$$^-4 \times {}^-2 = \boxed{?}$$
$$^-4 \times {}^-3 = \boxed{?}$$

3. Work these out:

(a) $^+7 \times {}^+5$ (d) $^-8 \times {}^-5$ (g) $^-2 \times {}^-13$

(b) $3 \times {}^-6$ (e) $^-9 \times {}^+8$ (h) $^-7 \times 12$

(c) $^-3 \times 7$ (f) $^+4 \times {}^-11$ (i) $^-15 \times {}^-6$

The line 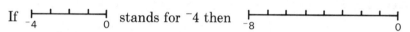 can stand for $^+3$ (that is, 3).

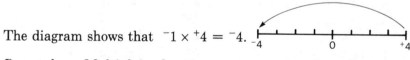 then stands for $2 \times {}^+3$. This new line is twice as long, so $2 \times {}^+3 = {}^+6$.

If ⊢──┤ stands for $^-4$ then ⊢────────┤ stands for $2 \times {}^-4$. Once again the new line is twice as long. This time, since the number $^-4$ is negative, the line showing $^-4$ is pointing to the left. The new line is twice as long and also points to the left, so $2 \times {}^-4 = {}^-8$.

Now if multiplication by $^-1$ causes a rotation through 180° and since ⊢──┤$_{+4}$ stands for $^+4$, then ⊢──┤$_{-4}$ stands for $^-1 \times {}^+4$. This can be more easily seen on one diagram:

The diagram shows that $^-1 \times {}^+4 = {}^-4$.

Remember   Multiplying by $^-1$ causes a rotation through 180°.

The diagram shows that $^-1 \times {}^-6 = {}^+6$.

Exercise 9

Work these out:

1. $^-1 \times {}^+3$ **5.** $^-1 \times {}^+6$ **9.** $^-1 \times {}^+19$

2. $^-1 \times 7$ **6.** $^-1 \times {}^-9$ **10.** $^-1 \times {}^-11$

3. $^-1 \times {}^-4$ **7.** $^-1 \times 9$ **11.** $^-1 \times {}^-17$

4. $^-1 \times {}^-7$ **8.** $^-1 \times 14$ **12.** $^-1 \times {}^-23$

The ideas used in Exercise 9 can now be used to help us to work out calculations such as $^-4 \times {}^-6$.

Since $^-4 = 4 \times {}^-1$, $^-6$ must be multiplied by both $^-1$ and 4. Multiplying $^-6$ by $^-1$ rotates a line that stands for $^-6$, so that it becomes $^+6$. Multiplying by 4 enlarges the $^+6$ line 4 times so that it becomes $^+24$,
so $^-4 \times {}^-6 = \underline{\underline{^+24}}$.

Exercise 10

Work these out:

A
1. $3 \times {}^-5$
2. $6 \times {}^-6$
3. $^-2 \times {}^-4$
4. $7 \times {}^-8$
5. $^-7 \times {}^-8$
6. $^-7 \times 8$
7. $^+7 \times {}^+8$
8. $^-9 \times 3$
9. $^-8 \times 9$
10. $^-6 \times {}^-12$
11. $^-12 \times {}^-3$
12. $^-11 \times {}^+5$

13. $^+9 \times {}^-7$
14. $12 \times {}^-4$
15. $^-13 \times 5$
16. $^-14 \times {}^-3$
17. $^-2 \times 5 \times {}^-4$
18. $3 \times {}^-6 \times {}^+4$
19. $^-10 \times {}^-3 \times {}^-2$
20. $6 \times 7 \times {}^-5$
21. $^-9 \times {}^-2 \times 6 \times {}^-2$
22. $^-8 \times {}^-5 \times {}^-4 \times {}^-3$
23. $7 \times {}^-10 \times {}^-3 \times 8$
24. $^-2 \times {}^-15 \times 6 \times {}^-4$

B
1. $4 \times (-5)$
2. $7 \times (-3)$
3. $(-2) \times (-6)$
4. $(+5) \times (+9)$
5. $(+5) \times (-9)$
6. $(-5) \times (+9)$
7. $(-5) \times (-9)$
8. $(-7) \times (+6)$
9. $(-9) \times (-7)$
10. $(-6) \times (+8)$
11. $(+9) \times (-8)$
12. $(-6) \times (-4)$

13. $(-9) \times 12$
14. $(+13) \times (-3)$
15. $(-12) \times (+6)$
16. $(-16) \times (-4)$
17. $(-3) \times (+2) \times (+5)$
18. $(-2) \times (-9) \times (-3)$
19. $(-4) \times (+5) \times (-7)$
20. $(+8) \times (-5) \times (+9)$
21. $(-2) \times (+5) \times (-3) \times (-7)$
22. $(+10) \times (-4) \times (+6) \times (-2)$
23. $(-1) \times (-5) \times (-9) \times (+6)$
24. $(-8) \times (+10) \times (+4) \times (-3)$

Exercise 11

A Copy these and fill in the missing numbers:

1. (a) $8 \times 3 = \boxed{?}$ (b) $24 \div 3 = \boxed{?}$

2. (a) $9 \times 6 = \boxed{?}$ (b) $54 \div 9 = \boxed{?}$

3. (a) $9 \times {}^-2 = \boxed{?}$ (b) ${}^-18 \div 9 = \boxed{?}$

4. (a) ${}^+7 \times {}^-6 = \boxed{?}$ (b) ${}^-42 \div {}^-6 = \boxed{?}$

5. (a) ${}^-5 \times {}^-7 = \boxed{?}$ (b) $35 \div {}^-5 = \boxed{?}$

6. (a) ${}^-8 \times {}^-10 = \boxed{?}$ (b) ${}^+80 \div {}^-10 = \boxed{?}$

7. (a) ${}^-9 \times {}^+5 = \boxed{?}$ (b) ${}^-45 \div {}^-9 = \boxed{?}$

8. (a) ${}^-7 \times {}^+11 = \boxed{?}$ (b) ${}^-77 \div {}^+11 = \boxed{?}$

9. (a) ${}^-8 \times {}^-9 = \boxed{?}$ (b) $72 \div {}^-9 = \boxed{?}$

10. (a) ${}^+9 \times {}^-12 = \boxed{?}$ (b) ${}^-108 \div {}^-12 = \boxed{?}$

B Work these out:

1. ${}^+12 \div {}^+3$

2. ${}^-18 \div {}^-2$

3. ${}^-20 \div {}^+5$

4. $\dfrac{24}{{}^-4}$

5. ${}^-28 \div {}^-4$

6. $\dfrac{{}^-63}{7}$

7. $40 \div {}^-5$

8. $\dfrac{{}^-54}{{}^+6}$

9. ${}^-30 \div {}^-5$

10. $\dfrac{{}^-56}{{}^-8}$

11. ${}^-63 \div 9$

12. $64 \div {}^-8$

13. $\dfrac{{}^-60}{{}^-12}$

14. $48 \div {}^-3$

15. ${}^-72 \div {}^+3$

16. $\dfrac{68}{{}^-4}$

C Work these out:

1. $\dfrac{(+18)}{(+3)}$

2. $(+21) \div (-7)$

3. $(-24) \div (+6)$

4. $\dfrac{(+27)}{(-9)}$

5. $(-32) \div (-4)$

6. $\dfrac{(+36)}{(-4)}$

7. $(-72) \div (+8)$

8. $(-39) \div (-3)$

9. $\dfrac{(-45)}{(+15)}$

10. $(+48) \div (-12)$

11. $\dfrac{(-81)}{(-9)}$

12. $(-54) \div (-3)$

13. $(-84) \div (+7)$

14. $\dfrac{(+75)}{(-15)}$

15. $(-56) \div (+14)$

Exercise 12

For each question, find the missing number that will make the statement correct:

1. $\boxed{?} \times {}^-3 = {}^-24$
2. ${}^-7 \times \boxed{?} = 35$
3. $\boxed{?} \div 2 = {}^-8$
4. $24 \div \boxed{?} = {}^-3$
5. $\boxed{?} \times {}^-5 = {}^-45$
6. $\dfrac{\boxed{?}}{{}^-2} = {}^-13$
7. ${}^-8 \times \boxed{?} = 40$
8. $\boxed{?} \div {}^-11 = 3$
9. $10 \times \boxed{?} = {}^-40$
10. $\boxed{?} \times {}^-6 = 54$
11. $\boxed{?} \times 7 = {}^-63$
12. ${}^-49 \div \boxed{?} = 7$

13. $\boxed{?} \times 9 = 72$
14. $\dfrac{\boxed{?}}{{}^-25} = {}^-4$
15. ${}^-13 \times \boxed{?} = 78$
16. $12 \times \boxed{?} = {}^-108$
17. $\boxed{?} \div {}^-12 = 7$
18. ${}^-12 \times \boxed{?} = {}^-84$
19. $\boxed{?} \times {}^-2 = {}^-34$
20. $\boxed{?} \times {}^-5 = {}^-70$
21. ${}^-15 \times \boxed{?} = {}^-105$
22. $\dfrac{{}^-65}{\boxed{?}} = {}^-5$
23. $57 \div \boxed{?} = {}^-19$
24. $\boxed{?} \times {}^-5 = 80$

Using a Calculator

Most calculators have a $\boxed{+/_-}$ key on them which allows negative numbers to be used. For instance, to key in ${}^-6$ you will probably need to key in $\boxed{6}\ \boxed{+/_-}$. (You normally need to key in the number before using the $\boxed{+/_-}$ key.)

e.g. 1 ${}^-5 - {}^-2 = \boxed{?}$

Key in: $\boxed{5}\ \boxed{+/_-}\ \boxed{-}\ \boxed{2}\ \boxed{+/_-}\ \boxed{=}$

${}^-5 - {}^-2 = \underline{\underline{{}^-3}}$

e.g. 2 ${}^-3 \times {}^+8 = \boxed{?}$

Key in: $\boxed{3}\ \boxed{+/_-}\ \boxed{\times}\ \boxed{8}\ \boxed{=}$

${}^-3 \times {}^+8 = \underline{\underline{{}^-24}}$

Exercise 13

Use a calculator to check your answers to Exercises 3, 10 and 11.

Exercise 14

Work these out *without* using a calculator:

1. $9 - 13$
2. $6 - {}^-13$
3. ${}^-9 + 8$
4. ${}^-7 \times {}^+5$
5. ${}^-56 \div 7$
6. $\dfrac{{}^-63}{{}^-9}$

7. ${}^-8 + {}^-9$
8. $13 + {}^-7$
9. $8 \times {}^-9$
10. $(-9) - (-6)$
11. ${}^-9 - {}^+8$
12. $\dfrac{(+70)}{(-5)}$

13. ${}^-6 \times {}^-7$
14. $(-14) \times (-5)$
15. ${}^-84 \div {}^-7$
16. ${}^-14 + {}^+9$
17. ${}^-8 - {}^-15$
18. $\dfrac{{}^-96}{12}$

Exercise 15   Magic Squares   **M**

Copy and complete the magic squares. The sum of the numbers in each row, column or diagonal, should always be the same:

1.

5	1	${}^-3$
		2

2.

${}^-2$		
3	${}^-1$	
		0

3.

	${}^-6$	${}^-1$
	${}^-2$	
	2	

4.

5		
${}^-2$		
3		${}^-1$

5.

${}^-3$		${}^-1$
	0	
1		

6.

	${}^-7$	${}^-2$
	${}^-3$	
${}^-4$		

7.

${}^-7$			5
		2	${}^-5$
6	${}^-1$	3	${}^-6$
		${}^-3$	

8.

0		11	${}^-3$
5			
1		6	4
12			9

187

9.

3			6
		1	‾5
	‾4	‾3	
‾9	5		‾6

10.

	‾4		‾5
		‾2	5
‾6		‾3	6
	‾1		‾8

11.

‾8			‾11
	‾5		
‾7	‾1	‾2	
4		‾9	1

12.

	‾3		‾2
			‾12
‾1	‾8	‾4	‾13
	‾6	‾10	

13.

2			‾7	0
	‾10		‾1	1
‾11			5	
‾5	‾3	4	6	‾12
‾4		10		

14.

2	3			
		1	8	‾11
‾12	‾6	0	6	12
11	‾8		‾1	5
			‾3	

15.

‾7		9		‾5
‾13	5		‾4	‾6
	4	‾3		
	‾2		‾11	7
‾1		‾15	8	

Exercise 16   Algebraic Substitution

1. If $x = {}^-8$, find the value of:
    (a) $3x$ (b) $x - 7$ (c) $2x + 5$ (d) $25 - 2x$

2. If $t = {}^-3$, find the value of:
    (a) $6t$ (b) $t + 8$ (c) $4t - 1$ (d) $14 + 3t$

3. If $n = {}^-5$, find the value of:
    (a) $8n$ (b) $9 - n$ (c) $3n + 10$ (d) $5 + 4n$

4. If $y = 2x - 9$, find the value of y when x equals:
    (a) 8   (b) 3   (c) 0   (d) ⁻4   (e) ⁻7

5. $y = 4x + 7$. Find the value of y when x equals:
    (a) 0   (b) 3   (c) ⁻1   (d) ⁻5   (e) ⁻10

6. If $s = 4t - 8$, find the value of s when t equals:
    (a) 0   (b) 5   (c) ⁻5   (d) 2   (e) 1

7. If $h = 15 - 2q$, find the value of h when q equals:
    (a) 0   (b) 4   (c) 9   (d) ⁻5   (e) ⁻12

8. If $x + y = 7$, find the value of y when x equals:
    (a) 2   (b) 10   (c) ⁻3   (d) 0   (e) ⁻9

9. If $M = a + b$, find the value of M when:
    (a) $a = 8$ and $b = $ ⁻3   (b) $a = $ ⁻4 and $b = $ ⁻9

10. If $R = s + t$, find the value of R when:
    (a) $s = $ ⁻2 and $t = 14$ (b) $s = $ ⁻10 and $t = $ ⁻8

11. If $P = 2y + c$, find the value of P when:
    (a) $y = 8$ and $c = $ ⁻3   (b) $y = $ ⁻3 and $c = 8$

12. If $a = 4b - c$, find the value of a when:
    (a) $b = 5$ and $c = 25$ (b) $b = $ ⁻2 and $c = $ ⁻3

13. If $h = p - 5q$, find the value of h when:
    (a) $p = 20$ and $q = 3$ (d) $p = 8$ and $q = $ ⁻2
    (b) $p = 15$ and $q = 4$ (e) $p = $ ⁻10 and $q = $ ⁻5
    (c) $p = 3$ and $q = 6$ (f) $p = $ ⁻25 and $q = $ ⁻6

14. If $x = $ ⁻5 and $y = $ ⁻8, find the value of:
    (a) $x + y$ (d) $3x + y$ (g) $x - 3y$
    (b) $x - y$ (e) $2x - y$ (h) $4x - 3y$
    (c) xy (f) $x + 2y$ (i) $5y - 2x$

15. If $a = $ ⁻6 and $b = $ ⁻7, find the value of n if:
    (a) $n = a + b$ (e) $n = 10 - 2a$ (i) $2a + 3b$
    (b) $n = a - b$ (f) $n = 3a - b$ (j) $4a - 2b$
    (c) $n = 7a$ (g) $n = 3b + a$ (k) $5b - 4a$
    (d) $n = 6b$ (h) $n = a - 2b$ (l) $3a + 4b$

16. If $c = 3$ and $d = {}^-5$, find the value of:

(a) $3(c + d)$

(b) $3(c - d)$

(c) $4(2c + d)$

(d) $2(4d + c)$

(e) $5(3c - 4d)$

(f) $c - (4 - 2d)$

(g) $3c + (8 - 3d)$

(h) $20 - (4c + 5d)$

Exercise 17 Mid-point of Two Numbers

A Which number lies exactly half-way between the given numbers?

1.

| 6 | ? | 22 |

4.

| ${}^-11$ | ? | 7 |

2.

| ${}^-9$ | ? | ${}^-1$ |

5.

| ${}^-9$ | ? | 17 |

3.

| ${}^-12$ | ? | ${}^+8$ |

6.

| ${}^-26$ | ? | 48 |

B Which number lies exactly half-way between the given numbers?

1. 4 and 20

2. 5 and 31

3. ${}^-6$ and ${}^+8$

4. ${}^-12$ and ${}^-1$

5. ${}^-11$ and ${}^+19$

6. ${}^-2$ and 26

7. ${}^-26$ and ${}^+2$

8. ${}^-13$ and ${}^+13$

9. 37 and 93

10. ${}^-15$ and ${}^-37$

11. ${}^-54$ and ${}^-18$

12. ${}^-47$ and 39

13. ${}^-91$ and ${}^-23$

14. ${}^-48$ and ${}^-98$

15. ${}^-79$ and ${}^+51$

Exercise 18 Puzzles

1. Using all three numbers ${}^-4$, ${}^-2$ and ${}^-8$ only, where each number is used once in every question, and using only the operations $+$, $-$, $\times$ and $\div$, write as many questions as you can that give a negative answer.

2. Repeat question 1 using the numbers ${}^-5$, ${}^-3$, ${}^-2$.

3. Using all the numbers ⁻7, ⁻5, ⁻3 and 4, and any of the operations +, −, ×, and ÷ (the operations may be used several times but the numbers must each be used only once in each question):
   (a) (i) Write a question that gives the largest possible answer.
       (ii) What is that largest possible answer?
   (b) (i) Write a question that gives the smallest possible answer.
       (ii) What is that smallest possible answer?

4. Repeat question 3 using the numbers ⁻8, ⁻5, 3 and 4.

Exercise 19 Sequences

A Give the next three terms of each of these sequences:

1. 8, 5, 2, ⁻1, ?, ?, ?

2. ⁺9, ⁺5, ⁺1, ?, ?, ?

3. 15, 13, 10, 6, 1, ?, ?, ?

4. 9, 6, 1, ⁻6, ?, ?, ?

5. 6, 4, 0, ⁻6, ?, ?, ?

6. ⁺1, ⁻1, ⁺3, ⁻5, ⁺11, ?, ?, ?

B Copy these sequences. Fill in the missing numbers.

1. ⁺11, ⁺8, ?, ⁺2, ?, ?, ⁻7, ...

2. ⁻4, ⁺8, ⁻12, ?, ⁻20, ?, ?, ...

3. 6, 5, 2, ?, ?, ⁻19, ?, ...

4. 16, 3, ?, ?, ⁻36, ?, ⁻62, ...

5. 1, ⁻2, 4, ⁻8, ?, ?, 64, ?, ...

6. ⁻10, ⁻1, ⁻8, 3, ⁻6, 7, ?, 11, ?, ?, ...

Exercise 20   A Graph of Temperatures

1. Using the following table, plot a graph to convert °C (Celsius) to °F (Fahrenheit). Use a scale of 20 mm to 20 °C on the horizontal axis and use 20 mm to 40 °F on the vertical axis.

°C	⁻60	0	100
°F	⁻76	32	212

2. Now use your graph to help you to change the given temperatures into the other system:

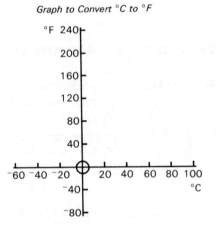

Graph to Convert °C to °F

(a) 25 °C   (g) 113 °F
(b) 50 °F   (h) 23 °F
(c) 5 °F   (i) ⁻25 °C
(d) 75 °C   (j) ⁻45 °C
(e) 50 °C   (k) ⁻31 °F
(f) ⁻20 °C   (l) ⁻55 °C

3. Which temperature has the same value in both systems? (That is, if x °F $= x$ °C, find the value of x.)

192

14 Relations between Two Sets

Consider the set of pupils and the set of shoe sizes. The relationship between the two sets can be shown on a *relation diagram* (sometimes called an *arrow diagram* or a *mapping diagram*).

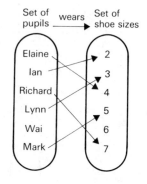

A *relation* is when we have two sets (which may be equal) and a statement that links any member or members of one set with any member or members of the other set in a given order.

Note Not all members of a set need to be used.

Exercise 1 ▬▬▬▬▬▬▬▬▬▬▬▬▬▬▬ **M**

Copy and complete each diagram to show the given relation for the two sets:

1. is one-third of

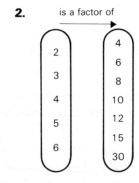

2. is a factor of

3.

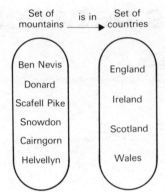

Set of mountains → is in → Set of countries

Set of mountains: Ben Nevis, Donard, Scafell Pike, Snowdon, Cairngorn, Helvellyn

Set of countries: England, Ireland, Scotland, Wales

5.

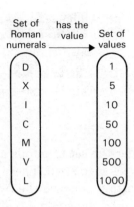

Set of Roman numerals → has the value → Set of values

Set of Roman numerals: D, X, I, C, M, V, L

Set of values: 1, 5, 10, 50, 100, 500, 1000

4.

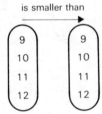

is smaller than →

9, 10, 11, 12   9, 10, 11, 12

6.

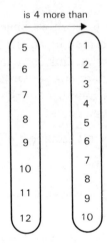

is 4 more than →

5, 6, 7, 8, 9, 10, 11, 12   1, 2, 3, 4, 5, 6, 7, 8, 9, 10

Exercise 2 ▬▬▬▬▬▬▬▬▬▬▬▬▬▬ **M**

For each question, two sets are given, together with a rule that relates them. Show each relation on a diagram as in Exercise 1.

1. $V = \{$Cotopaxi, Fuji-San, Hekla, Klyuchevskaya, Mauna Loa, Mt. Etna, Popocatépetl, Vesuvius$\}$

$C = \{$Ecuador, Iceland, Italy, Japan, Mexico, USA, USSR$\}$

Relation 'can be found in' from set V to C.

2. $T = \{$Aylesbury, Carlisle, Chelmsford, Ipswich, Maidstone, Matlock, Middlesbrough, Newcastle-upon-Tyne, Norwich, Preston, Reading, Taunton, Truro$\}$

$C = \{$Berkshire, Buckinghamshire, Cleveland, Cornwall, Cumbria, Derbyshire, Essex, Kent, Lancashire, Norfolk, Northumberland, Somerset, Suffolk$\}$

Relation 'is in' from set T to set C.

3. $A = \{2, 4, 6, 8, 10, 12\}$

$B = \{1, 2, 3, 4, 5, 6, 7, 8\}$

Relation 'is twice as big as' from set A to B.

4. $N = \{1, 2, 3, 4, 5, 6, 7, 8, 9, 10\}$

Relation 'is 3 less than' from set N to N.

5. $R = \{$Amazon, Mekong, Missouri-Mississippi, Nile, Volga, Yangtse$\}$

$S = \{$Atlantic, Caspian Sea, China Sea, Gulf of Mexico, Mediterranean Sea, North Pacific$\}$

Relation 'outflows into' from set R to S.

6. $Q = \{3.9 \times 4.2, \; 5.8 \times 4.1, \; 820 \div 51, \; 7.12 \times 28.4, \; 9.3 \times 1.89\}$

$A = \{12, 16, 18, 20, 24, 140, 210, 240\}$

Relation 'has an estimated answer of' from set Q to A.

7. $N = \{715, 263, 1053, 650, 9270, 3503, 345\}$

Relation 'has the same remainder when divided by 4 as' from set N to N.

8. $C = \{$Belgium, Chile, Egypt, France, Greece, Italy, Japan, Mexico, Portugal, Spain, Switzerland, Turkey, USA, USSR, Yugoslavia$\}$

$M = \{$Dinar, Dollar, Drachma, Escudo, Franc, Lira, Peseta, Peso, Pound, Rouble, Yen$\}$

Relation 'has as its currency' from set C to set M.

Exercise 3

For each question, write a relation that is true for all pairs of numbers that are linked in each arrow diagram:

1.

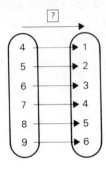

3.

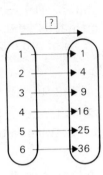

2.

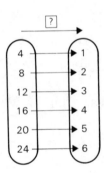

4.

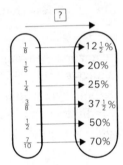

Exercise 4   M

1. (a) Copy and complete the mapping* diagram so that each solid maps to its number of vertices:
   (b) Which solid maps to 7?
   (c) Which solid maps to 5?

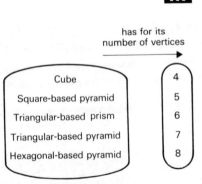

*See the glossary, p. 446.

2. (*a*) Copy and complete the mapping diagram so that each common fraction maps to the decimal having the same value.

(*b*) What maps to 0.6?

(*c*) What maps to 0.375?

(*d*) What does $\frac{2}{5}$ map to?

has the same value as
→

$\frac{3}{4}$ 　 0.125

$\frac{1}{8}$ 　 0.75

$\frac{3}{10}$ 　 0.1

$\frac{2}{5}$ 　 0.6

$\frac{1}{10}$ 　 0.875

$\frac{3}{8}$ 　 0.4

$\frac{3}{5}$ 　 0.3

$\frac{7}{8}$ 　 0.375

Note   The first set in a mapping is called the *domain.* The arrows used in a mapping diagram point from the domain. (The second set is called the *co-domain.**)

Functions and Function Notation

A *function* is a relation in which each member of the domain maps on to only one image (a many-one mapping or a one-one mapping). Mapping diagrams such as the two below show *functions*.

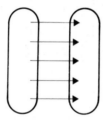 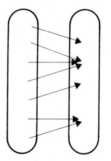

The relation 'is the square of' (shown here) is not a function. Members of the domain map to more than one image (for example, 4 maps to both ⁻2 and 2).

is the
square of

x ——→ y

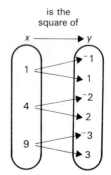

1 ⟨ ⁻1
    1

4 ⟨ ⁻2
    2

9 ⟨ ⁻3
    3

*See the glossary, p. 444.

197

The given mapping diagram shows the function $f(x) = 6x$ using the domain $\{1, 3, 4, 6, 9, 10\}$.

Note that since
$$f(x) = 6x$$
$$f(1) = 6 \times 1 = 6$$
$$f(3) = 6 \times 3 = 18$$
and so on.

Note also that $f(x) = 6x$ may be written as $f : x \longrightarrow 6x$

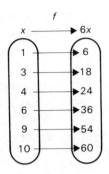

Exercise 5 **M**

A Copy and complete the mapping diagrams:

1.

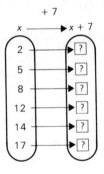

3.

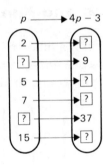

2.

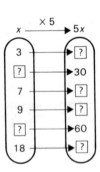

4.

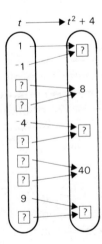

B 1. Copy and complete the mapping diagram to show the function $f(x) = 5x - 6$ using the domain $\{4, 5, 7, 8, 9, 12\}$:

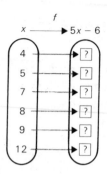

2. Draw a mapping diagram to show the function $h(x) = 2x + 9$ using the domain $\{1, 2, 3, 4, 5, 6, 7\}$.

3. Draw a mapping diagram for the function $g(x) = 3x - 5$ using the domain $\{4, 6, 8, 10, 12, 14\}$.

4. Draw a mapping diagram for the function $k(x) = \dfrac{18}{x}$ using the domain $\{1, 2, 3, 4, 6, 9, 18, \frac{1}{2}, \frac{1}{3}, \frac{1}{10}\}$.

5. Draw a mapping diagram for the function $h : t \longrightarrow 25 - t$ using the domain $\{0, 3, 8, 10, 12, 15, 25\}$.

6. Draw a mapping diagram for the function $g(t) = 20 - 3t$ using the domain $\{0, 1, 2, 3, 4, 5, 6, 7, 8\}$.

7. Draw a mapping diagram for the function $f : n \longrightarrow 2n + 5$ using the domain $\{7, 4, 1, 0, {}^-1, {}^-2, {}^-4, {}^-8\}$.

8. Draw a mapping diagram to show the function $g : n \longrightarrow \dfrac{n}{4}$ using the domain $\{24, 20, 16, 8, 1, 0, {}^-4, {}^-12, {}^-20\}$.

9. Draw a mapping diagram for the function $f(x) = 15 - 2x$ using the domain $\{10, 7\frac{1}{2}, 5, 2.5, 1, 0, {}^-4, {}^-8, {}^-10\}$.

10. The rule for a mapping is 'multiply by 6 then subtract 4'. Draw a mapping diagram using the domain $\{1, 2, 3, 4, 5, 6, 7, 8\}$.

11. The rule for a mapping is 'double then add 8.' Draw a mapping diagram using the domain $\{7, 5, 2, 1, 0, {}^-1, {}^-4, {}^-6, {}^-10\}$.

12. Draw a mapping diagram for the function $h(x) = x^2 - 3$ using the domain $\{{}^-5, {}^-4, {}^-3, {}^-2, {}^-1, 0, 1, 2, 3, 4, 5\}$. (Note that question 4 in section A may help you.)

199

Exercise 6

A Copy and complete the mapping diagram in each question so that pairs of elements that are linked by arrows are linked by the same function:

1.

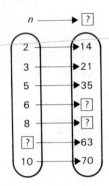

4.

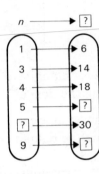

2.

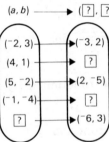

5.

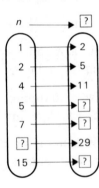

3.

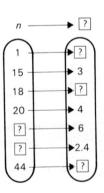

6.

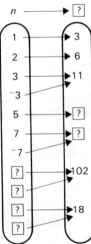

B Find the function:

1.

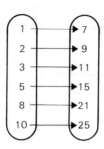

2.

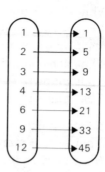

Exercise 7

1. For the mapping $n \longrightarrow 5n + 4$:
  (*a*) What does 6 map to?   (*b*) What number maps to 44?

2. For the mapping $t \longrightarrow 2t - 8$:
  (*a*) What does 7 map to?   (*d*) What does 20 map to?
  (*b*) What does 12 map to?   (*e*) What maps to 0?
  (*c*) What does 9 map to?   (*f*) What maps to 10?

3. For the mapping $x \longrightarrow 20 - 4x$:
  (*a*) What does 3 map to?   (*d*) What does 2 map to?
  (*b*) What does 0 map to?   (*e*) What maps to 0?
  (*c*) What does 4 map to?   (*f*) What maps to 16?

4. For the mapping $p \longrightarrow 3(p - 6)$:
  (*a*) What does 10 map to?   (*d*) What does 25 map to?
  (*b*) What does 15 map to?   (*e*) What maps to 0?
  (*c*) What does 12 map to?   (*f*) What maps to 3?

5. For the mapping $u \longrightarrow u - 6$:
  (*a*) What does 14 map to?   (*d*) What does ⁻5 map to?
  (*b*) What does 12 map to?   (*e*) What maps to 4?
  (*c*) What does 2 map to?   (*f*) What maps to 0?

6. For the mapping $m \longrightarrow 3m - 9$:
  (*a*) What does 6 map to?   (*d*) What does ⁻1 map to?
  (*b*) What does 10 map to?   (*e*) What maps to 0?
  (*c*) What does 0 map to?   (*f*) What maps to 3?

7. For the mapping $a \longrightarrow 15 - 2a$:
   (a) What does 2 map to?
   (b) What does 6 map to?
   (c) What does 8 map to?
   (d) What does ‾3 map to?
   (e) What maps to 9?
   (f) What maps to 0?

8. For the mapping $c \longrightarrow 4(c - 7)$:
   (a) What does 9 map to?
   (b) What does 15 map to?
   (c) What does 2 map to?
   (d) What does ‾4 map to?
   (e) What maps to 0?
   (f) What maps to 12?

Exercise 8

A **1.** Given that $f(x) = 9x$, find the value of:
   (a) $f(2)$ (b) $f(8)$ (c) $f(0)$ (d) $f(‾3)$

2. Given that $f(n) = 3n + 8$, find the value of:
   (a) $f(2)$ (b) $f(0)$ (c) $f(6)$ (d) $f(‾2)$

3. Given that $h(u) = 14 - u$, find the value of:
   (a) $h(7)$ (b) $h(0)$ (c) $h(20)$ (d) $h(‾4)$

4. If $f(t) = 6 - 2t$, find the value of:
   (a) $f(1)$ (b) $f(0)$ (c) $f(5)$ (d) $f(‾5)$

5. If $g(t) = \dfrac{(t - 7)}{2}$, find the value of:

   (a) $g(11)$ (b) $g(8)$ (c) $g(0)$ (d) $g(‾3)$

6. If $h(n) = 8n - 4$, find the value of:
   (a) $h(3)$ (b) $h(0)$ (c) $h(\frac{1}{2})$ (d) $h(‾2)$

7. (a) Find the value of $f(6)$ when $f(x) = 2x - 9$
   (b) Find the value of $f(‾3)$ when $f(x) = 2x + 11$.

8. (a) Find the value of $f(10)$ when $f(t) = (2t - 8)/4$.
   (b) Find the value of $f(‾6)$ when $f(t) = \dfrac{(t + 2)}{2}$

B **1.** If $y = 4x$, find the value of y when:

(a) $x = 6$ (b) $x = 0$ (c) $x = 12$ (d) $x = {}^-3$

2. If $y = \dfrac{x}{6}$, find the value of y when:

(a) $x = 30$ (b) $x = 0$ (c) $x = {}^-12$ (d) $x = 15$

3. If $y = 6x + 8$, find the value of y when:

(a) $x = 1$ (b) $x = 6$ (c) $x = {}^-1$ (d) $x = {}^-3$

4. If $y = 18 - x$, find the value of y when:

(a) $x = 10$ (b) $x = 0$ (c) $x = 18$ (d) $x = {}^-2$

5. If $y = 18 - 3x$, find the value of y when:

(a) $x = 6$ (b) $x = 0$ (c) $x = 10$ (d) $x = {}^-8$

6. If $y = \dfrac{(2x + 10)}{4}$, find the value of y when:

(a) $x = 3$ (b) $x = 0$ (c) $x = 4$ (d) $x = {}^-3$

7. If $y = 3(4x - 5)$, find the value of y when:

(a) $x = 4$ (b) $x = 0$ (c) $x = 1$ (d) $x = {}^-2$

8. If $y = 4(8 - x)$, find the value of y when:

(a) $x = 7$ (b) $x = 0$ (c) $x = 15$ (d) $x = {}^-4$

Exercise 9

A **1.** If $f(x) = x + 5$, find the value of x when:

(a) $f(x) = 8$ (b) $f(x) = 15$ (c) $f(x) = 21$ (d) $f(x) = 0$

2. If $f(x) = 8x$, find the value of x when:

(a) $f(x) = 16$ (b) $f(x) = 0$ (c) $f(x) = 32$ (d) $f(x) = 72$

3. If $f(x) = 2x - 3$, find the value of x when:

(a) $f(x) = 5$ (b) $f(x) = 11$ (c) $f(x) = 15$ (d) $f(x) = 0$

4. If $f(t) = 5t + 1$, find the value of t when:

(a) $f(t) = 6$ (b) $f(t) = 21$ (c) $f(t) = 1$ (d) $f(t) = 46$

5. If $g(t) = 9t - 4$, find the value of t when:

(a) $g(t) = 14$ (b) $g(t) = 32$ (c) $g(t) = 41$ (d) $g(t) = 59$

B **1.** If $y = x - 8$, find the value of x when:

(a) $y = 2$ (b) $y = 5$ (c) $y = 0$ (d) $y = 10$

2. If $y = 3x + 5$, find the value of x when:

(a) $y = 5$ (b) $y = 8$ (c) $y = 14$ (d) $y = 26$

3. If $y = 2x - 7$, find the value of x when:

(a) $y = 3$ (b) $y = 7$ (c) $y = 1$ (d) $y = 2$

4. If $y = 10 - x$, find the value of x when:

(a) $y = 4$ (b) $y = 10$ (c) $y = 0$ (d) $y = 8$

5. If $y = 8x + 6$, find the value of x when:

(a) $y = 22$ (b) $y = 6$ (c) $y = 30$ (d) $y = 10$

Exercise 10

A If $f(x) = 4x^2$, find the value of:

1. $f(2)$	**4.** $f(6)$	**7.** $f(-2)$	**10.** $f(-5)$
2. $f(3)$	**5.** $f(1)$	**8.** $f(-4)$	**11.** $f(-10)$
3. $f(0)$	**6.** $f(9)$	**9.** $f(-1)$	**12.** $f(-7)$

B If $y = 5x^2$, find the value of y when:

1. $x = 2$	**4.** $x = 0$	**7.** $x = {}^-1$	**10.** $x = {}^-8$
2. $x = 4$	**5.** $x = 7$	**8.** $x = {}^-3$	**11.** $x = {}^-9$
3. $x = 5$	**6.** $x = 10$	**9.** $x = {}^-6$	**12.** $x = {}^-12$

Exercise 11

A If $f(x) = 2x^2 + 3$, find the value of:

1. $f(2)$	**4.** $f(5)$	**7.** $f(-1)$	**10.** $f(-6)$
2. $f(3)$	**5.** $f(7)$	**8.** $f(-3)$	**11.** $f(-10)$
3. $f(0)$	**6.** $f(9)$	**9.** $f(-4)$	**12.** $f(-8)$

B If $y = 3x^2 - 12$, find the value of y when:

1. $x = 3$	**4.** $x = 1$	**7.** $x = {}^-3$	**10.** $x = {}^-2$
2. $x = 5$	**5.** $x = 2$	**8.** $x = {}^-5$	**11.** $x = {}^-6$
3. $x = 0$	**6.** $x = 4$	**9.** $x = {}^-1$	**12.** $x = {}^-10$

Exercise 12

A Write a statement for each function:

   e.g. $f : x \longrightarrow 3x + 7$
          <u>Multiply by 3 then add 7.</u>

1. $f : x \longrightarrow 2x - 8$

2. $f : x \longrightarrow 8x + 4$

3. $f : t \longrightarrow 9t - 12$

4. $h : t \longrightarrow 3(t - 6)$

5. $k : x \longrightarrow \dfrac{x}{4} + 9$

6. $g : t \longrightarrow \dfrac{(t - 7)}{4}$

7. $h : x \longrightarrow 4(2x + 3)$

8. $g : x \longrightarrow \dfrac{(4x - 9)}{3}$

9. $f : u \longrightarrow \dfrac{(u + 8)}{5} + 6$

10. $g : u \longrightarrow 2(u + 5) - 9$

B Write functions for the following statements (choose any letters you wish):

   e.g.   Multiply by 8 then add 12.
         <u>$f : x \longrightarrow 8x + 12$</u>

1. Double then add 9.

2. Multiply by 6 then subtract 8.

3. Divide by 4 then add 10.

4. Add 7 then multiply by 5.

5. Subtract 8 then multiply by 6.

6. Add 4 then divide by 7.

7. Multiply by 4, subtract 7 then multiply by 3.

8. Subtract 2, multiply by 3 then add 4.

9. Add 9, divide by 3 then subtract 15.

10. Multiply by 9, add 8, then halve.

Revision Exercises VIII to XIV

Revision Exercise VIII

1. Each line has been drawn to the given scale. Find the true length.
   (*a*) 1 cm represents 15 km

   _____

   (*b*) 1:400

   _____

2. Using a scale of 1 cm to 250 m, draw straight lines to represent the given lengths:
   (*a*) 1.5 km   (*b*) 2.25 km   (*c*) 1.875 km

3. (*a*) What is the bearing   (*b*) What is the bearing of:
   of Y from X?   (i) X from P?
                                          (ii) Y from P?

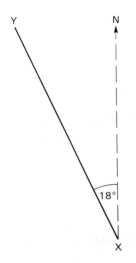
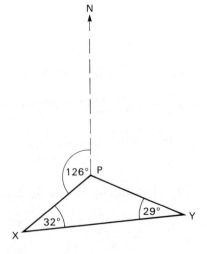

4. Dunvegan is 45 km from Leverburgh and on a bearing of 144°.
Clachan is 30 km from Leverburgh on a bearing of 219°. Make a
scale drawing to show all three places. Use a scale of 1 cm to 5 km.
(*a*) How far is Dunvegan from Clachan?
(*b*) What is the bearing of Clachan from Dunvegan?

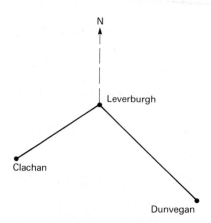

5. The angle of elevation of the top of a building, from a point that is
47 m away from the foot of the building, is 23°. Make a scale
drawing using the scale 1:500 then find the height of the building.

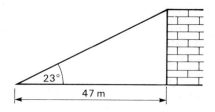

6. Make a scale drawing of the
front elevation of a desk. Use a
scale of 1 cm to 20 cm (that is
1:20). Its dimensions, given on
this diagram, are in centimetres.
The thickness of the top of the
desk is 20 mm.

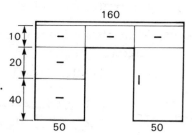

Revision Exercise IX

1. If there are 34 crosses:
   (a) How many groups of eight could there be?
   (b) How many crosses would be left over?
   (c) Write 34 in base 8.

2. Convert the following numbers from their given base into base ten:
   (a) 21_3 (b) 42_5 (c) 36_8 (d) 65_{12}

3. Convert the following numbers from base ten into the given base:
   (a) 36_{ten} to base 8   (b) 87_{ten} to base 12

4. Copy and complete:

   $326_8 = \boxed{?}$ sixty-fours, $\boxed{?}$ eights and $\boxed{?}$ units $= \boxed{?}_{ten}$

5. Convert the following numbers from the given base into base ten:
   (a) 314_5 (b) 302_4 (c) 1221_3 (d) 101101_2

6. Convert these from base ten to the given base:
   (a) 206_{ten} to base 8   (b) 55_{ten} to base 2

7. Work out what has been written in ASCII code:

   0110010
   1101110
   1100100
   1011001
   1100101
   1100001
   1110010

8. (a) Write $4C_{hex}$ in base ten.
   (b) Write 45_{ten} in hexadecimal.

9. Write these binary numbers in order of size from smallest to largest:

   11101_2, 110111_2, 100110_2, 100011_2, 11111_2, 101001_2

10. Which of these are even numbers?

    534_8, 207_9, 1058_9, 3132_4, 120110_3, 3431_5

Revision Exercise X

1. How many seconds are there in 9 min 27 s?

2. A film lasted 1 h 47 min. How many minutes was that?

3. How many days are there in 27 weeks?

4. In a 4×200 m women's relay event, the times for the legs were 21.87 s, 21.9 s, 22.64 s, 21.59 s. What was the total time?

5. Write the time 'quarter to seven in the evening' using:
   (a) the 24-hour clock notation, (b) the 12-hour clock notation.

6. Write these times in words:
   (a) 22.10   (b) 8.35 a.m.

7. Write 14.30 using the 12-hour clock notation.

8. Write 12.50 p.m. using the 24-hour clock notation.

9. I set off on a bus journey at 10.53. If the journey took 4 h 28 min, at what time did I arrive at my destination?

10. Using the train timetable on p. 148, find:
    (a) the time of arrival in Ledbury of the 08.15 train from Worcester Foregate St.,
    (b) the time the next train leaves after the train that leaves Great Malvern at 18.15.

11. How many days were there from:
    (a) noon on 21 October 1979 to noon on 14 November 1979?
    (b) noon on 11 February 1964 to noon on 30 March 1964?

12. If 16 June is a Monday, on what day is 19 July of the same year?

13. List the leap years from 1970 to 2000 inclusive.

14. Using the table given on p. 154, answer the following.
    Mr and Mrs Benson flew from Bristol to Corfu on 12 July.
    (a) At what time did they take off from Bristol?
    (b) How long was the flight?
    (c) When they landed in Corfu, what was the time:
       (i) in Bristol?   (ii) in Corfu?
    (d) What was the time in Corfu when they took off:
       (i) from Bristol   (ii) from Corfu?

Revision Exercise XI

1. A rectangular table top is 1.6 m long and 0.92 m wide. Calculate its area.

2. Am I definitely able to cut 45 dusters each measuring 55 cm by 40 cm from a rectangular piece of material that
   (a) measures 3.9 m by 2.8 m?
   (b) measures 3.6 m by 2.8 m?
   (c) has an area of 10 m²?

3. A rectangle of length 18 cm has an area of 144 cm²:
   (a) Calculate the width of the rectangle.
   (b) Calculate the area of a square that has the same-sized perimeter as the rectangle.

4. A room is 4.8 m long, 4 m wide and 2.4 m high. Calculate:
   (a) the area of the floor,
   (b) the total area of all four walls ignoring any doors and windows.

5. In each of the following, find d in terms of the other letters:
   (a) $A = ld$
   (b) $A = \frac{1}{2}Dd$

6. (a) Find the area: (b) Find the base, labelled b:

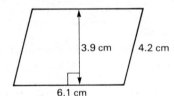   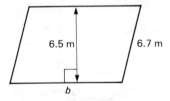

Area = 61.1 m²

7. Calculate:
   (a) the area of the parallelogram,
   (b) the perpendicular height, labelled h.

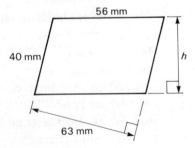

8. (*a*) Find the area:

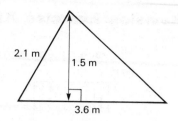

(*b*) Find the perpendicular
   height, labelled *h*, if the
   area is 18 cm².

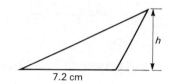

9. Calculate:
   (*a*) the area of the triangle,
   (*b*) the length of the base,
      labelled *b*.

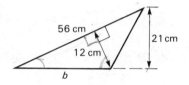

10. Calculate the area of the
   trapezium.

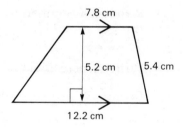

11. Calculate the area of:
   (*a*) a kite with diagonals measuring 12.6 cm and 8.7 cm,
   (*b*) a rhombus with the long diagonal measuring 7.9 cm and
      the short diagonal measuring 6.8 cm.

12. Construct a kite with sides measuring 50 mm and 25 mm,
   where the angle between a long and short side is 120°:
   (*a*) How long are the diagonals?
   (*b*) By measuring and calculating, find the area of the kite.

211

1. For each square, write what percentage has been shaded:

(a)   (b) 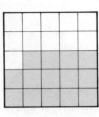   (c)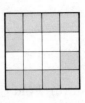

2. Using a 10 by 10 square, shade 52% of it.

3. Write 73% as a vulgar fraction.

4. Write $\frac{59}{100}$ as a percentage.

5. Write 70% as a decimal.

6. Write 0.08 as a percentage.

7. Write as a common fraction in its simplest terms:

  (a) 5%   (b) 56%   (c) $3\frac{1}{2}\%$

8. Write as percentages:

  (a) $\dfrac{13}{25}$ (b) $\dfrac{7}{8}$ (c) $\dfrac{13}{40}$

9. Bryn got 80% in a test. What was his mark out of 25?

10. Find:

  (a) 75% of 42 ℓ

  (b) $2\frac{1}{2}\%$ of £894

11. Find $33\frac{1}{3}\%$ of £69.

12. In a sale, a keyboard costing £199 was sold at a discount of 15%. Calculate:

  (a) the discount,

  (b) the selling price of the keyboard.

Revision Exercise XIII

1. Write the temperature shown on the given thermometer.

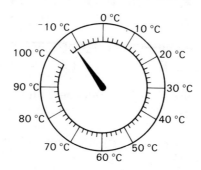

2. A thermometer showed the temperature to be 4 °C. If it then fell by 9 °C, what would the new temperature be?

3. Find the value of: $4 - 11 + 3 - 7$

4. Find the value of: $(-3) - (-11) + (-2)$

5. Find the value of: $^-8 + \,^-10 - \,^-1$

6. Find the missing numbers:
   (a) $\boxed{?} + \,^-6 = \,^-11$
   (b) $^-4 - \boxed{?} = 6$

7. Simplify where possible:
   (a) $4k - 2l - 9l - k + 5l + 6k - 2k$
   (b) $4mad - 3adm + 2dm - 5md + ma + 6mda$
   (c) $4x^2 - 3x + 5x - x^2 + 7 - 4x - 9$

8. Work these out:
   (a) $^-3 \times \,^+4 \times \,^-5$
   (b) $(+6) \times (-7) \times (+2)$

9. Work these out:
   (a) $^-42 \div \,^-7$
   (b) $\dfrac{(-36)}{(+4)}$

10. Find the missing numbers:
   (a) $\boxed{?} \times \,^-9 = 72$
   (b) $\boxed{?} \div \,^-7 = 8$

11. If $x = {}^-9$, find the value of:

    (a) $4x$ (b) $x - 10$ (c) $3x + 15$ (d) $10 - 2x$

12. If $y = 3x + 8$, find the value of y when x equals:

    (a) 0 (b) 5 (c) ${}^-2$ (d) ${}^-5$ (e) ${}^-10$

13. If $T = a - 6d$, find the value of T when:

    (a) $a = 7$ and $d = {}^-3$,   (b) $a = {}^-8$ and $d = 2$.

14. If $m = 4$ and $n = {}^-3$, find the value of:

    (a) $4(2m - n)$ (b) $10 - (m + 3n)$

15. Which number lies exactly half-way between:

    (a) ${}^-15$ and ${}^+31$?   (b) ${}^-68$ and ${}^-6$?

16. Copy the sequence and fill in the missing numbers:

$$9,\ 7,\ 3,\ \boxed{?},\ {}^-11,\ \boxed{?},\ \boxed{?},\ {}^-47$$

Revision Exercise XIV   **M**

1. If $C = \{$Amsterdam, Athens, Brussels, Copenhagen, Kabul, Oslo, Reykjavic, Stockholm, Vienna$\}$

    and $N = \{$Afghanistan, Austria, Belgium, Denmark, Greece, Iceland, Netherlands, Norway, Sweden$\}$,

    draw a diagram to show the relation 'is the capital of' from set C to set N.

2. Write a relation that is true for all pairs of numbers that are linked in the arrow diagram below.

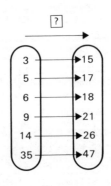

3. Copy and complete the mapping diagrams:

(a)

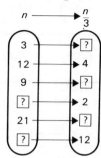

(b)

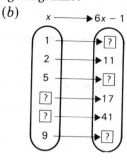

4. Draw a mapping diagram for the function $g(t) = 5t - 2$ using the domain $\{1, 2, 3, 4, 5, 6\}$.

5. Draw a mapping diagram for the function $f(x) = 18 - 2x$ using the domain $\{10, 5, 1, 0, {}^-1, {}^-6\}$.

6. Copy and complete the mapping diagram below so that pairs of elements that are linked by arrows are linked by the same function.

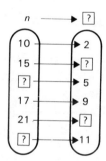

7. For the mapping $t \longrightarrow 12 - 3t$:
   (a) What does 3 map to?   (d) What does ${}^-2$ map to?
   (b) What does 0 map to?   (e) What maps to 0?
   (c) What does 6 map to?   (f) What maps to 6?

8. If $h(x) = 7x - 5$ find the value of:
   (a) $h(3)$ (b) $h(8)$ (c) $h(0)$ (d) $h({}^-2)$

9. If $y = 5(3x - 6)$ find the value of y when:
   (a) $x = 4$ (b) $x = 2$ (c) $x = 0$ (d) $x = {}^-2$

10. If $f(t) = 4t - 5$, find the value of t when:
   (a) $f(t) = 7$ (b) $f(t) = 23$ (c) $f(t) = 47$ (d) $f(t) = 1$

215

11. If $y = 6x + 1$, find the value of x when:

    (a) $y = 7$ (b) $y = 19$ (c) $y = 1$ (d) $y = 43$

12. If $f(x) = 3x^2 + 8$, find the value of:

    (a) $f(0)$ (b) $f(2)$ (c) $f(^-2)$ (d) $f(^-5)$

13. If $y = 4x^2 - 9$, find the value of y when:

    (a) $x = 3$ (b) $x = {}^-3$ (c) $x = 1$ (d) $x = {}^-5$

14. Write a statement for the function $f : x \longrightarrow 4(x + 7)$.

15. Write a function for the statement 'Multiply by 5 then add 7.'

15 Co-ordinates and Graphs

Plotting Points Using the Four Quadrants

Exercise 1

Draw a pair of axes as shown
(x ranges from $^-10$ to $^+10$ and y
from $^-8$ to $^+8$).

Answer all the following questions
using axes as shown:

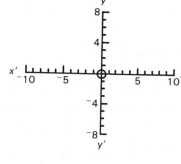

1. (a) Plot the points $(^-5, 2)$,
$(^-8, 2)$, $(^-9, ^-1)$, and
$(^-2, ^-1)$; then join them
with straight lines to make
a quadrilateral.

   (b) What is the name of the quadrilateral obtained in part (a)?

2. (a) Plot the points $(5, ^-2)$, $(10, ^-1)$, $(9, ^-6)$ and $(4, ^-7)$; then
join them with straight lines to make a quadrilateral.

   (b) What is the name of the quadrilateral obtained in part (a)?

   (c) Write the co-ordinates of the point of intersection of the
diagonals of this quadrilateral.

3. (a) Plot the points $P(5, 7)$, $Q(6, 4)$ and $R(1, 4)$; then join
P to Q and Q to R using straight lines.

   (b) Find the position of a point S, such that PQRS is a
parallelogram. Complete the drawing of the parallelogram.

   (c) Write the co-ordinates of S.

4. (a) Plot the points $W(^-10, 6)$, $X(^-8, 8)$ and $Y(^-3, 6)$; then
join W to X and X to Y using straight lines.

   (b) Find a point Z, and complete the drawing of quadrilateral
WXYZ where WY is a line of symmetry.

   (c) Write the co-ordinates of Z.

   (d) What sort of quadrilateral is WXYZ?

217

5. $(0, 2)$, $(^-2, 1)$, $(^-4, 5)$ and $(^-2, 6)$ are the vertices of a rectangle. Find the co-ordinates of the point of intersection of the diagonals.

6. $(^-3, ^-3)$, $(3, ^-1)$ and $(4, ^-4)$ are three vertices of a rectangle. Find the co-ordinates of the fourth vertex.

7. BD is a diagonal of square ABCD. B is the point $(^-4, ^-5)$ and D is $(^-10, ^-5)$. Find the co-ordinates of A and C, if the square is labelled anticlockwise.

8. $(3, 2)$, $(8, 4)$ and $(9, 0)$ are the co-ordinates of the vertices of a triangle. Draw the triangle and calculate its area.

Exercise 2

Answer all the following questions using axes as shown in Exercise 1.

1. A, B and C are the points $(10, 7)$, $(6, 7)$, $(6, 5)$ respectively. Find D, the fourth point, such that ABCD is a rectangle.

2. $P(^-1, 7)$ and $R(^-1, 3)$ are opposite vertices of a square, PQRS. Find the other two vertices if the square is labelled anticlockwise.

3. $X(9, 2)$ and $Y(9, ^-1)$ are two vertices of a right-angled, isosceles triangle. If the right-angle is at Y, find the co-ordinates of the third vertex, Z, where Z is to the left of Y.

4. Three vertices of a rhombus are $(^-1, ^-1)$, $(2, ^-2)$ and $(^-1, ^-3)$. Find the fourth vertex.

5. $J(^-9, 2\frac{1}{2})$, $K(^-6, ^-1)$ and $L(^-4, 0)$ are vertices of a parallelogram JKLM. Find the co-ordinates of M.

6. The diagonals of parallelogram TUVW intersect at $(^-7, 6)$. T is the point $(^-9, 7)$ and U is $(^-5, 8)$. Find the co-ordinates of V and W.

7. $(^-8, ^-4)$ is one vertex of a square. The diagonals of the square intersect at $(^-6, ^-5)$. Find the co-ordinates of the other vertices.

8. The diagonals of parallelogram DEFG intersect at $(7.5, ^-5)$. If D is the point $(8, ^-2)$ and E is $(5, ^-6)$, find the co-ordinates of vertices F and G.

218

9. $(1, ^-7)$ and $(3, ^-7)$ are the vertices of the base of an isosceles triangle. Find possible co-ordinates for the third vertex, if its y-value is a whole number and is bigger than $^-9$ and less than $^-3$.

10. KLMN is a rectangle. K is the point $(4, 4)$ while the opposite vertex, M, is $(0.5, 1)$. Vertex N lies on the y-axis. Find two possible pairs of co-ordinates for:
    (a) vertex N,   (b) vertex L.

Exercise 3 Graphs with Equations $x = c$ and $y = c$

1. (a) On graph paper, draw a pair of axes as shown, using a scale of 10 mm to 1 unit. $^-8 \leqslant x \leqslant ^+8$ and $^-10 \leqslant y \leqslant ^+10$.
   (b) Plot the points $(4, 3)$, $(4, 4)$, $(4, 5)$, $(4, 1)$, $(4, 0)$, $(4, 2)$, $(4, 2.5)$, $(4, 1.5)$, $(4, ^-2)$, $(4, ^-5)$, $(4, 6)$, $(4, ^-6)$, $(4, ^-3)$, $(4, 10)$, $(4, ^-2.5)$, $(4, ^-3.5)$.
   (c) What do you notice about all these points you have plotted on your graph paper?
   (d) Join the points to form a straight line. (Use a ruler.)
   (e) Look at the pairs of co-ordinates given in part (b) above. In each case, the first number is always 4. If the ordered pairs (or pairs of co-ordinates) are written as (x, y), then the x-value is always 4, that is, $x = 4$.

   The *equation of this line* is therefore $x = 4$. Label your line '$x = 4$'.

2. On the same piece of graph paper and using the same pair of axes, draw these lines:
   (a) $x = 3$ (b) $x = 1$ (c) $x = 5\frac{1}{2}$ (d) $x = ^-5$

3. Using the same pair of axes, draw:
   (a) $y = 3$ (b) $y = 6$ (c) $y = 7\frac{1}{2}$ (d) $y = ^-4$

219

4. Using the same pair of axes draw:
   (a) $x = 0$ (b) $y = 0$

5. What is special about the lines drawn in question 4?

6. What is the equation of the straight line that joins these points?
   $(^-7, ^-2)$, $(^-7, 4)$, $(^-7, 9)$, $(^-7, ^-6.5)$

7. What is the equation of the straight line that joins these points?
   $(^-1, 5)$, $(3, 5)$, $(2, 5)$, $(6, 5)$, $(^-5, 5)$, $(2.5, 5)$, $(^-7, 5)$

Graphs with Equations $y = x + c$

Exercise 4   **M**

A 1. (a) Consider the relation 'is 3 less than' for the set of real numbers*.

Copy and complete the mapping diagram.

(b) The relation 'is 3 less than' in part (a) can be shown using ordered pairs.

Copy these ordered pairs and fill in the missing y-values.

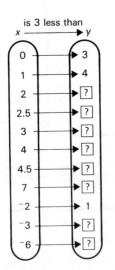

is 3 less than
$x \longrightarrow y$

0	3
1	4
2	?
2.5	?
3	?
4	?
4.5	?
7	?
$^-2$	1
$^-3$	?
$^-6$	?

(0, 3)

(1, 4)

(2, ?)

(2.5, ?)

(3, ?)

(4, ?)

(4.5, ?)

(7, ?)

($^-2$, 1)

($^-3$, ?)

($^-6$, ?)

*See the glossary, p. 447.

220

(c) The same relation, 'is 3 less than', can be shown in a table. Copy and complete the following table.

x	$^{-}6$	$^{-}3$	$^{-}2$	0	1	2	2.5	3	4	4.5	7
y	?	?	1	3	4	?	?	?	?	?	?

2. (a) Draw a pair of axes where x ranges from $^{-}6$ to $^{+}8$ ($^{-}6 \leqslant x \leqslant {}^{+}8$) and y from $^{-}10$ to $^{+}10$ ($^{-}10 \leqslant y \leqslant {}^{+}10$). Use a scale of 10 mm to 1 unit on both axes.

(b) Plot the points given by the relation, then join the points with a straight line. Since a straight line is obtained, the graph is called a *linear graph.*

3. For this relation, the x-value is 3 less than the y-value. So the y-value must be 3 more than the x-value. Copy and complete the statements in parts (a) and (b):

(a) The y-value = the x-value + ?.

(b) That is, $y = x +$?. This is called the *equation of the graph.*

(c) Write the equation of the graph along your graph.

B **1.** Draw a mapping diagram to show the relation 'is 2 less than'.

2. Show the relation as a set of ordered pairs.

3. For each of the ordered pairs, what must be added to the first number to obtain the second number?

4. Copy and complete these statements for the ordered pairs that satisfy the relation 'is 2 less than':

(a) The y-value = the x-value + ?.

(b) That is, $y = x +$?.

5. Using the same pair of axes as in part A, draw a graph to show the relation 'is 2 less than'. Label your graph with its equation.

C **1.** Find equations that are true for the given sets of ordered pairs:

   (a) $\{(0, 6),\ (1, 7),\ (2, 8),\ (4, 10),\ (7, 13),\ (10, 16),\ (12, 18),$
      $(14, 20)\}$

   (b) $\{(0, 4),\ (1, 5),\ (3, 7),\ (6, 10),\ (8, 12),\ (11, 15),\ (13, 17),$
      $(14, 18)\}$

2. Draw graphs of the equations in question 1. Use the same pair of axes as in part A.

D Using the same pair of axes as used in part A, draw graphs of:

1. the relation 'is 1 less than'

2. $y = x$

3. $y = x + 5$

If you have not already labelled each graph you have drawn, then write the equation of each graph on each line.

E Where would the graph of $y = x + 7$ cross the y-axis?

Exercise 5

Throughout this exercise, draw every graph using the same pair of axes as in Exercise 4.

A **1.** Copy and complete the mapping diagram for the relation 'is 2 more than'.

2. Since x is 2 more than y, then y is 2 less than x.
The y-value = the x-value − 2, that is, $y = x - 2$.
Find the value of y when:
(a) $x = 6$ (b) $x = {}^-3$

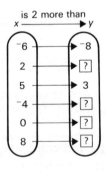

3. $(7, \boxed{?})$, $(3, \boxed{?})$, $(1, \boxed{?})$, $({}^-2 \boxed{?})$ and $({}^-2.5, \boxed{?})$ are ordered pairs that satisfy the equation $y = x - 2$. Find the missing numbers and write the five ordered pairs.

4. Draw the graph of $y = x - 2$. Label your graph.

222

5. Draw the graph of $y = x - 4$. Label it.

6. Draw the graph of the relation 'is 3 more than'.

7. Draw the graph of the relation 'is 1 more than'.

B 1. Write what you notice about all the graphs you draw in part A.

2. Where would the graph of $y = x - 6$ cross the y-axis?

Graphs with Equations $y = mx$

Exercise 6

Draw a pair of axes where x ranges from $^-8$ to $^+8$ and y ranges from $^-50$ to $^+50$. Use a scale of 1 cm to 1 unit on the x-axis and 1 cm to 5 units on the y-axis.

A 1. Graph the relations:

    (*a*) 'is $\frac{1}{2}$ of'   (*b*) 'is $\frac{1}{4}$ of'

2. Using the same pair of axes as for question 1, draw the following graphs:

    (*a*) $y = x$ (*e*) $y = 8x$

    (*b*) $y = 3x$ (*f*) $y = \frac{1}{2}x$

    (*c*) $y = 5x$ (*g*) $y = \frac{5}{2}x$

    (*d*) $y = 6x$ (*h*) $y = \frac{7}{2}x$

B 1. Write what you notice about all the graphs you drew in part A.

2. List the graphs in order of steepness, giving the steepest first.

Exercise 7

1. Using the same pair of axes as for Exercise 6, draw the following graphs:

    (*a*) $y = {}^-x$ (*d*) $y = {}^-\frac{1}{2}x$

    (*b*) $y = {}^-2x$ (*e*) $y = {}^-5x$

    (*c*) $y = {}^-3x$ (*f*) $y = {}^-\frac{3}{2}x$

2. Write what you notice about the graphs in question 1.

3. List the graphs in question 1 in order of steepness, giving the steepest first.

The *gradient* of a line is a measure of how steep it is.

Exercise 8

Given the equations of these linear graphs, find their gradients:

e.g. 1	$y = {}^-3x$	e.g. 2	$3y = 6x$

$$\text{Gradient} = \underline{\underline{{}^-3}}$$

$$y = 2x$$
$$\text{Gradient} = \underline{\underline{2}}$$

1. $y = 4x$

2. $y = {}^-7x$

3. $y = 12x$

4. $y = \frac{1}{2}x$

5. $y = 2\frac{1}{2}x$

6. $y = {}^-\frac{7}{2}x$

7. $y = \frac{3}{4}x$

8. $y = {}^-x$

9. $y = \frac{x}{3}$

10. $y = 0$

11. $2y = 8x$

12. $y = {}^-3\frac{1}{4}x$

13. $2y = {}^-6x$

14. $2x = y$

15. $x = 2y$

16. $2y = 9x$

Graphs with Equations $y = mx + c$

Exercise 9

Draw a pair of axes where x ranges from $^-7$ to $^+7$ and y ranges from $^-25$ to $^+25$. Use a scale of 1 cm to 1 unit on the x-axis and 2 cm to 5 units on the y-axis. Use this pair of axes for all the graphs in this exercise.

A Draw graphs of:

1. $y = 3x$

2. $y = 3x + 4$

3. $y = 3x + 2$

4. $y = 3x - 2$

5. $y = 3x - 1$

6. $y = 3x - 4$

B **1.** Write what you notice about all the graphs you drew in part A.

2. Where would the graph of $y = 3x + 5$ cross the y-axis?

224

Exercise 10

A Draw a pair of axes where $^-8 \leqslant x \leqslant {}^-8$ (use a scale of 1 cm to 1 unit on the x-axis) and $^-25 \leqslant y \leqslant {}^+25$ (use a scale of 2 cm to 5 units on the y-axis). Use this pair of axes for all the graphs throughout this exercise.

1. (a) If
$$y = {}^-2x + 3$$
   when $x = 2,$ $\quad y = {}^-4 + 3$
   $$= {}^-1$$
   This gives the point $(2, {}^-1)$. Plot $(2, {}^-1)$.
   (b) If $y = {}^-2x + 3,$ find y when $x = 6$. Plot the obtained point.
   (c) If $y = {}^-2x + 3,$ find y when $x = 0$. Plot the obtained point.
   (d) If $y = {}^-2x + 3,$ find y when $x = {}^-8$. Plot the obtained point.
   (e) Draw a straight line through all the marked points.
   (f) Label this linear graph with the equation $y = {}^-2x + 3$.

2. Draw the graph of:
   (a) $y = {}^-2x + 5$
   (b) $y = 8 - 2x$
   (c) $y = {}^-2x$
   (d) $y = {}^-2x - 4$
   (e) $y = 6 - 2x$
   (f) $y = {}^-2x + 9$

B 1. What do you notice about all the graphs you have drawn in part A?

2. (a) Where would the graph of $y = {}^-2x + 4$ cross the y-axis?
   (b) Where would the graph of $y = 7 - 2x$ cross the y-axis?

Gradient and y-intercept

Exercise 11

Write the gradient and y-intercept of each of the graphs that have the following equations:

1. $y = 2x + 1$
2. $y = 3x + 5$
3. $y = x$
4. $y = 5x$
5. $y = 7x + 2$
6. $y = 2x - 4$
7. $y = 3x - 5$
8. $y = 6x + 3$
9. $y = \frac{1}{2}x + 3$
10. $y = \frac{1}{2}x - 1$
11. $y = \frac{1}{4}x$
12. $4y = 8x$

225

13. $2y = 4x$
14. $2y = 4x + 2$
15. $3y = 9x + 6$
16. $3y = 6x - 3$
17. $2y = 6x + 2$
18. $2y = 2x + 1$

19. $3y = 6x + 1$
20. $5y = 5x - 1$
21. $2y = x + 2$
22. $6y = 3x + 6$
23. $2y = x - 1$
24. $y = {}^-x$

25. $y = {}^-x - 1$
26. $y = 2 - 4x$
27. $y = 3 - 2x$
28. $2y = 2 - 4x$
29. $3y = 6 - 9x$
30. $2y = 1 - 2x$

Exercise 12

Write the equations of graphs that have the given gradients and y-intercepts:

	Gradient	y-intercept
1.	2	3
2.	2	$^-5$
3.	4	0
4.	3	8
5.	5	$^-4$

	Gradient	y-intercept
6.	1	7
7.	6	1
8.	$^-2$	5
9.	$^-4$	9
10.	$^-3$	$^-2$

Exercise 13

In each question, select the equations that best describe the given graphs:

1. $y = 5x - 2$
$y = 3x - 4$
$y = x + 4$
$y = 4x$
$y = 3x + 4$

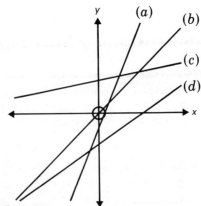

226

2. $y = \frac{1}{2}x$
   $y = x + 6$
   $y = 2x$
   $y = 4x - 3$
   $y = 3x + 4$

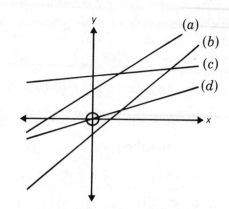

3. $y = 4$
   $x = 4$
   $y = {}^-4$
   $x = {}^-4$
   $y = 2x + 4$
   $y = 2x - 4$
   $y = 4 - 2x$
   $y = 6 - 4x$
   $y = {}^-2x$

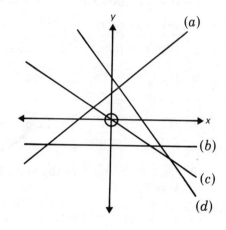

4. $y = \frac{1}{2}x - 3$
   $y = 2x - 3$
   $y = 5x - 3$
   $y = 3x + 7$
   $y = 6x + 4$
   $y = 8x + 7$

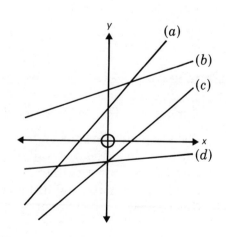

Exercise 14

1. Does the point $(4, 1)$ lie on the line $y = 2x - 7$?

2. Does the point $(3, 5)$ lie on the line $y = 3x + 4$?

3. Does the point $(^-2, 14)$ lie on the line $y = 3x + 8$?

4. Does the point $(^-1, 5)$ lie on the line $y = 4x + 9$?

5. Does the point $(^-4, 9)$ line on the line $y = 2x - 1$?

6. Find the missing numbers:
   (a) The point $(3, \boxed{?})$ lies on the line $y = 5x - 8$.
   (b) The point $(\boxed{?}, 14)$ lies on the line $y = 2x + 6$.
   (c) The point $(1, \boxed{?})$ lies on the line $y = 3x - 7$.
   (d) The point $(\boxed{?}, ^-5)$ lies on the line $y = 4x + 3$.

7. If $(3, a)$ and $(b, 2)$ lie on the line $y = 2x + 6$, then find the values of a and b.

8. If $(p, ^-2)$ and $(^-2, q)$ lie on the line $y = 5x + 3$, then find the values of p and q.

9. On which line does the point $(^-4, ^-10)$ lie, on $y = 3x + 2$ or on $y = 3x - 2$?

10. On which line does the point $(^-3, 14)$ lie, on $y = 2x + 8$ or on $y = 8 - 2x$?

Gradient

Reminder: The *gradient* of a line is a measure of how steep it is.

The steepness depends on how much the line rises vertically (the *rise*) compared with either its length or the horizontal distance (the *tread*).

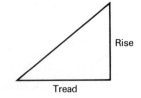

Rise

Tread

In mathematics we use:

$$\text{Gradient} = \frac{\text{rise}}{\text{tread}}$$

The gradient of any straight line can be found by drawing a right-angled triangle under the line, then dividing the rise by the tread. This is shown in the following examples.

e.g. 1   Find the gradient of the straight line joining the points (2, 4) and (6, 16).

From the diagram:

the rise $= 16 - 4 = 12$

the tread $= 6 - 2 = 4$

$$\text{Gradient} = \frac{\text{rise}}{\text{tread}} = \frac{12}{4} = \underline{\underline{3}}$$

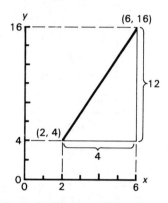

e.g. 2   Find the gradient of the straight line joining the points (⁻3, 13) and (2, 3).

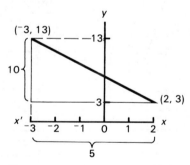

From the diagram:

the rise $= {}^{-}10$

the tread $= 5$

$$\text{Gradient} = \frac{\text{rise}}{\text{tread}} = \frac{{}^{-}10}{5} = \underline{\underline{{}^{-}2}}$$

(*Note*   The gradient is negative because the line slopes downwards.)

Exercise 15

A Find the gradient of each line segment given:

1.

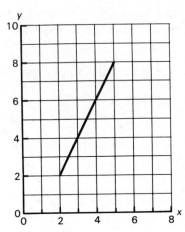

3.

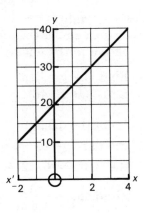

2.

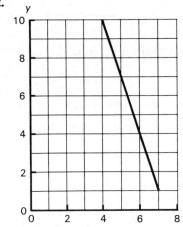

4.

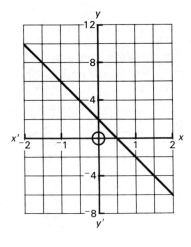

B Find the gradient of the straight-line segment joining each pair of points:

1. $(2, 8)$, $(5, 17)$

2. $(^-2, ^-12)$, $(3, 8)$

3. $(3, 1)$, $(^-1, 9)$

4. $(3, 2)$, $(5, 17)$

5. $(^-2, ^-17)$, $(0, 7)$

6. $(10, 10)$, $(18, 16)$

7. $(^-2, 12)$, $(5, ^-9)$

8. $(^-6, ^-4)$, $(^-18, ^-7)$

Exercise 16   Obtaining a Formula

Copy and complete:

From the diagram:

$$\text{the rise} = y_2 - y_1$$

$$\text{the tread} = \boxed{?}$$

$$\text{Gradient} = \frac{\text{rise}}{\text{tread}} = \frac{\boxed{?}}{\boxed{?}}$$

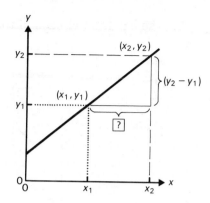

$$\text{Gradient of a line} = \frac{(y_2 - y_1)}{(x_2 - x_1)}$$

where the two points are (x_1, y_1) and (x_2, y_2).

Exercise 17

Find the gradient of the straight-line segment joining each pair of points:

e.g. 1 $(2, 4)$ and $(6, 16)$

Let $(x_1, y_1) = (2, 4)$ and $(x_2, y_2) = (6, 16)$

$$\text{Gradient} = \frac{(y_2 - y_1)}{(x_2 - x_1)} = \frac{(16 - 4)}{(6 - 2)} = \frac{12}{4} = \underline{\underline{3}}$$

e.g. 2 $(^-3, 13)$ and $(2, 3)$

Let $(x_1, y_1) = (^-3, 13)$ and $(x_2, y_2) = (2, 3)$

$$\text{Gradient} = \frac{(y_2 - y_1)}{(x_2 - x_1)} = \frac{(3 - 13)}{(2 - {}^-3)} = \frac{^-10}{5} = \underline{\underline{^-2}}$$

1. $(4, 13)$, $(6, 27)$

2. $(4, 2)$, $(2, 12)$

3. $(0, 0)$, $(7, 28)$

4. $(5, ^-1)$, $(1, 3)$

5. $(^-3, 25)$, $(3, ^-11)$

6. $(15, 2.5)$, $(8, ^-1)$

7. $(1.5, ^-13)$, $(^-1, 7)$

8. $(3\frac{1}{2}, 8)$, $(18\frac{1}{2}, 29)$

231

Find the equation of each of the following graphs:

1.

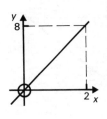

5.

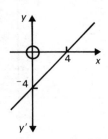

9.

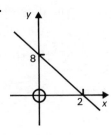

2.

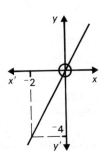

6.

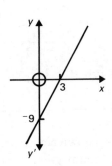

10.

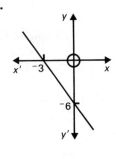

3.

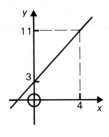

7.

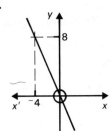

11.

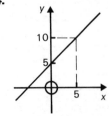

4.

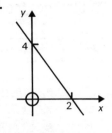

8.

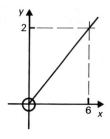

12.

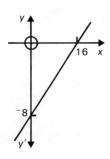

Exercise 19　Sketching Graphs

Sketch a graph of each of the following equations:

1. $y = 4x$
2. $y = 4x + 2$
3. $y = 4x - 4$
4. $y = 2x + 1$
5. $y = 3x - 6$
6. $y = {}^-3x$
7. $y = {}^-2x + 6$
8. $y = 8 - x$
9. $y = {}^-4x - 8$
10. $y = 6 - 3x$

Exercise 20　Graphs from Tables

1. In a sale, a dealer gave some discount. The following table shows the amount of discount for various prices of goods.

Normal price	0	30	75	105	150	210	300	360	480
Discount	0	10	25	35	50	70	100	120	160

Draw a pair of axes as shown then, using the given table, draw a graph to show the discount given by the dealer.

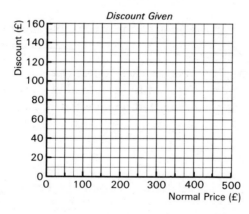

Use your graph to help you to answer these questions.
(a) How much discount is given when the normal price is:
   (i) £60?　　(ii) £270?　　(iii) £195?　　(iv) £375?
(b) Find the normal price when the discount is:
   (i) £60　　(ii) £75　　(iii) £135　　(iv) £105
(c) What percentage discount does the dealer give?

233

2. In a science experiment using pulleys, a table was produced showing the effort needed to lift various loads.

Load (N)	10	20	30	40	50	60	70
Effort (N)	7	10	13.5	15	20	22	24.5

Draw a pair of axes as shown.

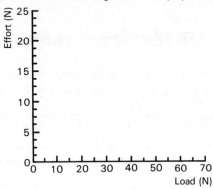

Use a scale of 2 cm to 10 N for the load and 4 cm to 5 N for the effort.

Plot points from the information in the table above then draw the line of best fit.

Use your graph to answer these questions.
(a) What effort is needed to lift a load of 45 N?
(b) What load can be lifted by an effort of 20 N?

Circumference and Area of a Circle

3.141 592 653 589 793 238 462 643 383 279 502 884 197 169 399 375 . . .

Circumference of a Circle

Exercise 1

For this exercise you need several
cylindrical objects such as jars, tins,
coins and so on. They should be
different sizes.

Find the diameter and the circumference of each circular base (or
cross-section) of each object you have collected.

To find the circumference: either wrap a tape measure around the
object; or wrap a piece of string around it, then measure the length
of the string.

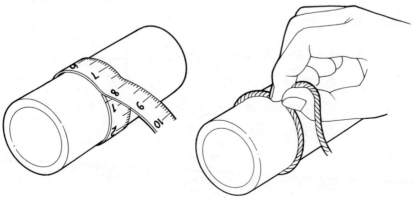

Show your results in a table as follows:

Object	Circumference, C	Diameter, d	$\dfrac{C}{d}$

Complete the last column by dividing the circumference by the diameter. Write what you notice.

From Exercise 1 you probably found that the circumference is slightly more than three times the diameter. In the Bible, when King Solomon was building his temple, the circumference was thought to be three times the diameter. In 1 Kings, chapter 7, verse 23, it says 'And he made a molten sea, ten cubits from the one brim to the other: it was round all about, and his height was five cubits: and a line of thirty cubits did compass it round about.' (See also 2 Chronicles, chapter 4, verse 2.) The molten sea was a very large bowl that contained over 500 barrels of water for the priests' use in washing themselves and the sacrifices. They also used the water for keeping the courts of the temple clean.

Exercise 2

Find the circumference of each circle.

Use: Circumference, $C = 3d$.

e.g. 1   Diameter, $d = 6$ cm

Circumference, $C = 3d$

$$C = 3 \times 6$$

∴ the circumference $= \underline{\underline{18 \text{ cm}}}$

6 cm

e.g. 2

Radius, $r = 2.4$ m

∴ diameter, $d = 4.8$ m

Circumference, $C = 3d$

$C = 3 \times 4.8$

∴ the circumference = 14.4 m

A The diameter is:
1. 19 cm
2. 52 mm
3. 8.5 m
4. 3.7 cm

B The radius is:
1. 13 cm
2. 4.6 m
3. 37 mm
4. 8.8 cm

π (pi)

Exercise 3

The circumference of a circle happens to be slightly more than 3 times the diameter.

The Greek letter π (pi) is used as a symbol for the ratio of the circumference to the diameter of any circle, so:

$$\pi = \frac{C}{d}$$

but we often re-write this as:

Circumference of a circle, $C = \pi d$.

Pi has not got an exact value. It is non-terminating and non-recurring when written as a decimal.

For thousands of years, mathematicians have tried to calculate more and more accurate values of pi.

(The value of pi to 48 decimal places has been given at the beginning of this chapter.)

A About 1580 BC, in the Rhind Papyrus, a method for calculating the area of a circle was given by Ahmes, the scribe. From this method, pi was found to be $\frac{256}{81}$. Use a calculator to change this to a decimal. Compare its accuracy with the decimal value given on p. 235.

B Over 2000 years ago, Archimedes (287–212 BC), a Greek mathematician, showed that the value of pi lies between $3\frac{10}{71}$ and $3\frac{1}{7}$. Use a calculator to change these two values of pi into decimals. Compare their accuracy using the decimal value given on p. 235. (Note that $3\frac{1}{7}$ is still used as a suitable approximation to pi.)

C About AD 150, Ptolemy, another Greek, found pi to have the value of 3°8′30″. This is:

$$3 + \frac{8}{60} + \frac{30}{3600} = 3\frac{17}{120} = \frac{377}{120}$$

Change $\frac{377}{120}$ to a decimal and compare it with the decimal value given on p. 235.

D In China, about AD 480, Tsu Ch'ung-Chih found quite an accurate value of pi. He gave the value $\frac{355}{113}$. Change $\frac{355}{113}$ to a decimal. Compare it with the decimal value given on p. 235. Note that this value together with $\frac{22}{7}$ can be used to find Ptolemy's value for pi:

$$\frac{355 + 22}{113 + 7} = \frac{377}{120}$$

E About AD 1430, the Persian mathematician, Jemshid Al-Kashi, gave pi to 16 decimal places.

F Ludolf van Ceulen (1540–1610), a German, found pi to 35 decimal places. He had worked on the problem for most of his life.

G About 1655, John Wallis gave pi as a *series*. This series can be written as:

$$\pi = 2 \times \frac{2}{1} \times \frac{2}{3} \times \frac{4}{3} \times \frac{4}{5} \times \frac{6}{5} \times \frac{6}{7} \times \frac{8}{7} \times \frac{8}{9} \times \frac{10}{9} \times \ldots$$

The numbers follow a pattern and continue for ever. The more numbers that are used, the more accurate is the value of pi. It takes a long time to find a reasonable approximation for pi using this series*. Try it for yourself on a calculator. The first few values are as follows:

$$\pi_1 = 2 \times \frac{2}{1} \quad = 4 \qquad\qquad \pi_5 = 2.8\dot{4} \times \frac{6}{5} \quad = 3.41\dot{3}$$

$$\pi_2 = 4 \times \frac{2}{3} \quad = 2.\dot{6} \qquad\qquad \pi_6 = 3.41\dot{3} \times \frac{6}{7} \quad = 2.9257$$

$$\pi_3 = 2.\dot{6} \times \frac{4}{3} = 3.\dot{5} \qquad\qquad \pi_7 = 2.9257 \times \frac{8}{7} = 3.3437$$

$$\pi_4 = 3.\dot{5} \times \frac{4}{5} = 2.8\dot{4} \qquad\qquad \pi_8 = 3.3437 \times \frac{8}{9} = 2.9722$$

and so on.

The values of pi can be shown on a graph. The above values are shown on the following graph.

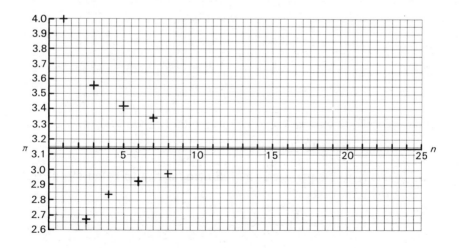

Copy the graph and plot some more points.

*A computer program is given in Appendix 4, p. 441.

H There have been a number of different series used to find pi over the years. For some of the following series work out some of the values of pi and show them on a graph (as in part G). Computer programs are given in Appendix 4, p. 441 for questions 1–4.

1. In 1673 Leibniz discovered the following series* that gives pi. (It was also discovered independently by James Gregory at a slightly later date.)

$$\pi = 4(1 - \tfrac{1}{3} + \tfrac{1}{5} - \tfrac{1}{7} + \tfrac{1}{9} - \tfrac{1}{11} + \ldots)$$

that is, $\pi = 4 - \tfrac{4}{3} + \tfrac{4}{5} - \tfrac{4}{7} + \tfrac{4}{9} - \tfrac{4}{11} + \ldots$

Note $\pi_1 = 4$, $\pi_2 = 2.\dot{6}$, $\pi_3 = 3.4\dot{6}$, $\pi_4 \approx 2.895$ and so on.

2. In 1680, John Wallis, together with Lord Brouncker, discovered the following continuous fraction that gives an approximation* of pi:

$$\pi = \cfrac{4}{1 + \cfrac{1}{2 + \cfrac{9}{2 + \cfrac{25}{2 + \cfrac{49}{2 + \cfrac{81}{2 + \text{etc.}}}}}}}$$

Note $\pi_1 = \tfrac{4}{1} = 4$ $\pi_2 = \cfrac{4}{1 + \tfrac{1}{2}} = \cfrac{4}{1.5} = 2.\dot{6}$

$$\pi_3 = \cfrac{4}{1 + \cfrac{1}{2 + \tfrac{9}{2}}} = \cfrac{4}{1 + \tfrac{1}{6.5}} = \cfrac{4}{1 + 0.538} = \cfrac{4}{1.538}$$

$= 3.4\dot{6}$ and so on.

3. In 1717, A. Sharp used the following series to calculate pi to 72 decimal places*:

$$\pi = \sqrt{12}\left(1 - \frac{1}{3 \times 3} + \frac{1}{3^2 \times 5} - \frac{1}{3^3 \times 7} + \frac{1}{3^4 \times 9} - \ldots\right)$$

Note $\pi_1 \approx 3.464$, $\pi_2 \approx 3.079$, $\pi_3 \approx 3.156$, $\pi_4 \approx 3.1379$ and so on.

*Computer programs are given in Appendix 4, p. 441.

4. About 1730, Euler calculated pi using the series*:

$$\frac{\pi}{4} = \frac{1}{2} - \frac{1}{3} \times \frac{1}{2^3} + \frac{1}{5} \times \frac{1}{2^5} - \frac{1}{7} \times \frac{1}{2^7} + \ldots$$

$$+ \frac{1}{3} - \frac{1}{3} \times \frac{1}{3^3} + \frac{1}{5} \times \frac{1}{3^5} - \frac{1}{7} \times \frac{1}{3^7} + \ldots$$

This can be written as

$$\pi = 4\left(\frac{1}{2} + \frac{1}{3}\right) - \frac{4}{3}\left(\frac{1}{2^3} + \frac{1}{3^3}\right) + \frac{4}{5}\left(\frac{1}{2^5} + \frac{1}{3^5}\right)$$

$$- \frac{4}{7}\left(\frac{1}{2^7} + \frac{1}{3^7}\right) + \frac{4}{9}\left(\frac{1}{2^4} + \frac{1}{3^9}\right) - \ldots$$

5. In 1770, J.H. Lambert discovered several approximations for pi. Work out these three:

(a) $\left(\dfrac{7}{4}\right)^2$ (b) $\left(\dfrac{16}{9}\right)^2$ (c) $\left(\dfrac{62}{35}\right)^2$

6. William Shanks (1853) used a series to find pi to 707 decimal places. However, the last 180 digits were incorrect. It took him about 20 years of calculating!

7. In 1914, Ramanujan suggested the following approximation for pi:

$$\pi = \sqrt{\sqrt{\frac{2143}{22}}}$$

Work it out (it is an excellent approximation).

8. In 1949, the ENIAC computer calculated pi to 2035 decimal places in 80 h of machine time.

9. In 1958, G.E. Felton used a Ferranti Pegasus computer to find pi to 10 021 places in 33 machine hours. (This would have taken about 100 years to work out on a calculator!)

10. Dr Daniel Shanks and Dr John W. Wrench Jr in New York in 1961, used an IBM 7090 computer to calculate pi to 100 265 places in 8 h 43 min.

*A computer program is given in Appendix 4, p. 441.

11. In 1981, Dr Kazunori Miyoshi of the University of Tsukuba in Japan worked out pi to two million decimal places in 137 h on a FACOM M200 computer.

12. In 1983, two other Japanese mathematicians, Yoshiaki Tamura and Yasumasa Kanada succeeded in working out pi to eight million decimal places in 7 h using a HITAC M280H computer.

13. On 8 Mar 1988, Yasumasa Kanada of Tokyo University, calculated pi to 208 326 000 decimal places in 5 h 57 min using a HITAC 802/80 computer.

14. The world record for memorising pi is held by Hideaki Tomoyori of Japan who memorised 40 000 decimal places in 17 h 21 min (including 4 h 15 min breaks) on 10 Mar 1987.

15. The British record of memorising 20 013 decimal places of pi is held by Creighton Carvello at Saltscar Comprehensive School, Redcar.

16. The first person to use the symbol π to stand for the ratio $\dfrac{C}{d}$, was probably an English writer called William Jones. He used π in 1706.

Exercise 4

In Exercise 3, several ratios were given for pi. Here are some more. Use a calculator to change these to decimals. In each case, state the number of decimal places that are correct, by comparing with the value given on p. 235.

1. $\dfrac{333}{106}$ **5.** $\dfrac{487}{155}$ **9.** $\dfrac{776}{247}$ **13.** $\dfrac{1021}{325}$

2. $\dfrac{421}{134}$ **6.** $\dfrac{531}{169}$ **10.** $\dfrac{820}{261}$ **14.** $\dfrac{1043}{332}$

3. $\dfrac{443}{141}$ **7.** $\dfrac{688}{219}$ **11.** $\dfrac{864}{275}$ **15.** $\dfrac{1354}{431}$

4. $\dfrac{465}{148}$ **8.** $\dfrac{732}{233}$ **12.** $\dfrac{908}{289}$ **16.** $\dfrac{1376}{438}$

Exercise 5

In Exercises 3 and 4 there are a number of different ratios that give good approximations for pi. Try to find some ratios of your own that give approximations for pi. Note that ratios such as $\frac{44}{14}$ are not allowed ($\frac{44}{14}$ can simplify to a ratio that has already been given, namely $\frac{22}{7}$).

Exercise 6

In Exercise 3, part D, two ratios were used to give another ratio:

$$\frac{355 + 22}{113 + 7} = \frac{377}{120}$$

Look at the ratios in Exercise 4, starting with question 2:

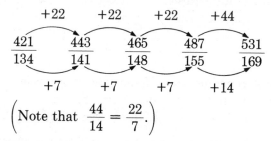

$$\left(\text{Note that } \frac{44}{14} = \frac{22}{7}.\right)$$

Investigate other ratios for pi in this way. Write about your findings.

Two mnemonics for pi given in the magazine *Mathematical Pie* are:

    How I like a cuddle
    3 . 1 4 1   6

and   How I wish I could recollect pi easily today
       3 . 1 4 1 5   9   2   6   5

(Count the number of letters in each word.)

Exercise 7

1. $\pi \approx \dfrac{399}{\boxed{?}}$ has three correct places of decimals. Find the denominator.

2. $\pi \approx \dfrac{\boxed{?}}{445}$ has four correct places of decimals. Find the numerator.

243

3. $\pi \approx \dfrac{1731}{\boxed{?}}$ has four correct places of decimals. Find the denominator.

4. The rational number $\dfrac{1753}{\boxed{?}}$ is an approximation for pi. Find the denominator so that it has four correct places of decimals.

5. $\dfrac{\boxed{?}}{671}$ is correct to four decimal places as an approximation for pi. Find the numerator.

6. $\dfrac{\boxed{?}}{544}$, as an approximation for pi, is correct to three decimal places (after rounding). Before rounding, four decimal places are correct. Find the numerator.

Exercise 8

Find the circumference of each of the following circles. Use the formula: Circumference of a circle, $C = \pi d$, and use the given value of π. As a check, estimate each answer using $\pi = 3$.

A Use $\pi = 3.14$ and give answers to two significant figures:

1. diameter = 25 cm
2. diameter = 7.6 m
3. radius = 4.7 cm
4. diameter = 38 mm

5. radius = 28 mm
6. radius = 3.2 cm
7. diameter = 86 mm
8. diameter = 9.3 m

B Use $\pi = 3.142$ and give answers to three significant figures:

1. diameter = 20 mm
2. radius = 15 mm
3. diameter = 8.3 cm
4. diameter = 5.7 m

5. radius = 2.25 m
6. diameter = 69 mm
7. diameter = 9.7 m
8. radius = 3.9 cm

C Use $\pi = 3\frac{1}{7}$:

1. diameter = 35 cm
2. diameter = 28 cm
3. radius = 21 m
4. radius = 14 cm

5. diameter = 49 mm
6. radius = 49 mm
7. diameter = $10\frac{1}{2}$ cm
8. radius = $1\frac{3}{4}$ in

Exercise 9

Answer the following using the given values of pi. Check each answer by estimating using $\pi = 3$.

1. A bicycle wheel has a diameter of 460 mm:
   (a) Calculate its circumference in metres (use $\pi = 3.14$).
   (b) Calculate the distance travelled by a cyclist when the wheels make 2500 revolutions.

2. A pedal bin has a circular rim of diameter 21 cm. Calculate the distance around the rim. (Use $\pi = 3\frac{1}{7}$.)

3. A tin has a diameter of 72 mm. Calculate the length of a label that fits around the tin exactly once. Use $\pi = 3.142$ and give the answer correct to the nearest millimetre.

4. A circular mirror has a diameter of 15 cm. Calculate the length of a metal strip that fits around the rim of the mirror. (Use $\pi = 3.14$.)

5. The diameter of the roller on my lawn mower is 220 mm. If it makes 35 revs when I mow one length of my lawn, calculate the length of the lawn. (Use $\pi = 3.1$.)

6. Calculate the perimeter of the given shape, if
   $AC = BD = 63$ mm.
   (Use $\pi = \frac{22}{7}$.)

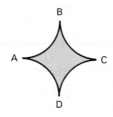

7. How many complete revolutions does a bicycle wheel with a diameter of 580 mm make in travelling 1 km? (Use $\pi = 3.14$.)

8. The diagram shows a running track. If the 'straights' are 100 m and the distance between opposite straights is 49 m, how far would a runner run who runs 8 laps. Use $\pi = \frac{22}{7}$ and give the answer in metres.

9. If the radius of the Earth is 3980 miles, calculate the distance around the Earth at the Equator. Use $\pi = 3.142$ and give the answer correct to the nearest mile.

10. Calculate the distance around circle of latitude 46 °N if its radius is 4425 km. (Use $\pi = 3.14$.)

11. A $2\frac{1}{2}\ell$ tin of paint has a diameter of 160 mm. In making the tin, an extra 15 mm of metal must be allowed to form a seam which must be leakproof.

Wired edge

Seam

PAIN

3 mm

160 mm

Wired edge

(a) Calculate the length of the piece of metal needed to make the curved face of the tin. (Use $\pi = 3.142$ and do not forget to allow 15 mm extra for the seam.)

(b) The wired edge at the top rim of the can is made from wire that is 3 mm thick (diameter = 3 mm). Calculate the length of wire needed (with no overlap). (Find the distance around the wired edge following the centre of the wire all the way round. (Use $\pi = 3.142$.))

12. A coffee jar has a diameter of 62 mm. Calculate the length of a label that goes around the jar once then overlaps itself by 14 mm. (Use $\pi = 3.14$ and give the answer correct to the nearest millimetre.)

13. There are two cars. The wheel diameter of one is 510 mm, while the other has a wheel diameter of 590 mm. How much further does the car with the larger wheels travel, when both sets of wheels make 80 000 revs? (Use $\pi = 3.14$.)

14. (a) A bicycle wheel has a diameter of 26 in. How many yards would the bicycle travel if the wheels turned 1800 times? (Use $\pi = 3.14$. Note that 12 in = 1 ft and 3 ft = 1 yd.)

(b) How far would the bicycle have travelled if the diameter of the wheels were half the size?

15. A protractor, as shown, is in the shape of a semi-circle, with a base diameter of 100 mm, together with a rectangular piece measuring 100 mm by 5 mm. Calculate the perimeter of the protractor. (Use $\pi = 3.14$.)

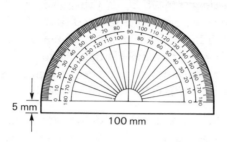

5 mm

100 mm

Exercise 10

1. Draw a pair of axes as shown. Use a scale of 1 cm to 1 cm for the diameter, and 2 cm to 5 cm for the circumference.

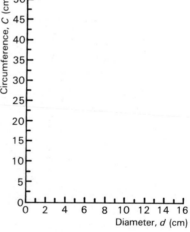

2. (a) Choose any diameter that is less than or equal to 15 cm.
(b) Calculate the circumference of the circle using $\pi = 3.14$.
(c) On your graph paper, plot a point to show the circumference and the diameter.

3. Repeat question 2 using other sizes of diameter that are less than 15 cm.

4. Write what you notice about the points you have plotted.

Exercise 11

1. Draw another pair of axes as in Exercise 10.

2. Use the measurements that you took in Exercise 1, p. 235. For each cylindrical object that you used, plot the measured circumference against the measured diameter. (If the diameter was more than 15 cm, just ignore that measurement — otherwise you would have to draw another pair of axes with larger diameters and circumferences marked on them.) Continue until you have plotted a point for each object that was measured.

3. This time, the points probably do not give a straight line. They are probably scattered about as shown in the diagram below (question 4). The points should suggest a straight line. Draw 'the line of best fit' as in Chapter 15, Exercise 20, p. 233.

4. Choose any diameter (10 cm has been chosen on this diagram).

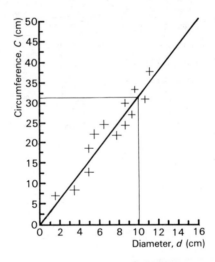

Draw a straight line, as shown, up to the graph, then draw a line across to the circumference axis. Read the value of the circumference.

Divide this value of the circumference by the diameter.

5. What do you notice about the answer obtained in question 4? If you do not notice anything, repeat question 4 using a different size of diameter.

Length of an Arc

Exercise 12

1. What fraction of the circumference is each arc?

(a)

(b)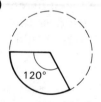

(c)

2. In each question, the angle subtended* at the centre of a circle by an arc is given (angle θ in the diagram).

   What fraction of the circumference is each of the following arcs?

   (a) 240°   (e) 210°   (i) 72°
   (b) 60°   (f) 30°   (j) 108°
   (c) 45°   (g) 150°   (k) 75°
   (d) 135°   (h) 36°   (l) 105°

Exercise 13

In each question, the radius of a circle is given, together with the angle subtended at the centre of the circle by an arc, and a value of π. Calculate the length of each arc.

1. $r = 15$ cm $\theta = 60°$ (Use $\pi = 3.14$.)
2. $r = 12$ m $\theta = 90°$ (Use $\pi = 3.142$.)
3. $r = 4.8$ cm $\theta = 30°$ (Use $\pi = 3$.)
4. $r = 4.5$ cm $\theta = 80°$ (Use $\pi = 3.1$.)
5. $r = 84$ mm $\theta = 210°$ (Use $\pi = 3.14$.)
6. $r = 56$ mm $\theta = 225°$ (Use $\pi = 3\frac{1}{7}$.)
7. $r = 135$ mm $\theta = 56°$ (Use $\pi = 3.142$.)
8. $r = 68$ mm $\theta = 81°$ (Use $\pi = 3.142$.)

*See the glossary, p. 448.

249

Area of a Circle

Exercise 14

1. Cut two circles out of coloured, gummed paper. Use two different colours and make the circles the same size; the diameters should be less than 50 mm.

2. Divide both circles into sixteen equal sectors, but do not cut them out.

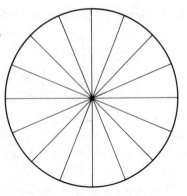

3. Cut both circles in half, giving four semi-circles.

4. Cut out the sectors of two of the semi-circles, one of each colour. (You should now have two semi-circles, one of each colour, eight sectors in one colour and eight sectors in the other colour.)

5. Stick the two semi-circles on to your page to give a full circle then stick the sectors on to your page as shown in the following sketches:

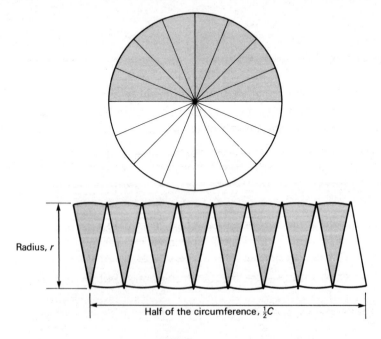

Radius, r

Half of the circumference, $\frac{1}{2}C$

Area of the circle = area of the parallelogram

$$= b \times h$$
$$= \tfrac{1}{2}C \times r$$
$$= \tfrac{1}{2}\pi d \times r \quad \text{(since } C = \pi d\text{)}$$
$$= \tfrac{1}{2}\pi \times 2r \times r \quad \text{(since } d = 2r\text{)}$$
$$= \pi \times r \times r$$

So the area of a circle $= \underline{\underline{\pi r^2}}$

6. Copy the above text that shows how to obtain a formula for the area of a circle.

Exercise 15

Calculate the areas of the following circles:

e.g. Diameter = 24 cm, so radius r = 12 cm.

$$\text{Area of a circle} = \pi r^2$$
$$\text{so area of the circle} = 3.14 \times 12^2 \text{ cm}^2$$
$$= 3.14 \times 144 \text{ cm}^2$$
$$= 452.16 \text{ cm}^2$$
$$= \underline{\underline{452 \text{ cm}^2}} \text{ (to 3 s.f.)}$$

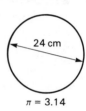

24 cm

$\pi = 3.14$

A Use $\pi = 3$:

1. radius = 7 cm
2. diameter = 36 cm
3. radius = 6.2 m

4. radius = 47 mm
5. diameter = 78 mm
6. diameter = 18.6 cm

B Use $\pi = 3.14$ and give answers to two significant figures:

1. radius = 2 m
2. radius = 60 cm
3. diameter = 18 m

4. radius = 16 cm
5. diameter = 15 m
6. radius = 43 mm

C Use $\pi = 3.142$ and give answers to three significant figures:

1. radius = 3 cm
2. radius = 8 cm
3. diameter = 2.6 m

4. diameter = 13.6 cm
5. radius = 54 mm
6. diameter = 58 mm

Exercise 16

1. A circular shaving mirror has a diameter of 16 cm. Calculate its area correct to two significant figures.
   (Use $\pi = 3.14$.)

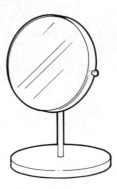

2. Calculate the area of the top of a circular chocolate cake, if the radius of its top is 10 cm. (Use $\pi = 3.142$.)

3. An LP record has a radius of 15 cm. Calculate the area of one side of the record. (Use $\pi = 3.14$ and ignore the hole in the centre.)

4. A circular metal tray has a radius of 14 cm. Calculate its area. (Use $\pi = \frac{22}{7}$.)

5. The diameter of a circular window in a church is 2.2 m. What area of glass was used in making it? (Use $\pi = 3.1$.)

6. A circular protractor has a radius of 52 mm. Calculate its area correct to two significant figures using $\pi = 3.14$.

7. Calculate the shaded area shown in the diagram.
   (Use $\pi = 3.14$.)

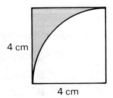

4 cm

4 cm

8. A circle of radius 6 cm is cut out of a rectangular piece of paper measuring 21 cm by 15 cm. Calculate the area of the remaining piece of paper. Use $\pi = 3.142$ and give your answer correct to three significant figures.

9. Calculate the area of the shape shown if the diameter of the two semi-circular ends is 7 m. (Use $\pi = 3\frac{1}{7}$.)

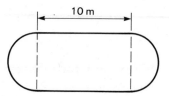

10 m

10. Calculate the area of the protractor given in Exercise 9, question 15, p. 247. (Use $\pi = 3.14$.)

17 Transformation Geometry

We live in a world where many things move. It can be useful to study how they move.

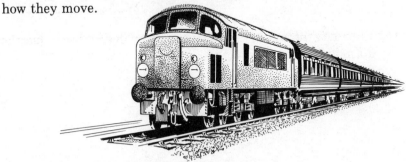

A train travelling on straight railway tracks shows movement in a straight line. We call movement in a straight line a *translation*. The movement may be in any direction but must be in a straight line for it to be a translation. The object being moved must not turn. The shape and size of the object do not change but its position does.

A wheelbarrow being tipped shows a different type of movement. It turns about a point. This type of movement is called a *rotation*.

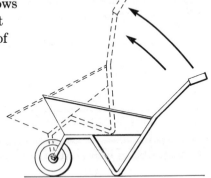

The handle on a tap needs to be turned (another example of a rotation). Once again, the shape and size of the object do not change but its position does.

If you look in an ordinary mirror you will see a *reflection* of yourself. Although you yourself do not move, your *image* can be seen in a different position. Once again your shape and size do not change but your image is in a different position from yourself. The image can be seen of any object placed in front of a mirror. Any point or mark on the object maps to a similar point or mark on the image. An object can be drawn, and its image can be drawn in a different position.

For translations and rotations we can use the same words, *object* and *image*. Consider the train: the original position can be referred to as the object and the new position as the image. Each point on the object maps to a similar point on the image (as for reflections). Also for the wheelbarrow, each point on the wheelbarrow in its original position (the object) maps to a similar point on the wheelbarrow in its new position (the image).

With translations, reflections and rotations, changes have happened — each point on the object has been mapped to a new position (the image position).

Translations, reflections and rotations are called *transformations*. A transformation is the relation between each point on an object and its image point.

Exercise 1 ■■■■■■■■■■■■■■■■■■■■■■■■■■■■■■■■ **M**

A Write the type of transformation: translation, reflection or rotation, for each of these movements:

e.g. The movement of a snooker cue during a game is a translation.

1. An aeroplane as it taxies along a runway.

2. The movement of a tennis racket when the player is serving.

3. The closing of a door with a hinge.

4. The opening of a sliding window.

5. The opening of a book.

6. The turning of a key in a lock.

7. Opening a drawer.

8. The movement of the drum in a washing machine.

B **1.** Write two other examples of a translation.

2. Write two other examples of a rotation.

Make a copy of this L-shape. Cut out your copy. (It may be better made out of card.)

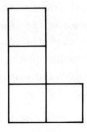

Use your L-shape in the following exercises.

Translations

Exercise 2

The shaded L-shape in the diagram has been *translated* 4 squares to the left. (The unshaded L-shape is the *image* of the shaded one.)

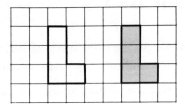

Use 1 cm squared paper throughout this exercise.

1. Draw your L-shape, then translate it 5 squares to the right. Draw the image.

2. Draw your L-shape, then translate it 6 squares downwards. Draw the image.

3. Draw your L-shape, then draw the image of a translation 4 squares upwards.

4. Draw your L-shape. Draw the final image position after a translation 3 squares to the right followed by a translation 5 squares downwards.

5. Draw your L-shape in the position shown. Now draw its image after a translation 4 squares to the right, followed by a translation 1 square downwards.

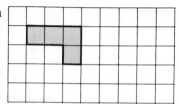

Note Under any translation, the object is moved in a straight line but *never* turned. An object and its image always remain the same way up.

Reflections | enoitɔelʇeЯ

Exercise 3 ▬▬▬▬▬▬▬▬▬▬▬▬▬▬▬ M

On a piece of squared paper, draw the L-shapes and the mirrors in the positions suggested by the diagrams. For each one, reflect the L-shape in the given mirror and draw the image. (Note that a shape can be reflected in either side of the mirror.)

1.
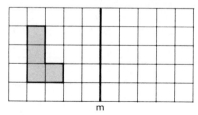

3.
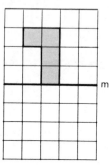

2.
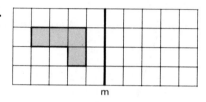

4.
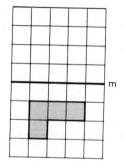

5.

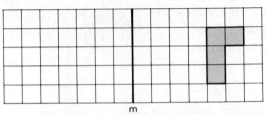

7.

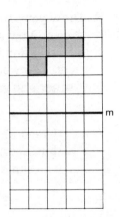

6.

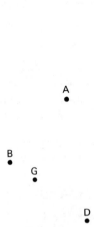

8.

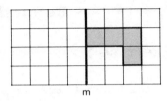

Exercise 4

1. Trace the mirror line and the nine points given on the previous page on to tracing paper. By folding the tracing paper along the mirror line, find the images of the nine points after a reflection in the mirror line, m. Label each image. (The image of A is A′, B′ is the image of B, C′ of C, and so on.)

2. (a) Join each object to its image using a straight line.
   (b) Write what you notice about each straight line and the mirror line. (At what angle do they cross?)

3. Write what you notice about the distance of an object from the mirror line when compared with the distance of its image from the mirror line.

4. Plot any point as the object and find its image. Label the object X and its image X′.

   Now reflect X′ in the same mirror line. Write what you notice. (Draw as many objects and images as you need to help you with this.)

5. Write what you notice about the points that lie on a mirror line and their images after a reflection in that mirror line.

Exercise 5 ▰▰▰▰▰▰▰▰▰▰▰▰▰▰▰▰▰▰▰▰▰ **M**

Copy the following mirror lines and points. Draw and label the image of each object point when reflected in the mirror line (label the image of A as A′, the image of B as B′ and so on).

1.

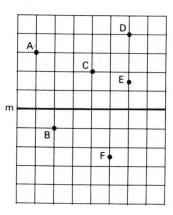

2.

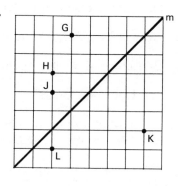

259

3.

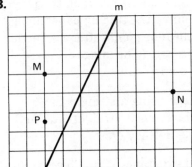

5.

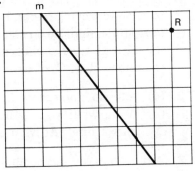

4.

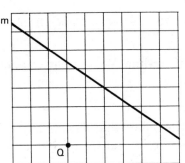

6.

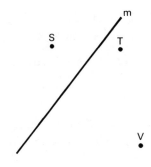

Exercise 6

1. On tracing paper, draw any mirror line.

2. Draw a line, AB, on the tracing paper. (This is the object.)

3. By folding along the mirror line, find and draw the image A′B′.

4. (*a*) How long is AB?   (*b*) How long is A′B′?

5. Write what you notice about the length of the image compared with the length of the object.

6. A line is 65 mm long. How long is its image under a reflection?

7. An image is a line of 51 mm long. How long is the object line?

Exercise 7

1. Trace the two points on to tracing paper. (A′ is the image of A after a reflection in a mirror line.)

A′
•

A
•

2. By folding the tracing paper, find the mirror line.

3. How many different positions of the mirror line are there?

4. Answer the questions above for any two other points.

5. Write what you discover.

Exercise 8 　M

Copy the following, then draw the image of each shape after a reflection in the given mirror line:

1.

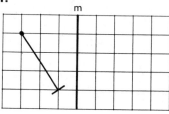

3.

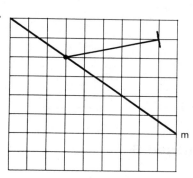

2.

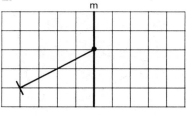

4.

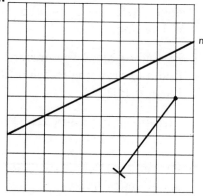

261

5.

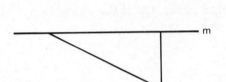

7.

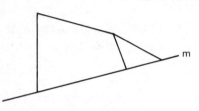

6.

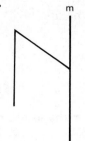

8.

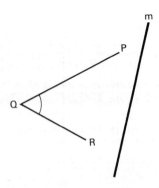

Exercise 9

1. On tracing paper, draw any angle PQR, as shown, and any mirror line.

2. By folding along the mirror line, find and draw the image of PQR. Label it P'Q'R'.

3. Measure ∠PQR and ∠P'Q'R', then write what you notice.

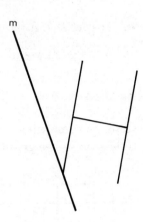

4. Repeat questions 1 to 3 for different-sized angles and write about your findings.

Exercise 10

Make any triangle out of card (let the sides measure between 30 mm and 50 mm).

A 1. (*a*) Draw round your triangle on tracing paper. Label the three vertices, A, B and C as shown.

(*b*) Draw any mirror line.

(*c*) By folding along the mirror line, find the image of △ABC. Label the image A'B'C', where A maps to A', B maps to B' and C maps to C'.

(*d*) Is △A'B'C' the same shape or different from △ABC?

(*e*) Is △A'B'C' bigger, smaller or the same size as △ABC?

2. On the same piece of paper, draw a different mirror line. Answer question 1, parts (*c*), (*d*) and (*e*) using this new mirror line.

3. (*a*) Write what you notice about the shape of any reflected image when compared with its object.

(*b*) Write what you notice about the size of any reflected image when compared with its object.

(If you are unable to answer question 3, repeat question 2 using a different mirror line.)

B 1. Draw round your triangle on another piece of tracing paper. Label the tracing LMN.

2. Draw any mirror line.

3. By folding, reflect △LMN in the mirror line and draw and label its image L'M'N' as in part A, question 1(*c*).

4. Is the object labelled clockwise or anticlockwise?

5. Is the image labelled clockwise or anticlockwise?

6. Repeat questions 1 to 5 above.

7. Write about your findings.

263

Exercise 11   Reflections and Polygons

A Make a right-angled triangle ABC
out of card where AB = 15 mm,
BC = 30 mm and ∠ABC = 90°.

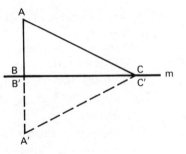

When △ABC is reflected in a mirror
line where side BC lies on the mirror
line, the object and image make an
isosceles triangle, as shown.

1. What shape do the object and image make if the triangle is
   reflected in a line on which the side AB lies?

2. What shape do the object and image make if the triangle is
   reflected in a line on which the side AC lies?

B Experiment with other sizes and types of triangle. (Make them out
of card.) Reflect each triangle you make in a mirror line that lies
along one of the sides of the triangle. Try to make the following
shapes with a triangle and its image. If it is possible to obtain a
certain shape, show, as in the example and diagram given above,
how you obtained it; otherwise write 'IMPOSSIBLE'.

1. a square
2. a rectangle
3. a parallelogram
4. a rhombus
5. a trapezium

6. an equilateral triangle
7. a right-angled isosceles triangle
8. a right-angled triangle that is
   not isosceles

C In parts A and B a triangle was reflected in a line along one of its
sides, and the object and image together formed either three- or
four-sided shapes:

1. Experiment with four-sided shapes as for the triangles. Reflect
   each shape in a line along one of its sides. For each new shape
   obtained from the object and image combined, note the number
   of sides. Find all possible numbers of sides for the newly obtained
   shapes.

2. Repeat question 1 by reflecting:
   (*a*) five-sided shapes
   (*b*) six-sided shapes
   (*c*) seven-sided shapes
   (*d*) eight-sided shapes

Rotations

Each of these diagrams shows a rotation about a point. In the first diagram, a point is being rotated, in the second, a straight line and in the third, a triangle.

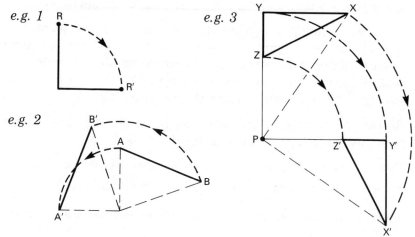

e.g. 1

e.g. 2

e.g. 3

The rotation can be clockwise or anticlockwise. The amount of turning can vary. In the examples, the rotation is 'a quarter turn'.

The curved lines need not be drawn to show the actual turning. In fact, only the shapes themselves need be drawn. The two diagrams below show the triangle in *e.g. 3* again being rotated through a quarter turn clockwise.

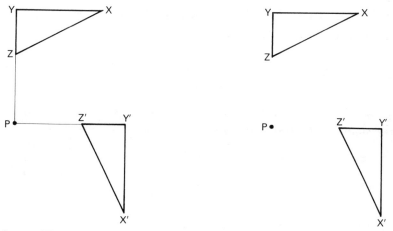

Note The point about which a shape rotates is called *the centre of rotation*.

265

Exercise 12

Draw any triangle in your exercise book and mark any centre of rotation. Label the centre of rotation C.

Trace your triangle and the centre on to tracing paper.

Keep the tracing paper in position and place a pencil point at C to hold the tracing paper in place. Now rotate the tracing paper about C to any new position. Copy your triangle into your exercise book in this new position. (You could use a pin to prick through the tracing on to your page to mark the image positions.)

Repeat the process above until you have at least three image positions of the triangle in your exercise book.

Now use your drawings to help you to answer these questions:

1. Are all the images the same size or of different sizes?

2. Are the images smaller than, bigger than, or the same size as the object?

3. When a shape is rotated, does its shape change?

4. Measure the distances of certain points on the object from C. Measure the distances of the images of these same points from C. Write what you notice about object and image distances from the centre of rotation.

5. If the object is labelled clockwise, will its image be labelled clockwise or anticlockwise?

Exercise 13

A In each drawing, an object and its image are given. In each case, is the point C the centre of rotation?

1.

2.

3. D _____ E

C •

E' _____ D'

6. J _____ K • C

K'

J'

4. F _____ G

G'

• C

F'

7.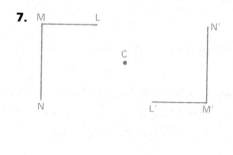

5. H | C • | H'

I | | I'

8.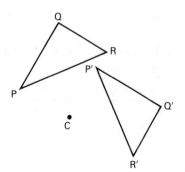

B Explain why C is not the centre of rotation in each of the following diagrams:

1. S
•

• C

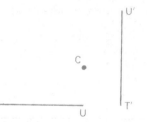

S'
•

3. V———————W

4.

X———————Y   •C

V'

Y'———————X'

C •

W'

Exercise 14   **M**

A Trace the following shapes. Rotate each one as instructed about the given centre of rotation, C. (Use tracing paper to help you.)

1. Rotate P 90° clockwise about C:

C
•

P
•

4. Rotate PQ clockwise through 180° about C:

P————————————————Q

2. Rotate AB 270° clockwise about C:

A————————————B

•
C

5. Rotate RS anticlockwise through 180° about C:

•
C

R————————————————S

3. Rotate CD 90° anticlockwise about C:

•
C

6. Rotate ∠ABC 180°
anticlockwise about C:

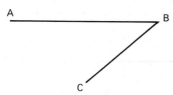

7. Rotate ∠BCD 180°
clockwise about C:

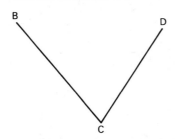

8. Rotate △ABC 90°
clockwise about C:

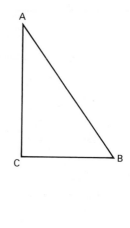

B Copy each of the following on to squared paper. Rotate each one
about the given centre of rotation, C.

1. Rotate 90° anticlockwise:

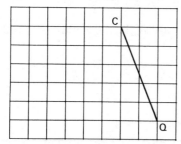

3. Rotate 180° clockwise:

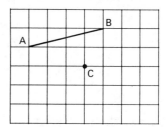

2. Rotate 270° anticlockwise:

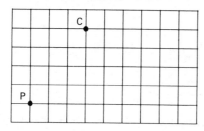

4. Rotate 90° anticlockwise:

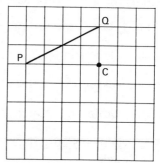

5. Rotate 90° clockwise:

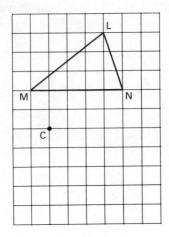

Exercise 15   Rotations and Quadrilaterals

e.g. A scalene triangle can be rotated through 180° about the mid-point of one of its sides. The diagram shows how the object and image together give a parallelogram.

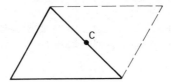

Answer these questions. (You may use tracing paper to help you.) In each question, the rotation is a half-turn about the mid-point of one of the sides. (For each triangle, use all three sides.)

What types of quadrilateral can be made by rotating:

1. a scalene triangle?

2. an isosceles triangle?

3. an equilateral triangle?

4. a right-angled triangle? (Try also a right-angled isosceles triangle.)

270

Translations, Reflections and Rotations

Exercise 16

For each diagram, write whether it shows a translation, a reflection or a rotation:

1.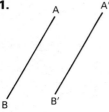

2.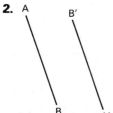

3.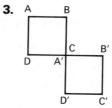

4.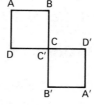

5.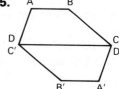

6.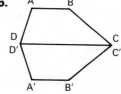

Exercise 17 **M**

Copy the diagram on to squared paper.

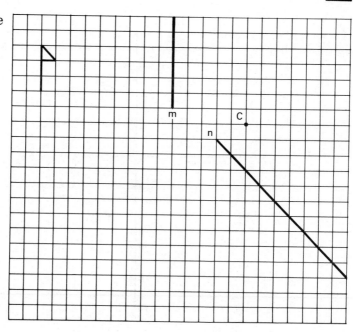

271

On the squared paper draw the following images.

1. Translate the flag 6 squares to the right.

2. Reflect the image of question 1 in mirror m.

3. Rotate the image from question 2 90° clockwise about C.

4. Reflect the image from question 3 in mirror n.

5. Translate the image from question 4 7 squares to the left followed by 2 squares upwards.

Transformations and Co-ordinates

Exercise 18   Translations

Draw a pair of axes as shown. Let 1 cm represent 1 unit on both axes. If you are unable to answer all of the following questions using the one pair of axes, draw as many as you need.

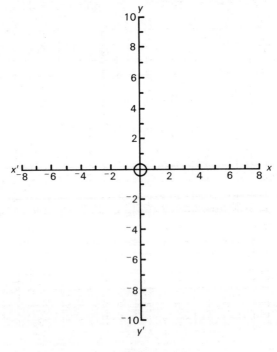

A 1. Plot the points A($^-$2, 8), B(0, 9) and C(1, 7), then join them to form a triangle. Translate ABC 5 cm to the right (parallel to the *x*-axis), then draw and label its image A'B'C'.

2. Plot some points of your own, then translate them to the right or to the left (parallel to the *x*-axis). Note the co-ordinates of the objects and of their images. Write what you notice.

B 1. Plot the points P(3, $^-$2), Q(1, $^-$4) and R($^-$1, $^-$2), then join them to form a triangle. Translate PQR 3 cm upwards (parallel to the *y*-axis) then draw and label its image P'Q'R'.

2. Plot some points of your own, then translate them upwards or downwards (parallel to the *y*-axis). Note the co-ordinates of the objects and their images. Write what you notice.

Exercise 19

Answer the following without plotting any points. Find the co-ordinates of the images under the given translations.

1. A(1, 5) is translated 5 units to the right.

2. B(2, 4) is translated 3 units to the left.

3. C(4, $^-$1) is translated 6 units upwards.

4. D($^-$1, $^-$2) is translated 3 units downwards.

5. E($^-$2, $^-$4) is translated 3 units to the right, followed by 2 units upwards.

6. F($^-$1, $^-$1) is translated 2 units to the left, followed by 5 units upwards.

7. G(1, 4) is translated 4 units to the left, followed by 4 units downwards.

8. H(0, 3) is translated 7 units to the right, followed by 5 units downwards.

Exercise 20   Reflections

Draw another pair of axes as for Exercise 18.

A 1. Plot X($^-$4, 7), Y($^-$5, 5) and Z($^-$1, 4), then join them to form a triangle. Reflect XYZ in the y-axis, then draw and label its image X'Y'Z'. Compare the co-ordinates of XYZ with those of X'Y'Z' and write what you notice.

2. Using straight lines, join J(2, 1) to K(6, 1) to L(5, $^-$2) to M(1, $^-$2) to J, giving a parallelogram. Reflect JKLM in the y-axis, then draw and label its image J'K'L'M'. Compare the co-ordinates of JKLM with those of J'K'L'M' and write what you notice.

3. Plot some points of your own, then reflect them in the y-axis. Compare the co-ordinates of each object with those of its image and write what you notice.

B 1. Reflect △XYZ, plotted in part A, question 1, in the x-axis then draw and label its image X"Y"Z". Compare the co-ordinates of XYZ with those of X"Y"Z" and write what you notice.

2. Plot some points of your own, then reflect them in the x-axis. Compare the co-ordinates of each object with those of its image and write what you notice.

Exercise 21   Rotations

By plotting points and rotating them, then by comparing the co-ordinates of each object and with those of its image, investigate how the following rotations affect the co-ordinates of the objects:

1. a rotation of 180° about the origin,

2. a rotation of 90° clockwise about the origin,

3. a rotation of 90° anticlockwise about the origin.

Exercise 22   Translations, Reflections and Rotations

Although you may draw a pair of axes and plot points in this exercise if you need to do so, try to answer the questions without plotting points:

1. The image of P(2, 5) is P'($^-$2, 5), while Q($^-$1, $^-$3) moves to (1, $^-$3). What sort of transformation is it?

   Note that we can show the transformation as follows:
   $$P(2, 5) \longrightarrow P'(^-2, 5)$$
   $$Q(^-1, ^-3) \longrightarrow Q'(1, ^-3)$$

2. Describe the following transformations:
   (a) A(3, $^-$2) $\longrightarrow$ A'($^-$1, $^-$2)
        B(6, 1) $\longrightarrow$ B'(2, 1)
   (b) C(2, $^-$3) $\longrightarrow$ C'(2, 3)
        D(7, 4) $\longrightarrow$ D'(7, $^-$4)
   (c) E(3, 4) $\longrightarrow$ E'($^-$3, $^-$4)
        F(5, $^-$2) $\longrightarrow$ F'($^-$5, 2)
        G($^-$1, 7) $\longrightarrow$ G'(1, $^-$7)
   (d) H(2, $^-$4) $\longrightarrow$ H'(4, 2)
        I($^-$3, 1) $\longrightarrow$ I'($^-$1, $^-$3)
        J($^-$4, $^-$5) $\longrightarrow$ J'(5, $^-$4)

Exercise 23   Rotations Giving Solids

Name the solid obtained when the shaded shape is rotated through 360° about the given line:

1.

2.

3.

Enlargements

Enlargements are another kind of transformation. In translations, reflections and rotations, sizes did not change; but in enlargements, sizes *do* change.

Exercise 24

Enlarge these shapes. Use squared paper.

1. Make each side twice as long:

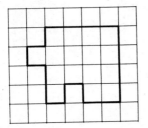

3. Make each side three times as long:

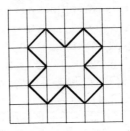

2. Make each side twice as long:

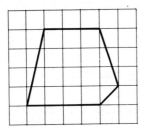

4. Make the perimeter four times as long:

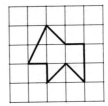

18 Indices and Square Roots

Indices

Exercise 1

A Find the value of:

1. 2^2	**6.** 3^4	**11.** 2^{12}	**16.** $10^3 \div 2^3$
2. 9^2	**7.** 4^5	**12.** 3^7	**17.** $\dfrac{12^3}{4^2}$
3. 12^2	**8.** 6^4	**13.** $2^4 \times 3^2$	
4. 30^2	**9.** 8^3	**14.** $5^3 \times 2^3$	**18.** $\dfrac{7^3}{10^4}$
5. 25^2	**10.** 10^5	**15.** $2^5 \times 9^4$	

B Which has the larger value:

1. 9^2 or 2^9?	**3.** 4^3 or 3^4?	**5.** 2^7 or 7^2?
2. 5^3 or 3^5?	**4.** 10^2 or 2^{10}?	**6.** 3^6 or 6^3?

C Work these out on a calculator. Where necessary, give an answer correct to four significant figures.

1. 17^2	**6.** 21^2	**11.** 6.18^2	**16.** 50.8^2
2. 1.9^2	**7.** 1.26^2	**12.** 1.61^3	**17.** 732^2
3. 8^6	**8.** 1.4^3	**13.** 8.71^2	**18.** 24^5
4. 3^9	**9.** 32^2	**14.** 0.38^2	**19.** 3.9^3
5. 2.1^2	**10.** 0.46^2	**15.** 97.2^2	**20.** 6.1^4

D Find, without using a calculator, the value of:

	(a)	(b)	(c)	(d)	(e)
1.	3^2	30^2	300^2	3000^2	$30\,000^2$
2.	5^2	50^2	500^2	5000^2	$50\,000^2$
3.	400^2	40^2	4^2	0.4^2	0.04^2
4.	600^2	60^2	6^2	0.6^2	0.06^2
5.	200^2	20^2	2^2	0.2^2	0.02^2
6.	8^2	0.8^2	0.08^2	0.008^2	0.0008^2
7.	1^2	0.1^2	0.01^2	0.001^2	0.0001^2
8.	9^2	0.9^2	0.09^2	0.009^2	0.0009^2

E Find the value of:

1. $\left(\dfrac{3}{5}\right)^2$

2. $\left(\dfrac{2}{3}\right)^2$

3. $\left(\dfrac{3}{2}\right)^2$

4. $\left(\dfrac{5}{8}\right)^2$

5. $\left(3\dfrac{1}{2}\right)^2$

6. $\left(1\dfrac{2}{3}\right)^2$

7. $\left(\dfrac{3}{6}\right)^2$

8. $\dfrac{3^2}{6}$

9. $\dfrac{3}{6^2}$

10. $\left(\dfrac{5}{2}\right)^2$

11. $\left(\dfrac{5^2}{2}\right)$

12. $\dfrac{5}{2^2}$

Exercise 2

1. If $y = x^2$, find the value of y when x equals:
   (a) 8   (b) 0   (c) $^-4$ (d) $^-7$ (e) $^-6$

2. If $y = 2x^2$, find the value of y when x equals:
   (a) 5   (b) 7   (c) $^-3$ (d) $^-4$ (e) $^-10$

3. If $y = x^2 + 5$, find the value of y when x equals:
   (a) 9   (b) 0   (c) $^-1$ (d) $^-2$ (e) $^-9$

4. If $y = x^2 - 9$, find the value of y when x equals:
   (a) 7   (b) 0   (c) $^-2$ (d) 3   (e) $^-3$

5. $A = l^2$ gives the area of a square with side l units. Find the area of a square when the length, l, is:
   (a) 6 cm   (b) 11 cm   (c) 14 cm   (d) 1.8 m

6. $A = 3r^2$ gives an estimate of the area of a circle with radius r units. Find the area of a circle when the radius, r, is:
   (a) 5 cm   (b) 1.6 cm   (c) 35 mm   (d) 6.7 cm

7. $A = \frac{3}{4}d^2$ gives an approximate value of the area of a circle with diameter d units. Find the area of a circle with diameter:
   (a) 6 cm   (b) 28 mm   (c) 15 cm   (d) 1.3 m

8. $V = l^3$ gives the volume of a cube with edge l units. Find the volume of a cube when length l equals:
   (a) 4 cm   (b) 6 m   (c) 10 cm   (d) 3.1 m

Exercise 3

1. Fold a piece of paper in half.
   (A sheet of newspaper will do.)
   After one fold it is 2 sheets thick.
   $(2^1 = 2)$

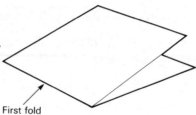

First fold

2. Fold it in half again.
   After 2 folds, it is 4 sheets thick.
   $(2^2 = 4)$

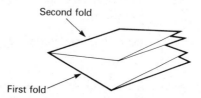

Second fold

First fold

3. Fold it in half again. After 3 folds it is 8 (or 2^3) sheets thick.

4. How many sheets thick is it after:
   (a) 4 folds?   (b) 7 folds?   (c) 12 folds?

5. Try to fold it in half 7 times, then tear it in half.

6. Write about your findings.

Exercise 4

1. Will the fifth power of every number always end in the same digit as the number itself? For example, consider the number 3.

   $$3^5 = 243, \text{ which ends in } 3.$$

   Also $15^5 = 759\,375$. Note that both $759\,375$ and 15 end in 5. (It is not necessary to work out the value of a number raised to its fifth power to find the units digit. Try to find and use a quick method.)

2. Find other powers which, when numbers are raised to that power, give the same units digit as the number itself. For example 14^7 ends in 4 so the power 7 appears to work. However 13^7 ends in 7, not 3, so the power 7 does not work.

279

Exercise 5   **M**

The following table may help you to check your answers to Exercise 4.

The main body of the table contains the last digit when n is raised to the given power.

e.g. 1 $2^4 = 16$, so the last digit, 6, is entered in the 2-row and the 4-column.

e.g. 2 $7^2 = 49$, so the last digit, 9, is entered in the 7-row and the 2-column.

Copy and complete the table.

						Power (or index)													
		1	2	3	4	5	6	7	8	9	10	11	12	13	14	15	16	17	18 etc.
	0	0	0						0		0	0							0	
	1	1			1															
	2	2			6		4					8				8				
	3	3	9	7	1								1							9
n	4	4																		
	5		5											5						
	6				6									6						
	7	7	9				9						1			3				
	8							2	6								6	8		
	9	9	1				1													

1. Look carefully at the completed table and write about any patterns you notice.

2. Which rows contain the same numbers throughout?

3. (*a*) Which columns are the same as the 1-column?
   (*b*) Which columns are the same as the 2-column?
   (*c*) Which columns are the same as the 3-column?
   (*d*) Which columns are the same as the 4-column?

4. Which columns would the 25-column be like?

Exercise 6   Number Patterns

Copy and check the number patterns and give the next three steps for each.

1. $(1+2)^2 = 1^3 + 2^3$
$(1+2+3)^2 = 1^3 + 2^3 + 3^3$
$(1+2+3+4)^2 = 1^3 + 2^3 + 3^3 + 4^3$

and so on

2. (*a*) $1^3 = 1^2$
$1^3 + 2^3 = 3^2$
$1^3 + 2^3 + 3^3 = 6^2$
$1^3 + 2^3 + 3^3 + 4^3 = 10^2$

and so on

(*b*) List the first seven triangular numbers. Compare the triangular numbers with the pattern in part (*a*) and write what you notice.

3. (*a*) $1^2 + 2^2 = 3^2 - 2^2$ *Note* $1 \times 2 = 2$
$2^2 + 3^2 = 7^2 - 6^2$ $2 \times 3 = 6$
$3^2 + 4^2 = 13^2 - 12^2$ $3 \times 4 = 12$
$4^2 + 5^2 = 21^2 - 20^2$ $4 \times 5 = 20$

and so on

(*b*) Compare the sequence 2, 6, 12, 20, ... with the triangular numbers and write what you notice.

4. $1^3 = 1 \times 1$
$2^3 = 2(1+2+1)$
$3^3 = 3(1+2+3+2+1)$
$4^3 = 4(1+2+3+4+3+2+1)$

and so on

5. $2^3 - 1^3 = 4^2 - 3^2$
$3^3 - 2^3 = 10^2 - 9^2$
$4^3 - 3^3 = 19^2 - 18^2$
$5^3 - 4^3 = 31^2 - 30^2$

and so on

Exercise 7

A List the squares of all the whole numbers from 1 to 16.

B Where possible, write each of the following numbers as the sum of two squares:

1. 45	**3.** 60	**5.** 80	**7.** 130	**9.** 146	**11.** 337
2. 52	**4.** 74	**6.** 113	**8.** 140	**10.** 261	**12.** 365

C Write five positive *integers** that can be written as a sum of two squares in more than one way. List the different sums that give each of these five integers. (Note that $25 + 4$ is the same as $4 + 25$. These are *not* two different sums.)

Exercise 8

Which of the following numbers are the products of two squares, where 1 is not allowed to be one of the square numbers used? Write each product as in the example.

e.g. $144 = 4 \times 36$

1. 729	**3.** 1156	**5.** 5929	**7.** 675	**9.** 529	**11.** 1372
2. 3025	**4.** 1521	**6.** 486	**8.** 3969	**10.** 324	**12.** 2025

Exercise 9   Graph of $y = x^2$ M

1. Draw a pair of axes as shown. Use a scale of 1 cm to 1 unit on the x-axis and 2 cm to 5 units on the y-axis.

   Let $^-7 \leqslant x \leqslant 7$
   and $0 \leqslant y \leqslant 50$.

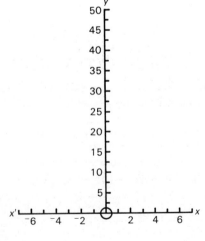

*See the glossary, p. 445.

282

2. Copy and complete:

    (*a*) the mapping diagram,   (*b*) the table.

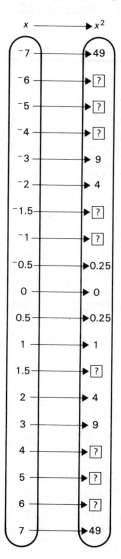

x	$y = x^2$
$^-7$	49
$^-6$	?
$^-5$	?
$^-4$	?
$^-3$	9
$^-2$	4
$^-1.5$	?
$^-1$	?
$^-0.5$	0.25
0	0
0.5	0.25
1	1
1.5	?
2	4
3	9
4	?
5	?
6	?
7	49

3. Draw a graph of $y = x^2$ using the results in your table.

4. Use your graph to estimate the value of:

    (*a*) 4.3^2 (*d*) 5.5^2 (*g*) $\sqrt{18}$ (*j*) $\sqrt{39}$

    (*b*) $(^-3.6)^2$ (*e*) $(^-6.4)^2$ (*h*) $\sqrt{6}$ (*k*) $\sqrt{13}$

    (*c*) $(^-2.4)^2$ (*f*) 1.4^2 (*i*) $\sqrt{33}$ (*l*) $\sqrt{26}$

Square Roots

Exercise 10

A Use a calculator to find:

1. (a) $\sqrt{4}$	**2.** (a) $\sqrt{25}$	**3.** (a) $\sqrt{6400}$
(b) $\sqrt{40}$	(b) $\sqrt{250}$	(b) $\sqrt{640}$
(c) $\sqrt{400}$	(c) $\sqrt{2500}$	(c) $\sqrt{64}$
(d) $\sqrt{4000}$	(d) $\sqrt{25\,000}$	(d) $\sqrt{6.4}$
(e) $\sqrt{40\,000}$	(e) $\sqrt{250\,000}$	(e) $\sqrt{0.64}$
(f) $\sqrt{400\,000}$	(f) $\sqrt{2\,500\,000}$	(f) $\sqrt{0.064}$
(g) $\sqrt{4\,000\,000}$	(g) $\sqrt{25\,000\,000}$	(g) $\sqrt{0.0064}$

B Write what you notice about the answers to the questions above.

Exercise 11

Estimate the following square roots by giving two numbers between which each square root lies. (Give the numbers correct to one significant figure.)

e.g. 1 $\sqrt{52}$ lies between 7 and 8.

e.g. 2 $\sqrt{81\,600}$ lies between 200 and 300.

e.g. 3 $\sqrt{0.0075}$ lies between 0.08 and 0.09.

1. $\sqrt{30}$	**6.** $\sqrt{200}$	**11.** $\sqrt{92.8}$	**16.** $\sqrt{0.14}$
2. $\sqrt{7}$	**7.** $\sqrt{470}$	**12.** $\sqrt{5.7}$	**17.** $\sqrt{0.06}$
3. $\sqrt{56}$	**8.** $\sqrt{1800}$	**13.** $\sqrt{9.28}$	**18.** $\sqrt{0.9}$
4. $\sqrt{84}$	**9.** $\sqrt{4230}$	**14.** $\sqrt{75\,560}$	**19.** $\sqrt{0.053}$
5. $\sqrt{840}$	**10.** $\sqrt{63.5}$	**15.** $\sqrt{234\,500}$	**20.** $\sqrt{0.0046}$

Exercise 12

Find, without using a calculator, the value of:

A 1. $\sqrt{9}$	**4.** $\sqrt{0.09}$	**7.** $\sqrt{0.0016}$
2. $\sqrt{16}$	**5.** $\sqrt{0.16}$	**8.** $\sqrt{0.25}$
3. $\sqrt{6400}$	**6.** $\sqrt{0.0009}$	**9.** $\sqrt{0.01}$

10. $\sqrt{0.49}$ **15.** $\sqrt{6.25}$ **20.** $\sqrt{0.000\,036}$

11. $\sqrt{0.0004}$ **16.** $\sqrt{10.24}$ **21.** $\sqrt{0.0121}$

12. $\sqrt{0.0064}$ **17.** $\sqrt{0.000\,004}$ **22.** $\sqrt{0.0225}$

13. $\sqrt{196}$ **18.** $\sqrt{0.000\,025}$ **23.** $\sqrt{0.000\,000\,49}$

14. $\sqrt{256}$ **19.** $\sqrt{0.0081}$ **24.** $\sqrt{0.000\,000\,09}$

B **1.** $\sqrt{\frac{9}{16}}$ **6.** $\sqrt{\frac{64}{25}}$ **11.** $\sqrt{1\frac{21}{100}}$ **16.** $\frac{\sqrt{81}}{3^2}$

2. $\sqrt{\frac{4}{25}}$ **7.** $\sqrt{\frac{100}{81}}$ **12.** $\sqrt{6\frac{1}{4}}$ **17.** $\frac{16^2}{\sqrt{16}}$

3. $\sqrt{\frac{81}{100}}$ **8.** $\sqrt{2\frac{1}{4}}$ **13.** $\sqrt{5\frac{4}{9}}$ **18.** $\frac{6^2}{\sqrt{25}}$

4. $\sqrt{\frac{25}{49}}$ **9.** $\sqrt{2\frac{7}{9}}$ **14.** $\sqrt{2\frac{2}{49}}$ **19.** $(\sqrt{81})^2$

5. $\sqrt{\frac{49}{36}}$ **10.** $\sqrt{1\frac{9}{16}}$ **15.** $\sqrt{1\frac{17}{64}}$ **20.** $\sqrt{49^2}$

Exercise 13

Use a calculator to find these (to four significant figures):

1. $\sqrt{34}$ **7.** $\sqrt{6700}$ **13.** $\sqrt{0.0435}$

2. $\sqrt{93}$ **8.** $\sqrt{8900}$ **14.** $\sqrt{0.865}$

3. $\sqrt{3}$ **9.** $\sqrt{1250}$ **15.** $\sqrt{0.0071}$

4. $\sqrt{7.5}$ **10.** $\sqrt{7.46}$ **16.** $\sqrt{0.000\,463}$

5. $\sqrt{940}$ **11.** $\sqrt{2.308}$ **17.** $\sqrt{0.005\,52}$

6. $\sqrt{670}$ **12.** $\sqrt{517.9}$ **18.** $\sqrt{0.0303}$

Square Roots by Successive Approximation

It is possible to use a calculator to find a square root without using the square root key.

e.g. Find $\sqrt{12}$:

Notes

$$\text{If } x = \sqrt{12}$$
$$x^2 = 12$$

Dividing by x: $\dfrac{x^2}{x} = \dfrac{12}{x}$

that is, $x = \dfrac{12}{x}$

so, when $x = \dfrac{12}{x}$ then $x = \sqrt{12}$.

First guess $x = 3$, then $\dfrac{12}{x} = \dfrac{12}{3} = 4$

This means $\sqrt{12}$ lies between 3 and 4. Try 3.5.

Second guess $x = 3.5$, then $\dfrac{12}{x} = \dfrac{12}{3.5} = 3.429$ (to 4 s.f.).

So $\sqrt{12}$ lies between 3.429 and 3.5. Try 3.464.

Third guess $x = 3.464$, then $\dfrac{12}{x} = \dfrac{12}{3.464} = 3.4642$.

So $\sqrt{12}$ lies between 3.464 and 3.4642. We could continue if we require greater accuracy.

$$\underline{\sqrt{12} = 3.464 \text{ correct to 4 s.f.}}$$

Instead of setting the work out as above, a table can be used:

Guess x	$\dfrac{12}{x}$	Next estimate
First, 3	4	3.5
Second, 3.5	3.429	3.464
Third, 3.464	3.4642	3.4641

So $\sqrt{12} = \underline{3.464}$ (to 4 s.f.)

Exercise 14

Use the method given in the example above (make a table) to find the following to four decimal places:

1. $\sqrt{8}$ **2.** $\sqrt{19}$ **3.** $\sqrt{21.6}$ **4.** $\sqrt{7.48}$

Multiplication and Division involving Indices

Exercise 15

Simplify, leaving answers in index form:

A 1. $x^5 \times x^4$ **5.** $c^2 \times c^7$ **9.** $u^9 \times u^7$

2. $d^3 \times d^5$ **6.** $m^4 \times m^6$ **10.** $w^{10} \times w^2$

3. $n^7 \times n^4$ **7.** $y^4 \times y$ **11.** $z^5 \times z^7$

4. $e^9 \times e^2$ **8.** $t \times t^8$ **12.** $f^6 \times f^{11}$

B 1. $x^2 \times x^6 \times x^3$

2. $k^4 \times k^3 \times k$

3. $h^3 \times h^9 \times h^2$

4. $v \times v^2 \times v^3$

5. $a^7 \times a \times a^6$

6. $g^2 \times g \times g^{10}$

7. $r^5 \times r^4 \times r^6$

8. $b^6 \times b \times b^8$

9. $n^9 \times n^3 \times n^6$

10. $l^8 \times l^4 \times l^7$

11. $w^4 \times w^8 \times w^9$

12. $p \times p \times p^{14}$

C 1. $x^6 \times y^3 \times y^6 \times x^4$

2. $m^7 \times n^5 \times m^5 \times n^2$

3. $d^3 \times e^4 \times d^2 \times d^5$

4. $b^4 \times a^2 \times b^4 \times a^5$

5. $t^7 \times u^4 \times u^9 \times t^9$

6. $c^8 \times c \times d^3 \times c^5$

7. $p^6 \times q \times p^7 \times q$

8. $v^8 \times w^8 \times w \times v^5$

9. $z^9 \times f^5 \times z^4 \times f^5$

10. $r^2 \times s^3 \times s^{12} \times r^{13}$

Exercise 16

Simplify:

A 1. $4t^2 \times 2t^3$

2. $3t^3 \times 2t^2$

3. $5x \times 3x^3$

4. $2y^6 \times 8y$

5. $4n^7 \times 6n^3$

6. $2p^6 \times 6p^2$

7. $7h^4 \times 2h^5$

8. $9u^9 \times 3u^3$

9. $6a^{10} \times 3a^4$

10. $3c^8 \times 7c^6$

11. $10d \times 5d^5$

12. $8q^{12} \times 9q^7$

B 1. $x^3y^2 \times x^4y^2$

2. $a^4b \times a^3b^6$

3. $p^6q^4 \times q^2p^3$

4. $h^3k^7 \times hk^6$

5. $2cd^2 \times 5c^2d$

6. $m^2n^5 \times 8m^4n^3$

7. $7t^2u^3 \times 4t^6u^3$

8. $4f^7e^5 \times 5e^6f^2$

9. $2k^3l^8 \times 9k^7l^2$

10. $6r^6s^6 \times 5r^5s^8$

11. $5v^5w^8 \times 7w^3v^8$

12. $8zg \times 6g^9z^{12}$

Exercise 17

Simplify, leaving your answers in index form:

1. $n^5 \div n^2$

2. $x^9 \div x^4$

3. $\dfrac{c^8}{c^2}$

4. $\dfrac{a^{12}}{a^{10}}$

5. $d^7 \div d$

6. $p^6 \div p^5$

7. $\dfrac{8e^9}{2e^2}$

8. $6f^6 \div 3f^3$

9. $9k^3 \div 3k^2$

10. $10b^{11} \div 2b^6$

11. $\dfrac{12z^{12}}{4z^4}$

12. $\dfrac{20m^{12}}{5m^5}$

13. $\dfrac{g^5p^4}{g^3p^3}$

14. $h^6l^8 \div hl^4$

15. $\dfrac{r^{10}s^7}{r^4s^5}$

16. $q^{11}t^8 \div q^2t^7$

17. $12u^7v^6 \div 6u^3v^4$

18. $20w^9y^{11} \div 5v$

19. $\dfrac{24a^5c^8}{4ac^3}$

20. $\dfrac{35m^7e^9}{7e^5m^4}$

21. $\dfrac{40n^7r^9}{2n^6r}$

22. $18b^8d^4 \div 9b^5d$

23. $\dfrac{28n^{13}e^4t^3}{4n^5e^2t^3}$

24. $16a^6c^3e^8 \div 8a^2ce^6$

Exercise 18

Simplify:

A
1. $x^4 \times x^4 \times x^4$
2. $n^5 \times n^5 \times n^5 \times n^5$
3. $y^8 \times y^8 \times y^8 \times y^8$
4. $2g^3 \times 2g^3 \times 2g^3$

5. $5h^5 \times 5h^5 \times 5h^5$
6. $2t^6 \times 2t^6 \times 2t^6 \times 2t^6$
7. $3u^2 \times 3u^2 \times 3u^2 \times 3u^2$
8. $4p^4 \times 4p^4 \times 4p^4$

B
1. $(a^3)^2$
2. $(b^4)^3$
3. $(c^2)^5$
4. $(d^5)^4$

5. $(e^7)^5$
6. $(f^9)^6$
7. $(g^6)^8$
8. $(h^4)^4$

9. $(2k^3)^3$
10. $(4l^4)^2$
11. $(3m^5)^4$
12. $(2n^7)^5$

13. $(3p^4)^3$
14. $(8q^9)^2$
15. $(2r^{12})^6$
16. $(5s^6)^3$

19 Basic Algebra

Construction and Use of Formulae

Exercise 1

1. To change kilometres into miles, multiply by 5 then divide by 8. Change 112 km into miles.

2. To change miles into kilometres, multiply by 1.6. Change 85 miles into kilometres.

3. To change gallons into litres, multiply by 4.5. Change 11 gal into litres.

4. The diagram shows one way of changing kilograms into pounds:

   Kilograms ———— × 2.2 ————▶ Pounds

   (a) Use it to change 75 kg into pounds.
   (b) Try to change 121 lb into kilograms.
   (c) Simon weighs 7 st 1 lb:
      (i) Change 7 st 1 lb into pounds (14 lb = 1 st).
      (ii) Change 7 st 1 lb into kilograms.

5. The hire-purchase price of an item is the sum of the loan and the interest. Find the hire-purchase price, if the loan totals £169.95 and the interest is £40.79.

6. The volume of a cylinder can be found by multiplying the area of its base by its perpendicular height. Find the volume of a cylinder with a base area of 38 cm^2 and a perpendicular height of 9 cm.

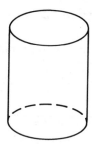

7. The area of a kite is half the product of its diagonals. Find the area of a kite with diagonals that measure 4.6 cm and 3 cm.

8. To find the diameter of a circle, the circumference can be divided by π. Find the diameter of a circle with circumference 88 mm. Use $\pi = \frac{22}{7}$.

9. The difference between the gross pay and the net pay gives the deductions. We can write:

$$\text{Deductions} = \text{gross pay} - \text{net pay}$$

Use the formula to find the deductions when the gross pay is £213.75 and the net pay is £146.80.

10. Each interior angle of a regular polygon can be found by dividing the sum of the interior angles, S, by the number of sides, n (which is the same as the number of angles). The formula can be written as $A = \dfrac{S}{n}$.

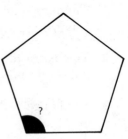

For a pentagon, $S = 540$. Find each interior angle.

11. The square root of the area of a square gives the length of each side. We can write, $l = \sqrt{A}$. Find l when the area of the square is 22.09 cm².

12. The surface area of a sphere can be found by squaring the radius and multiplying the answer obtained by 4π. We can write, $A = 4\pi r^2$.

Find the surface area of a sphere where the radius $r = 3.5$ cm and $\pi = 3.14$.

Exercise 2

Here are some more formulae:

1. Use $m = \dfrac{s}{60}$ to find m when $s = 420$.

2. Use $l = \dfrac{P}{4}$ to find l when $P = 26$.

3. If $A = \dfrac{V}{h}$, find A when $V = 288$ and $h = 8$.

4. Use $V = 30 - 10t$ to find V when:
(a) $t = 2$ (b) $t = 2.5$

5. If $s = 90(2n - 4)$, find s when:
(a) $n = 5$ (b) $n = 13$

6. If $C = \frac{5}{9}(F - 32)$, find C when:
(a) $F = 77$ (b) $F = 104$

7. Use $I = \dfrac{Prn}{100}$ to find I when $P = £650$, $r = 7$ and $n = 3$.

8. If $V = l^3$, find V when:
(a) $l = 6$ (b) $l = 3.5$

9. Given that $A = \pi r^2$, find A when $r = 2.1$ and $\pi = 3.142$. (Give the answer correct to three significant figures.)

10. Use $l = \sqrt{\dfrac{V}{h}}$ to find l when $V = 112$ and $h = 7$.

Exercise 3

1. Find a formula for the perimeter, P, of a regular hexagon in which each side is l units long. Find P when each side measures 4.7 cm.

2. Some building equipment costs £8 per day to hire. Write a formula to give the total cost of hire, $£C$, in terms of the number of days, n. Find C when $n = 7$.

3. If n articles cost h pounds each, write a formula to find the total cost, $£C$, in terms of n and h. Use the formula to find the cost of 14 articles at £15 each.

4. For the diagram, write a formula giving a in terms of b. Find the value of a when $b = 67$.

5. The volume of a cuboid, V cm³, is given by the product of its length, l cm, its breadth, b cm, and its height h cm. Write a formula and use it to find the value of V when $l = 6$, $b = 5$ and $h = 13$.

6. The volume, V cm³, of a pyramid is given as $\frac{1}{3}$ of the product of the area of its base, A cm², and its perpendicular height, h cm. Calculate the volume of a pyramid with a base area of 10.2 cm² and a perpendicular height of 4 cm.

7. Write a formula to change l inches into centimetres (use t). Give t in terms of l, if there are 2.54 cm in 1 in. Use the formula to find the number of centimetres in 8 in.

8. Write a formula giving c in terms of a and b. Find the value of c when $a = 39$ and $b = 104$.

9. Write a formula giving the total surface area of a cube, A units², in terms of its length of side, l units. Find the surface area of a cube with side 1.7 cm.

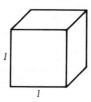

10. The volume (V units³) of a cuboid, with a square base, can be found by multiplying the square of the length (l units) of each edge of the base and the perpendicular height (h units). Write a formula giving V in terms of l and h, then use the formula to find V when $l = 2.3$ and $h = 4$.

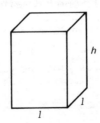

292

Generalised Arithmetic

Exercise 4

1. In a cricket match, Ishaq scored 23 runs in his first innings and r runs in his second innings. How many runs did he score altogether?

2. How old is Peter if he is twice as old as Arlene, if Arlene is y years old?

3. Sandra is x years old today:
   (a) How old will she be in 7 years' time?
   (b) How old was she d years ago?

4. A piece of wood is w metres long. If a length of c metres is cut off, what length remains?

5. On a certain day, Class 1A borrowed 27 books from the school library, Class 2A borrowed t books, Class 3A borrowed 18 books and Class 4A borrowed f books. How many books were borrowed altogether by the four classes?

6. Find the cost, in pence, of 8 tins of soup at n pence each.

7. Find the cost of 6 pencils if they cost q pence a dozen.

8. Oranges cost w pence each. How much change would there be from £1 if you bought:
   (a) 3 oranges?   (b) g oranges?

9. Hazel took $7k$ tablets each week. How many will she have taken in 8 weeks?

10. A car travels at v km/h. How far does it go in:
    (a) 6 hours?   (b) t hours?

11. How many pencils can you buy for £y if they cost 25 p each?

12. A piece of wood is y metres long. If two pieces, each measuring c metres, are cut off, what length remains?

13. Barry has h sweets. If Cathy has 7 more sweets than Barry but 2 less than Sue, how many sweets has Sue got?

14. A rectangular room measures l metres by w metres. Find its perimeter.

15. Suzanne is x years older than Dyfed and she is 4 years younger than Angela, who is y years of age. Find Dyfed's age.

16. Con is twice the age of Marion and half the age of Dean. If Dean is d years old, what is Marion's age?

Exercise 5

1. How many millimetres are there in k cm?

2. (*a*) Change £a to pence.
(*b*) Change £$4y$ to pence.

3. (*a*) Change n pence to pounds.
(*b*) Change $5d$ pence to pounds.

4. There are 12 in in 1 ft:
(*a*) How many inches are there in f feet?
(*b*) How many feet are there in h inches?

5. (*a*) How many months are there in t years?
(*b*) How many years are there in b months?

6. How many metres are there in l cm?

7. How many 10 p pieces are there in:
(*a*) £q?
(*b*) £$4u$?

8. How many metres are there in:
(*a*) e kilometres?
(*b*) $6f$ kilometres?

9. If you have w 20 p pieces, how much is that in pounds?

10. How many days are there in x hours?

Exercise 6

A Consider the expression $2n + 1$, where n can be any whole number:

1. By substituting some values for n, find at least six values for $2n + 1$.

2. What sort of numbers does the expression $2n + 1$ give when n is a whole number?

B 1. Write an expression for an even number.

2. Write an expression for a multiple of 5.

3. Write an expression for a whole number that is exactly divisible by 9.

4. Write an expression for a number that is always 1 less than a multiple of 4.

5. What is the next whole number bigger than n?

6. If k is even, what is the next highest even number?

7. d is a multiple of 3. What is the next highest multiple of 3?

8. y is a whole number. Write the next three consecutive whole numbers that are bigger than y.

Sequences

Exercise 7

A Copy the sequences and fill in the missing numbers:

1. 12, 23, 34, 45, ?, 67, ?, 89, ...

2. 56, 53, 49, 44, ?, 31, 23, ?, 4, ...

3. 2, 5, 10, 17, ?, 37, ?, 65, ...

4. 2, 3, 5, 9, 17, ?, 65, ?, ...

5. 29, 26, 21, ?, 5, ⁻6, ?, ⁻34, ...

6. 1, 7, 14, 22, $\boxed{?}$, ...

7. 6, 9, 15, $\boxed{?}$, 36, ...

8. 12, 14, $\boxed{?}$, 26, ...

B Copy the following sequences, and for each question, underline the one term that is incorrect:

1. 4, 7, 10, 13, 17, 19, 22, ...   **4.** 5, 8, 15, 26, 39, 60, 83, ...

2. 4, 7, 12, 21, 28, 39, 52, ...   **5.** 3, 4, 6, 10, 16, 34, 66, ...

3. 32, 23, 15, 9, 2, ⁻3, ...

Exercise 8   Graphing a Sequence

1. (*a*) Draw a pair of axes as shown.

    (*b*) Here is a sequence with two of the first eight terms missing:

        2, 5, 8, $\boxed{?}$, 14, $\boxed{?}$, 20, 23, ...

    Graph this sequence and find the missing values.

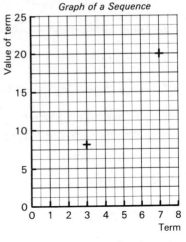

Graph of a Sequence

2. (*a*) Draw a pair of axes as shown.

    (*b*) Graph the sequence:

        1, 3, 7, 15, 31, $\boxed{?}$, 127, ...

    and find the missing value.

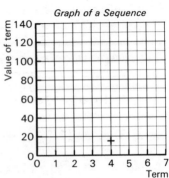

Graph of a Sequence

296

*n*th Term of a Sequence

Exercise 9

T_n stands for nth term of a sequence.

Consider the sequence 5, 9, 13, 17, 21, 25, 29, ...
The first term is 5 so we can write $T_1 = 5$.
The sixth term is 25 so we can write $T_6 = 25$.

1. Find T_2.

2. Find the third term.

3. Find T_5.

4. Find T_7.

5. Find T_8.

6. Try to find a quick way of working out T_{100}.

To find T_{100} by listing 100 terms would take some time. A formula would be useful.

Consider the formula

$$T_n = 4n + 1$$
$$T_1 = 4 \times 1 + 1 = 5$$
$$T_2 = 4 \times 2 + 1 = 9$$
$$T_3 = 4 \times 3 + 1 = 13$$
$$T_4 = 4 \times 4 + 1 = 17$$

and so on.

The formula $T_n = 4n + 1$ gives the sequence of Exercise 9. Since $T_n = 4n + 1$:

$$T_{100} = 4 \times 100 + 1 = 401$$

Exercise 10

A For each of the following sequences, a formula for the nth term is given. Write the first five terms of each sequence.

1. $T_n = 2n + 7$

2. $T_n = 2n - 1$

3. $T_n = 3n + 4$

4. $T_n = 6n$

5. $T_n = 24 - n$

6. $T_n = n^2$

7. $T_n = n^2 + n$

8. $T_n = n^2 - n + 3$

9. $T_n = 2n^2 + 1$

10. $T_n = \frac{1}{2}n^2 + \frac{1}{2}n + 4$

297

B **1.** $T_n = 2n + 5$, find T_{12}.

2. $T_n = 5n - 3$, find T_7.

3. $T_n = 4n + 2$, find the ninth term.

4. $T_n = 7n - 5$, find T_{20}.

5. Find T_{15} if $T_n = 3n + 8$.

6. Find the fifth term if $T_n = 10n - 7$.

7. $T_n = 6n - 4$, find T_8.

8. $T_n = 60 - 3n$, find T_{16}.

C For each of these sequences, try to find a formula for the nth term:

1. 3, 6, 9, 12, 15, 18, ...

2. 4, 7, 10, 13, 16, 19, ...

3. 4, 10, 16, 22, 28, 34, ...

4. 19, 18, 17, 16, 15, 14, ...

5. 4, 7, 12, 19, 28, 39, ...

6. 0, 2, 6, 12, 20, 30, ...

Exercise 11 ━━━━━━━━━━━━━━━━━━━━━━━ **M**

The following triangular pattern can be made with matches:

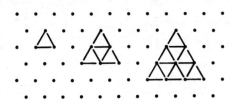

1. On triangular dotty paper, draw the next diagram in the pattern.

2. Count the number of matches used in each pattern, then write the sequence (give seven terms). It starts:

3, 9, ?, ?, ?, ?, ?, ...

3. Try to explain how to find the number of matches used for any size of triangle without just simply counting.

4. How many matches are used when there are 100 small triangles in one diagram of the pattern?

Like Terms

Exercise 12

Where possible, simplify the following expressions; if there is no shorter form, then write 'NO SHORTER FORM':

1. $5n + 3u - 2n + 4u$
2. $3a + 2c - 5a + c$
3. $9k - 4l - 6k + 6l$
4. $10t - 2t + 4t - v$
5. $12ab + 7ac - 5ab + 2ac$
6. $7xy - 3pq + 4yx - 2yx$
7. $am + ma - 3an + 6am$
8. $td - 8fe + 4dt + 5fe$
9. $3cad + 5acd - acd + 2dac$
10. $9mve + 3mek - 7vem - ekm$
11. $5a^2 + 4a + 3a - 7$
12. $e^2 - 6e + 4e + 8$
13. $17 - f + 2f^2 + 3f + 5f^2 - 4$
14. $2s^2 - 14s + 6s - 2$
15. $3x^2 - 4x + 5x - 7$
16. $4x^2 - 6x + 6x - 9$
17. $x^2 + 3x - x - 4$
18. $8 - y + 4y - y^2$
19. $3 + q - 4 - q^2 + 5q$
20. $v^2 - 5v + 8v - 7$
21. $5p^2 + 3pq - 5pq + q^2$
22. $wd + d^2w - wd^2$
23. $s^2t + t^2s + 4s^2t$
24. $d^2a + a^2d - 3ad$
25. $4ua^2 - 2u^2a + 5a^2u$
26. $2k^2 - l^2 + kl - 3l^2 + 2lk$
27. $abc + 4a^2bc - a^2cb$
28. $ap^2q - p^2aq^2 + qap^2$
29. $3xyz^2 - 2x^2yz + xy^2z$
30. $5n^2ut - 2ut^2n + 7nut^2$

Removal of Brackets

Exercise 13

A Multiply out:

1. $3(a + 5)$
2. $4(d - 3)$
3. $7(2 - x)$
4. $2(3n + 4)$
5. $5(5c - 1)$
6. $3(2 + 3q)$
7. $9(7 - 5t)$
8. $3p(g + 4)$
9. $2h(6u - 5)$
10. $2e(9 + 8r)$
11. $5k(7m + 3)$
12. $9y(1 + 2e)$
13. $4v(f + 6w)$
14. $z(3l - 5b)$
15. $6r(3s - 7t)$
16. $8p(4q + 3g)$
17. $\frac{1}{2}(10v + 12)$
18. $\frac{1}{4}(16 - 24l)$
19. $\dfrac{(18u + 21h)}{3}$
20. $\dfrac{(42f + 12d - 54c)}{6}$
21. $4(3x - 6y + z)$
22. $5(9a + b - 6m)$
23. $\frac{1}{5}(20s - 10k + 25l)$
24. $7(10n - 2w - 4g)$
25. $9(d + 4p - 6u)$

B Simplify each of the following by removing the brackets, then by collecting like terms:

1. $(2q + 9) + (5q + 2)$
2. $(3f + 8) + (2f - 3)$
3. $(4k + 6l) + (5k + l)$
4. $(9a + 2c) + (3a - c)$
5. $(6e + h) + (e + 5h)$

6. $2(3r + 7) + (7r + 4)$
7. $5(4n + 6) + (3n - 8)$
8. $7(2t + 4) + (t - 12)$
9. $6(5v + 3w) + (4v + 3w)$
10. $8(4x + 2y) + (5x - 9y)$

Exercise 14

Multiply out:

1. $^-2(x - 6)$
2. $^-4(m + 4)$
3. $^-3(5b + 6)$
4. $^-5(2d - 9)$
5. $^-7(3u - 8)$

6. $^-8(4 - 5p)$
7. $^-6(9 + 7n)$
8. $^-9(2y - 9z)$
9. $^-3(9l + 4m)$
10. $^-6(5f - 8e)$

11. $^-2(8s + 4t)$
12. $^-7(5g - 9h)$
13. $^-4(7w - 6z)$
14. $^-5(4q + 5r)$
15. $^-8(3a - 8c)$

Exercise 15

A Rewrite each of the following without brackets. The diagram illustrates the example.

e.g. Multiply out:
$$x(2x + 3) = \underline{\underline{2x^2 + 3x}}$$

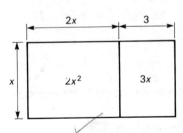

1. $d(d + 4)$
2. $p(p - 9)$
3. $g(2 + g)$
4. $u(8 - u)$
5. $n(2n + 6)$
6. $e(5e - 4)$

7. $3h(h + 5)$
8. $4a(a - 9)$
9. $7q(2q - 1)$
10. $6t(3t + 8)$
11. $9c(2c - 7)$
12. $3r(8 - 4r)$

13. $4m(m^2 - 3)$
14. $5y(2y^2 - 4y + 3)$
15. $2v^2(4v + 8)$
16. $6s^2(5s^2 + 2s - 9)$
17. $8k^2(k^3 - 2k^2 - 5)$
18. $7b^3(2b^2 - 5b + 3)$

B Multiply out:

1. $^-f(f - 3)$
2. $^-w(4w + 6)$
3. $^-z(4 - 9z)$

4. $^-y(3y + 5)$
5. $^-2d(3d + 4)$
6. $^-4c(2c - 3)$

300

7. $^-5x(3-5x)$

8. $^-3t(2t-7)$

9. $^-7p(4p+7)$

10. $^-6g(7+6g)$

11. $^-9u(3u^3-5u)$

12. $^-8e^2(9e^3-4)$

Exercise 16

Simplify: Even nos.

A
1. $6+(h+2)$
2. $7+(q-3)$
3. $5+(2x-3)$
4. $3u+(4u-5)$
5. $2d+(4d-1)$
6. $5a+(6-3a)$
7. $(6c-2)-5$
8. $(4w-7)+9$
9. $(9k-8)+2$
10. $(3v-6)+4v$

11. $8-(t+3)$
12. $7-(f-5)$
13. $4g-(2g-3)$
14. $7p-(6-5p)$
15. $6e-(5+2e)$
16. $5y-(3+8y)$
17. $9n-(4n-6)$
18. $7z-(z-9)$
19. $2b-(4+b)$
20. $8m-(3m-7)$

B
1. $(2x-5)+(x+1)$
2. $(3l+9)+(4l-5)$
3. $(6r+1)+(2r+3)$
4. $(4v-3)+(6v-5)$
5. $(5p+2q)+(2p-q)$
6. $(7s-3k)+(2s+8k)$
7. $(9z-4r)+(z+2r)$
8. $(f+6g)+(3f-8g)$

9. $(3t+8)-(t-3)$
10. $(4h-3)-(6-h)$
11. $(3x+2)-(x+7)$
12. $(4w-3e)-(2w+7e)$
13. $(8y+2d)-(3y-4d)$
14. $(7n+6a)-(2n+3a)$
15. $(5b-4c)-(2c+4b)$
16. $(6l-m)-(4l-9m)$

Exercise 17

Simplify:
1. $7+2(4t+3)$
2. $11+3(5g-2)$
3. $12+5(6-4n)$
4. $4+4(2h-7)$
5. $2y+3(4y-2)$
6. $7a+3(2a-3)$
7. $24p+7(3-2p)$
8. $9u+6(2u+6)$

9. $8-2(3m+2)$
10. $13-3(2+4e)$
11. $9-4(3-2s)$
12. $10-6(4d-3)$
13. $2v-4(2-3v)$
14. $19c-5(3c-7)$
15. $8x-3(4+2x)$
16. $14w-2(2w+3)$

301

Exercise 18

Multiply and simplify your answers:

e.g. 1
$$x(x-2) + 3(x-2)$$
$$= x^2 - 2x + 3x - 6$$
$$= \underline{x^2 + x - 6}$$

e.g. 2
$$a(a-5) - 3(a-5)$$
$$= a^2 - 5a - 3a + 15$$
$$= \underline{a^2 - 8a + 15}$$

1. $c(c+6) + 2(c+6)$

2. $u(u-4) + 3(u-4)$

3. $h(h+5) + 4(h-2)$

4. $n(n-3) + 3(n-3)$

5. $e(e+8) + 2(e+1)$

6. $r(r-2) + 5(r-3)$

7. $t(t-7) + 6(t+2)$

8. $w(w-6) + 7(w-6)$

9. $f(f-5) + 5(f-5)$

10. $y(y+8) + 2(y+8)$

11. $z(z-8) - 2(z-8)$

12. $k(k+4) - 9(k+4)$

13. $b(b+6) - 6(b+6)$

14. $g(g-3) - 3(g-3)$

15. $p(p+3) - 3(p+3)$

16. $s(s+3) - 3(s-3)$

17. $m(m-5) - 4(m-5)$

18. $v(v-5) - 5(v-5)$

19. $d(d+5) - 5(d+5)$

20. $q(q-8) - 7(q+4)$

Exercise 19

e.g.
$$(x+3)(x+5)$$
$$= x(x+5) + 3(x+5)$$
$$= x^2 + 5x + 3x + 15$$
$$= \underline{x^2 + 8x + 15}$$

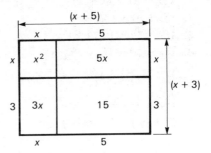

Multiply out and simplify your answers:

1. $(x+4)(x+2)$

2. $(x+3)(x+2)$

3. $(x+4)(x+1)$

4. $(x+2)(x-4)$

5. $(x+3)(x-5)$

6. $(x-4)(x+6)$

7. $(x-7)(x+3)$

8. $(x+4)(x-4)$

9. $(x-7)(x+7)$

10. $(x-2)(x-6)$

11. $(x-2)(x-9)$

12. $(x+2)(x+9)$

13. $(x-2)(x+9)$

14. $(x+2)(x-9)$

15. $(x+8)(x+3)$

16. $(x-1)(x-6)$

17. $(x-5)(x+6)$

18. $(x-10)(x-3)$

19. $(x+7)(x-8)$

20. $(x-5)(x-7)$

FACTORISING

Common Factors

Exercise 20

A Find the value of:

1. (a) $8 \times 6 + 8 \times 3$
  (b) $8 \times (6 + 3)$
2. (a) $9 \times 7 + 9 \times 3$
  (b) $9 \times (7 + 3)$
3. (a) $7 \times 9 - 7 \times 4$
  (b) $7 \times (9 - 4)$
4. (a) $4 \times 15 - 4 \times 12$
  (b) $4(15 - 12)$

5. (a) $5 \times 65 + 5 \times 35$
  (b) $5(65 + 35)$
6. (a) $12 \times 10 - 7 \times 12$
  (b) $12(10 - 7)$
7. (a) $6 \times 53 - 4 \times 53$
  (b) $53 \times (6 - 4)$
8. (a) $8 \times 49 + 8 \times 51$
  (b) $8(49 + 51)$

B **1.** 6 apples and 8 bananas are put into 2 boxes having the same number in each box:
  (a) How many apples and bananas are put into each box?
  (b) Copy and complete: $6a + 8b = 2(\boxed{?} + \boxed{?})$

2. Copy and complete:

  (a) $8a + 10b = 2(\boxed{?} + \boxed{?})$
  (b) $12a + 8b = 4(\boxed{?} + \boxed{?})$
  (c) $9a + 6b = 3(\boxed{?} + \boxed{?})$
  (d) $24a + 18b = 6(\boxed{?} + \boxed{?})$

  (e) $10a + 15b = \boxed{?}(2a + 3b)$
  (f) $16a + 2b = \boxed{?}(8a + b)$
  (g) $14a + 21b = \boxed{?}(2a + 3b)$
  (h) $20a + 12b = \boxed{?}(5a + 3b)$

C The rectangle shows that
$3x + 6 \equiv 3(x + 2)$
(The symbol $\equiv$ shows that the two expressions are identical to each other.)

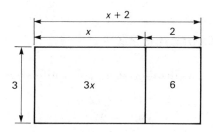

Draw rectangles to show that:

1. $6x + 12 \equiv 6(x + 2)$
2. $12x + 16 \equiv 4(3x + 4)$
3. $3p + 9q \equiv 3(p + 3q)$

4. $15c + 20d \equiv 5(3c + 4d)$
5. $14m + 10n \equiv 2(7m + 5n)$
6. $21e + 18f \equiv 3(7e + 6f)$

303

Exercise 21

A Factorise:

e.g. $8g + 10h = \underline{\underline{2(4g + 5h)}}$

1. $6m + 3$

2. $8k - 12$

3. $25d - 15$

4. $7x + 14$

5. $18t + 12$

6. $16a - 8$

7. $16p + 12$

8. $8c - 10$

9. $30e + 18f$

10. $15q - 12r$

11. $28n - 21u$

12. $10y + 35z$

13. $30v - 20w$

14. $27s - 36b$

15. $56e + 32f$

16. $28p + 42q$

17. $x^2 + 3x$

18. $t^2 - 8t$

19. $4n^2 + 3n$

20. $6c^2 + c$

21. $2a^2 - 6a$

22. $6u^2 + 9u$

23. $10g^2 - 15g$

24. $16y^2 - 12y$

B Find the value of the following by factorising:

1. $64 \times 29 - 64 \times 19$

2. $35 \times 59 + 35 \times 41$

3. $49 \times 37 + 49 \times 63$

4. $74 \times 146 - 74 \times 46$

5. $58 \times 39 - 29 \times 58$

6. $3.4 \times 61 + 3.4 \times 39$

7. $4.7 \times 12.4 - 4.7 \times 2.4$

8. $77 \times 56 + 23 \times 56$

9. $58 \times 47 + 53 \times 58$

10. $6.3 \times 4.9 + 5.1 \times 6.3$

Exercise 22

Multiply out and simplify your answers:

e.g.
$$(x + 2)(x - 2)$$
$$= x(x - 2) + 2(x - 2)$$
$$= x^2 - 2x + 2x - 4$$
$$= \underline{\underline{x^2 - 4}}$$

1. $(x + 8)(x - 8)$

2. $(x + 10)(x - 10)$

3. $(x + 1)(x - 1)$

4. $(x + 15)(x - 15)$

304

Factorising by Difference of Two Squares

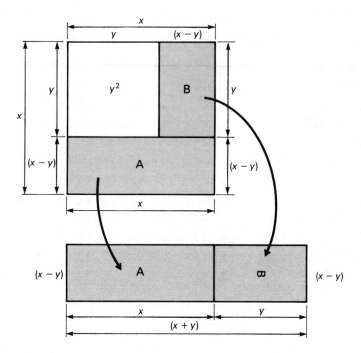

A small square with side y units fits inside a large square with side x units.

Area of large square $= x^2$

Area of small square $= y^2$

Difference between areas $= x^2 - y^2$

But the difference between the areas of the two squares leaves rectangles A and B.

So: Total area of rectangles A and B $= x^2 - y^2$

The two rectangles can be put together to form one long rectangle as shown above.

The length of the long rectangle $= (x + y)$ units

The breadth of the long rectangle $= (c - y)$ units

So the area of the long rectangle $= (x + y)(x - y)$ units²

So the total area of rectangles A and B $= (x + y)(x - y)$ units²

Hence, $x^2 - y^2 = (x + y)(x - y)$

Exercise 23

A Factorise:

e.g. $x^2 - 4 = \underline{(x + 2)(x - 2)}$

1. $x^2 - 16$
2. $x^2 - 64$
3. $y^2 - 49$
4. $p^2 - 81$

5. $x^2 - 100$
6. $a^2 - 1$
7. $c^2 - 121$
8. $y^2 - 144$

9. $m^2 - 225$
10. $n^2 - 400$
11. $x^2 - 169$
12. $y^2 - 256$

B Find the value of the following by factorising:

1. $9^2 - 7^2$
2. $34^2 - 31^2$
3. $84^2 - 16^2$
4. $18^2 - 8^2$
5. $76^2 - 24^2$
6. $63^2 - 53^2$

7. $57^2 - 43^2$
8. $173^2 - 73^2$
9. $49^2 - 44^2$
10. $6.8^2 - 3.2^2$
11. $4.6^2 - 3.6^2$
12. $8.9^2 - 1.1^2$

13. $734^2 - 266^2$
14. $9.7^2 - 0.3^2$
15. $7264^2 - 2736^2$
16. $81.4^2 - 18.6^2$
17. $5.37^2 - 4.63^2$
18. $9.02^2 - 0.98^2$

20 Statistics

Exercise 1   Drawing Graphs

1. 150 people were asked which newspaper they bought. Draw a bar chart to show the results of the survey as given in the table.

Newspaper	Number of people
Chronicle	19
Courier	23
Gazette	38
Guardian	22
Herald	14
Post	34

2. The table shows the number of people getting off buses at the terminus. Draw a pictogram to show the information.

Time	08.45	09.45	10.45	11.45	12.45	13.45
Number of people	20	12	8	10	15	7

3. The table shows the number of second-year pupils who stayed for school dinners during a particular week. Show these results on a jagged-line graph.

Day	Mon	Tue	Wed	Thur	Fri
Number of pupils	95	70	79	74	86

4. A survey of vehicles passing a school's gates during a morning was carried out. The results are given in the table below.

Draw a pie chart.

Type of vehicle	Number of vehicles
Cars	30
Buses	5
Lorries	8
Vans	12
Tractors	2
Motor bikes	3

Averages (Mode, Median and Mean)

Exercise 2

Here are the shoe sizes of nine pupils:

5, 6, 4, 6, 7, 4, 8, 3, 4

1. Which size was the most common?
(The one that occurs the most is called the *mode*.)

2. (*a*) Write the nine sizes in order of size.
(*b*) Which is the middle size?
(The middle size or value is called the *median*.)

3. Total the nine sizes and divide the total by the number of different sizes (by 9 in this instance).
(This time, the average found is called the *arithmetic mean* or more usually just the *mean*.)

4. If you owned a shoe shop, which of the above three averages would be the most useful in helping you to order your shoes? Give a reason for your answer.

Exercise 3

A Find the mode:

1. 4, 5, 3, 4, 6, 5, 3, 4

2. 5, 1, 8, 8, 1, 2, 6, 7, 8, 3, 4

3. 13, 16, 12, 13, 14, 14, 19, 16, 13, 11, 12

4. 37, 44, 61, 44, 21, 83, 79, 36, 45, 28, 50

5. x, g, h, g, x, y, g, m, n, f, n

6. 2, 4, 2, 6, 4, 2, 6, 8, 4, 4, 2, 8

(*Note*   There could be more than one mode.)

7. 5, 3, 3, 5, 1, 3, 1, 1, 4, 1, 5, 3, 4

8. 18, 12, 15, 12, 14, 12, 15, 14, 15, 15, 18

B Find the median:

1. 9, 5, 6, 8, 2, 5, 4

2. 28, 20, 24, 31, 24, 25, 26

3. 1, 14, 9, 6, 1, 3, 10, 4, 10

4. 7, 6, 7, 5, 6, 8, 8, 5, 9, 8, 5

5. 12, 5, 7, 8, 4, 12, 13, 10

(*Note*   When there is an even number of items, the median lies half-way between the two items in the middle. In question 5, the median lies half-way between the fourth and fifth items when they are written in order of size.)

6. 4, 14, 9, 6, 10, 14, 16, 4, 17, 17, 1, 14

7. 16, 12, 10, 19, 17, 19, 5, 3, 24, 24, 9, 25, 15, 21

8. 5, 7, 4, 5, 0, 0, 3, 7, 1, 4, 3, 4, 7, 1, 8, 6

C Calculate the mean:

1. 15, 9
2. 8, 3, 9, 4
3. 19, 23, 18
4. 5, 1, 6, 3, 5
5. 6, 9, 4, 8, 3, 6
6. 19, 12, 11, 18

7. 76, 72, 74
8. 68, 73, 45
9. 9, 5, 12, 4, 7, 8, 4
10. 9, 4, 15, 6
11. 31, 44, 76, 44, 45, 45
12. 110, 121, 108, 106, 120

Exercise 4

Find (a) the mode, (b) the median and (c) the mean, of each set of data:

1. 8, 7, 3, 9, 8, 2, 3, 8, 6
2. £35, £32, £37, £35, £39, £32, £29, £44, £32
3. 20 cm, 15 cm, 18 cm, 18 cm, 16 cm, 22 cm, 17 cm
4. 65 ft, 80 ft, 75 ft, 73 ft, 31 ft, 71 ft, 85 ft, 71 ft, 45 ft, 54 ft, 76 ft
5. 7 ℓ, 5 ℓ, 10 ℓ, 4 ℓ, 11 ℓ, 3 ℓ, 13 ℓ, 3 ℓ
6. £146, £164, £160, £123, £133, £157, £148, £135, £157, £152
7. 47 kg, 73 kg, 82 kg, 66 kg, 63 kg, 66 kg, 67 kg, 63 kg, 63 kg, 40 kg
8. 10 m, 6 m, 8 m, 8 m, 14 m, 12 m, 17 m, 6 m, 7 m, 3 m, 13 m, 4 m

Exercise 5

In nine tests, each marked out of 20, Zoe scored 11, 11, 11, 12, 12, 19, 19, 20, 20; while Nathan scored 1, 1, 2, 3, 13, 13, 13, 13, 13.

1. Who did better?

2. (a) Find the mode of Zoe's marks.
   (b) Find the mode of Nathan's marks.
   (c) Whose mode was higher?

3. (a) Find the median of Zoe's marks.
   (b) Find the median of Nathan's marks.
   (c) Whose median was higher?

4. (a) Find the mean of Zoe's marks.
   (b) Find the mean of Nathan's marks.
   (c) Whose mean was higher?

5. (a) Which average is the most suitable for deciding who did better in the tests?
   (b) Explain your answer.

Exercise 6

1. Rudi spent the following sums of money over nine months:

   £18, £32, £46, £25, £14, £45, £32, £21, £28

   Find:
   (a) the mode,   (b) the median,   (c) the mean.

2. A hockey team scored the following goals in 18 matches:

   2, 0, 1, 1, 3, 2, 0, 2, 4, 1, 6, 2, 1, 3, 0, 1, 2, 1

   Find the mode.

3. Two dice were thrown 20 times and their total score for each throw was noted. The totals were:

   3, 11, 2, 5, 7, 8, 6, 8, 10, 7,
   5, 9, 12, 7, 6, 10, 12, 7, 6, 8

   Find:
   (a) the mode,   (b) the median.

4. Twenty-five people were asked how many library books they borrowed last week. Their replies were:

   1, 0, 0, 2, 2, 3, 1, 2, 2, 0, 3, 4, 1,
   1, 2, 1, 2, 3, 1, 0, 0, 1, 2, 2, 0

   Find:
   (a) the mode,   (b) the median.

5. The pulse rates of several people were taken. The numbers of beats per minute were as follows.

   67, 66, 74, 79, 80, 72, 71, 64, 75, 72,
   78, 68, 70, 81, 68, 72, 75, 71, 74, 73

   Find:
   (a) the mode,   (b) the median,   (c) the mean.

6. The numbers of ray florets (petals) were counted on several daisies. The results were:

> 41, 40, 36, 42, 43, 41, 39, 44, 35, 43, 42, 42,
> 36, 45, 38, 40, 42, 39, 42, 37, 42, 40, 38, 39

Find:

(*a*) the mode, (*b*) the median, (*c*) the mean.

Mean

Note If the word 'average' is used in a question and it is not clear whether the mode, median or mean is wanted, then it will probably be the mean that must be found.

Exercise 7

1. Calculate Jackie's average exam mark if her marks were:

> English 63%, French 68%, mathematics 76%,
> geography 55%, history 51%, science 71%

2. Mr Askew bought the following amounts of petrol:

> 43 ℓ, 28 ℓ, 34 ℓ, 29 ℓ, 32 ℓ, 37 ℓ, 25 ℓ, 36 ℓ

What was the average quantity of petrol bought?

3. The midday temperatures during one week were:

> 9.7 °C, 10.8 °C, 11.4 °C, 9.3 °C, 9.8 °C, 10.4 °C, 10.7 °C

Calculate the average temperature.

4. The heights of ten pupils were:

> 1.59 m, 1.63 m, 1.55 m, 1.57 m, 1.61 m,
> 1.58 m, 1.62 m, 1.56 m, 1.68 m, 1.61 m

Calculate the average height.

5. The circumference and diameter of nine cylinders were measured. The results of the calculation $\dfrac{\text{circumference}}{\text{diameter}}$ were found to be:

> 3.15, 3.2, 3.1, 3.04, 3.08, 3.11, 3.23, 3.16, 3.19

Calculate the average of these results.

6. Daily barometer readings were:

754 mm, 750 mm, 751 mm, 749 mm, 758 mm, 753 mm, 756 mm

Calculate the average daily reading.

7. Five pupils are aged:

11 years 7 months, 11 years 3 months, 12 years 1 month, 11 years 10 months and 11 years 2 months

Calculate their average age.

8. A cricketer scored:

73, 126, 61, 31, 14, 96, 119, 0, 50, 49, 82, 37

(*a*) Calculate his average score.

(*b*) What would his average be if in one of these innings he was not out?

$$\left(\text{Note that the average score} = \frac{\text{total scored}}{\text{number of times out}} \right)$$

Exercise 8

1. (*a*) Find the total of the five numbers 9, 6, 3, 8, 9.

(*b*) Calculate the mean.

(*c*) Explain how to find the total of any set of numbers when you know their mean and how many numbers there are.

2. If the mean of six numbers is 47, what do the six numbers total?

3. The average number of children in eight families is 2.5. Find the total number of children.

4. There was an old woman who lived in a shoe. She had so many children, with an average age of 15 years and a total age of 345 years, that she didn't know what to do. How many children did she have?

5. A cyclist averaged 73 miles per day for five days:

(*a*) What was the total distance travelled in the five days?

(*b*) If the cyclist travelled 298 miles during the first four days, how far did she travel on the fifth?

6. Roger's average mark in eight tests was 58%:

(*a*) Find his total mark.

(*b*) Find his mathematics mark if his other results were: English 49%, French 61%, chemistry 48%, biology 45%, physics 74%, geography 72%, history 49%.

7. Penny's average mark in seven tests was 62%. If six of the test marks total 375, calculate the seventh mark.

8. Bryan saved, on average, £2.80 per week for eight weeks. If on the ninth week he saved £3.70, calculate his average savings for the nine weeks.

9. In a class of 15 girls and 12 boys, the girls obtained an average of 63% in a test while the boys averaged 54%. Calculate the average mark for the whole class.

10. The average of thirteen numbers is 21. If the first seven numbers average 18 and the next five numbers average 29, find the thirteenth number.

Exercise 9

In a cricket match, two bowlers, S. Batty and I. Ball, had identical bowling averages after the first innings. Both took 4 wickets for 48 runs, an average of 12 runs per wicket (the lower the average the better the bowler). In the second innings, Batty took 1 wicket for 17 runs (an average of 17 runs per wicket), while Ball took 8 wickets for 120 runs (an average of 15 runs per wicket), so Ball had the better average in the second innings.

Who had the better bowling averages for the whole match?

Exercise 10

Answer these. If an answer is not possible, write 'IMPOSSIBLE'.

1. Write six numbers that have a mode of 9.

2. Write six numbers that have a median of 9.

3. Write six numbers that have a mean of 9.

4. Find three numbers where the mode is 7 and the mean is 8.

5. Find three numbers where the median = the mode = 8, and the mean = 6.

6. Find four whole numbers where the mean is 5, the mode is 7, and where two of the numbers are less than 7.

7. Find four whole numbers where the mean is 6, the mode is 7, and where two of the numbers are bigger than 7.

8. 2, 8, x, y, z have a mode of 11 and a median of 10. Find x, y and z, if they are whole numbers.

Exercise 11

1. Consider the numbers 3, 6, 2, 2, 8, 5, 2.
   (*a*) What is the mode?
   (*b*) Add 10 to each number.
   (*c*) What is the mode of the new set of numbers?

2. Repeat question 1 for the median.

3. Repeat question 1 for the mean.

4. Investigate adding any number to a given set of numbers. Find out what happens to the mode, median and mean. Write what happens.

5. Find the mean of:
   (*a*) 6, 3, 8, 1, 8 and 4
   (*b*) 46, 43, 48, 41, 48 and 44

6. Find the mode of the numbers in question 5.

7. Find the median of the numbers in question 5.

8. On 1 September, seven girls were aged 11 years 2 months, 11 years 9 months, 11 years 5 months, 11 years 7 months, 11 years 5 months, 11 years 10 months and 11 years 4 months.
   (*a*) Find their average age.
   (*b*) Find their average age on 1 January of the following year.

Histograms

Exercise 12

The *histogram** given below shows the marks out of 10 obtained by some pupils in a test:

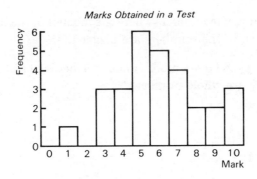

Marks Obtained in a Test

1. How many pupils took the test?

2. Which mark was:
(*a*) the mode?   (*b*) the median?

3. Calculate the mean.

Exercise 13   **M**

Here are some marks. They are out of 100.

43	51	62	52	61	38	19	46	54	72	68	24
58	35	44	28	27	92	74	31	56	52	43	37
25	57	84	75	40	18	60	36	61	73	68	74
46	53	39	9	38	49	84	51	70	54	67	50
52	18	62	56	60	62	59	47	48	61	52	69

1. What is the *range* of the marks? (The range is the difference between the largest and smallest marks.)

2. Copy and complete the tally chart (or *frequency table*) opposite. Write the marks in groups 0–9, 10–19, 20–29, and so on. (Each group is called a *class interval*.)

*See the glossary, p. 445.

Marks	Tally	Frequency
0–9		?
10–19		?
20–29		4
30–39		?
40–49		?
50–59		?
60–69		?
70–79		6
80–89		?
90–99		?

3. Draw a histogram.

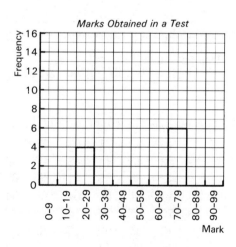

4. Which is the modal class? (The *modal class* is the class interval where the greatest frequency occurs. It is the class where the highest bar is on the graph.)

Exercise 14

For each of the surveys below:

1. Find the range.
2. Make a frequency table using the given class intervals.
3. Draw a histogram.
4. Give the modal class.

A The scores obtained by 66 cricketers are given below:

7	70	74	41	108	21	0	6	112	65	34
45	85	24	38	34	26	12	45	1	0	49
72	0	53	86	3	45	129	71	22	136	2
25	40	59	25	35	34	100	3	64	21	30
18	148	104	0	66	60	48	55	78	3	49
39	52	37	8	76	31	50	24	47	36	58

Use the class intervals
0–19, 20–39, 40–59, 60–79, 80–99, 100–119, 120–139, 140–159.

B The ages of some swimmers are:

11	7	23	42	9	12	6	35	53	8
28	34	41	63	13	24	48	29	15	40
18	30	17	46	33	12	54	31	6	8
36	5	57	22	12	49	14	32	9	

Use the class intervals
0–9, 10–19, 20–29, 30–39, 40–49, 50–59, 60–69.

C The masses (in kilograms) of 80 people are:

46	35	71	63	59	42	54	71	45	38
32	43	45	48	41	53	57	52	40	44
47	65	36	41	35	62	76	51	39	51
44	31	53	64	78	54	46	49	62	54
70	55	37	74	33	47	42	46	41	56
42	45	56	45	36	51	60	45	65	70
46	39	44	61	47	58	69	71	78	74
62	48	53	59	41	49	73	63	67	72

Use the class intervals 30–34, 35–39, 40–44, 45–49, 50–54, 55–59,
60–64, 65–69, 70–74, 75–79.

D The heights of 72 trees (measured in metres) are:

13	18	12	16	21	22	8	22	24	20	19	15
6	24	16	20	3	27	13	5	17	17	28	6
21	23	4	9	14	31	18	21	27	26	23	14
5	9	14	22	21	25	22	21	5	12	16	25
18	25	22	28	23	10	14	15	24	17	17	21
27	23	18	21	25	26	16	29	26	19	22	30

Use the class intervals
0–3, 4–7, 8–11, 12–15, 16–19, 20–23, 24–27, 28–31.

Exercise 15

Carry out at least one of the surveys below. For each survey carried out:

1. Find the range.
2. Make a frequency table (decide on the class interval).
3. Draw a histogram.
4. Give the modal class.

A Find the heights of the pupils in your class. (Work to the nearest centimetre.)

B Find the times taken for the pupils in your class to come to school. (Work to the nearest minute.)

C For each pupil in your class (or year group), find the total time spent per week watching television. (Work to the nearest hour.)

Scattergrams

Exercise 16

The graph shown is called a *scattergram* or *scatter diagram* (because the points are scattered).

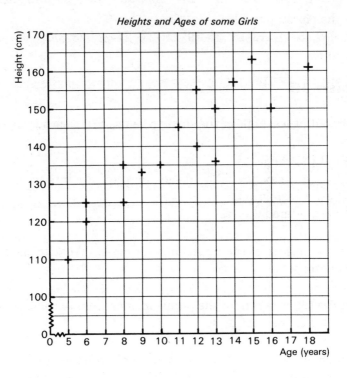

Such a graph shows two independent *variables* at the same time. Height and age are both variables because they vary from person to person.

1. How many girls are shown on the graph?
2. How tall is the tallest girl?
3. What is the age of the youngest girl?
4. What is the difference in height between the 12-year-old girls?

From the graph, it can be seen that some younger girls are taller than some older girls. However, it is still clear from the graph that older girls tend to be taller than younger girls.

The total height of the girls is $(110 + 120 + 125 + 125 + 135 + 133 + 135 + 145 + 140 + 155 + 136 + 150 + 157 + 163 + 150 + 161)$ cm, which is 2240 cm.

Their mean height $= \dfrac{\text{total height}}{\text{total number of girls}} = \dfrac{2240}{16}$ cm $= 140$ cm

Exercise 17

1. Calculate the mean age of the girls given in the scattergram in Exercise 16.

2. Copy the scattergram in Exercise 16, including the jagged lines on both axes. They are called *broken scales**.

3. Plot the mean height against the mean age. Use a cross and circle it.

4. Now draw the *line of best fit*. The line of best fit should pass through the point that was plotted from the two means. It should also have about the same number of points on each side.

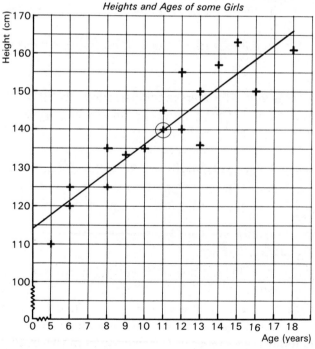

Heights and Ages of some Girls

*See the glossary, p. 443.

5. Use your graph to find the probable height of a girl aged 7 years.

Exercise 18

For each survey:
- (a) draw a scattergram,
- (b) calculate and plot the mean for both variables,
- (c) draw the line of best fit if there is one (sometimes there is no line of best fit!),
- (d) answer the questions using your graph.

1. Here are 12 pupils' results on two mathematics papers:

Paper 1	90	85	75	74	63	57	53	46	36	35	26	20
Paper 2	75	68	65	56	54	45	38	30	28	20	12	13

From your graph, find:
- (i) the probable mark on Paper 2 when the mark on Paper 1 was 70,
- (ii) the probable mark on Paper 1 for someone who got 28 marks on Paper 2.

2. The table gives the average temperatures (in degrees Celsius) at certain times of the year and the amount of gas used (in therms) by the Aldridge household:

Temp (°C)	7	19	16	13	10	5	6	20	9	22	8	16	18	7	4
Gas used (therms)	37	10	16	19	30	33	38	6	27	3	26	12	7	26	40

From your graph, find:
- (i) the probable number of therms used when the temperature was 10 °C,
- (ii) the probable temperature when 16 therms were used.

3. The following table gives the geography marks of 15 pupils and the number of days each was absent.

Days absent	31	10	15	0	20	5	29	38	30	20	3	38	5	2	24
Geog. mark	18	63	43	78	40	60	35	25	20	50	76	20	72	64	41

From your graph, find:
- (i) the probable geography mark for someone who was absent for 30 days,
- (ii) the probable number of days absence for someone who obtained 62 marks.

4. The house numbers and English marks of 15 pupils are given in this table:

House no.	64	134	84	150	116	146	47	5	85	6	121	40	107	12	28
Eng. mark	64	24	45	85	65	57	13	26	18	87	34	35	89	73	82

Write what you notice about the graph and comment on what it suggests.

5. Sixteen golfers played two rounds of golf in a competition. Here are their scores:

Player number	1	2	3	4	5	6	7	8	9	10	11	12	13	14	15	16
Round 1	68	72	71	73	75	68	70	71	73	70	74	67	71	69	74	70
Round 2	67	67	69	73	73	68	70	73	70	72	74	68	70	67	72	67

DO NOT DRAW A SCATTERGRAM UNTIL YOU READ THESE NOTES:

The scores in Round 1 range from 68 to 75 (a very narrow range). Similarly, Round 2 has a narrow range: from 67 to 74.

If you used a full scale from 0 to 75, then the graph would be drawn on a small part of the page and would be too small to use (see the diagram).

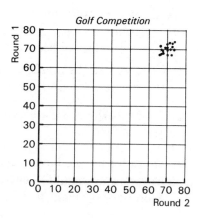

323

Since the axes ought to be labelled from zero, a *broken scale* is used on both axes (see the diagram). Now draw your scattergram setting your work out using a broken scale as shown.

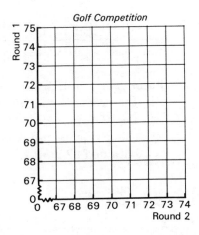

6. The masses (in kilograms) and heights (in centimetres) of 12 people are as follows:

Mass (kg)	40	55	67	35	52	45	50	65	70	47	41	57
Height (cm)	153	167	170	143	164	157	158	176	175	155	142	160

(i) Find the probable height of someone with a mass of 40 kg.

(ii) Find the probable mass of someone with a height of 1.71 m.

Exercise 19

For each survey:

(a) draw a scattergram,

(b) calculate and plot the mean for both variables,

(c) draw the line of best fit (if there is one).

1. Compare maths marks with the sizes of pupil's heads (measure the distance around) for pupils in your class.

2. Compare shoe sizes with the sizes of people's heads (the distance around).

3. Do taller people have bigger feet?
Measure the height of each pupil in your class and the length of each person's right foot.

4. For pupils in your class, find each person's height and each person's arm span (measured from fingertip to fingertip).

5. Compare the test marks for any two subjects.

Probability

Exercise 20

Here are some words that we probably use when we decide whether or not something is likely to happen (we are, in fact, describing *probabilities*):

impossible, highly unlikely, fifty-fifty chance, most probable, certain.

For each of the following sentences, select from the five choices above, the word (or words) that best describes what is likely to happen:

1. The next person you see in the street will be smaller than you.

2. The next person you see in the street will be over 14 ft tall.

3. The next person you see in the street will be female.

4. You will listen to the radio today.

5. Next year, it will rain on every Saturday in the year.

6. When you throw an ordinary die, the number you get will be:
(*a*) bigger than 6,   (*b*) less than 5.

7. The next vehicle you see travelling along the road will be a tractor.

8. You will eat something today.

9. When you toss a coin you will obtain a tail.

10. You will get full marks in your next mathematics test.

Exercise 21

1. Try this game.

Three people should play. Two coins are needed. Before you start to play the game, decide who you think will win.

(*a*) Copy this table first:

Name	Outcome	Tally	Frequency
?	2 heads		?
?	1 head and 1 tail		?
?	2 tails		?

(*b*) The two coins should be tossed together. Record the result.
The first person gets a point if two heads are shown.
The second person gets a point for a head and a tail.
The third person gets a point for two tails.

(*c*) Repeat part (*b*). Toss the two coins about 40 times altogether.
The winner is the person who gets the most points.

(*d*) Show your results on a bar chart.

(*e*) Write a sentence about your bar chart.

(*f*) Which *outcome** is most likely to win, two heads, a head and a tail or two tails?

2. If you tossed two coins 80 times, how many times would you expect to get two heads?

Let us look at the game in question 1 where two coins were tossed.

The possible outcomes are:

First coin	Second coin
heads	heads
heads	tails
tails	heads
tails	tails

There are four possible outcomes.

*See the glossary, p. 446.

326

Using H for heads and T for tails,
the first person wins if the outcome is HH
the second person wins if the outcome is HT or TH
the third person wins if the outcome is TT.

Since the second person can win with two outcomes while the others can win with only one outcome, the second person has the best *chance* of winning.

Since the second person can win with 2 out of 4 outcomes
the probability that the second person wins is $\frac{1}{2}$ (2 out of 4 $= \frac{2}{4} = \frac{1}{2}$)
the probability that the first person wins is $\frac{1}{4}$ and
the probability that the third person wins is $\frac{1}{4}$.

Since one of them must win and since $\frac{1}{2} + \frac{1}{4} + \frac{1}{4} = 1$, it can be seen that a probability of 1 means that the *event* * is certain to happen.

Also, a probability of 0 means the event will definitely not happen.

Exercise 22 $\blacksquare$ M

1. Make out a table to show the possible outcomes when three coins are tossed. The table has been started for you.

2. How many different outcomes are there?

Tossing Three Coins

First coin	Second coin	Third coin
H	H	H
H	H	T
H	T	H

3. How many of these outcomes show:
   (a) 3 heads?
   (b) 2 heads?
   (c) 1 head?
   (d) 0 heads?

*See the glossary, p. 445.

4. Make out a tally chart and carry out an experiment with three coins. Toss the coins 120 times.

Number of heads	Tally	Frequency
3		?
2		?
1		?
0		?

5. Draw a bar chart to show your results.

6. Write what you notice. Compare the theoretical results with the experimental results.

Tree Diagrams

Here is a *tree diagram*. It shows the outcome from tossing two coins.

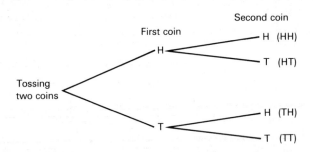

Exercise 23   **M**

1. Copy and complete the diagram opposite for tossing three coins.

The route marked with a heavy line shows the outcome tail, head, tail.

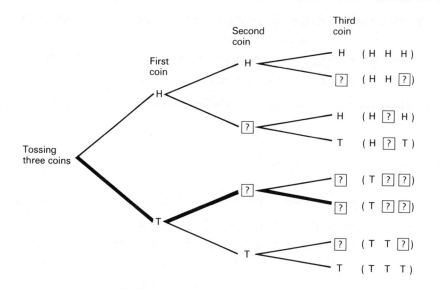

2. (a) Draw a tree diagram for tossing four coins.

(b) List the outcomes as follows:

    H H H H
    H H H T
    H H T H

   and so on.

(c) Copy this table. Write the results of parts (a) and (b) in your table.

Tossing Four Coins

Outcome	Number of ways
4 heads	?
3 heads	?
2 heads	?
1 heads	?
0 heads	?

3. There are 6 different ways of getting two heads out of a total of 16 different outcomes.

We say that the *probability* * of two heads is $\frac{3}{8}$ (since $\frac{6}{16} = \frac{3}{8}$).
(*a*) What is the probability of three heads?
(*b*) What is the probability of three tails?

Exercise 24

In throwing a die, there are 6 possible outcomes (1, 2, 3, 4, 5 or 6).

e.g. The probability of getting a 2 or a 5 is $\frac{1}{3}$
(since these are 2 events out of 6 outcomes
and 2 out of 6 $= \frac{2}{6} = \frac{1}{3}$).

What is the probability when throwing an ordinary die of getting:

1. a 1 or a 6?

2. an even number?

3. a prime number?

4. 4 or more?

5. 1 or more?

6. a number less than 3?

7. a factor of 6?

8. a multiple of 8?

Exercise 25

A Find the probability of:

1. choosing a king from a pack of 52 playing cards,

2. choosing a heart from a pack of 52 playing cards,

3. choosing a number card from a pack of 52 playing cards,

4. choosing a vowel in a game of Scrabble, if there are 6 vowels and 8 consonants to choose from,

5. choosing the correct key from a key-ring which has 4 similar keys on it,

6. choosing a red jelly-baby from a bag containing 9 red and 12 black jelly-babies,

*See the glossary, p. 447.

7. choosing a £10 note from a wallet containing £240 in £5 and £10 notes, if exactly one-third of the money is in £10 notes,

8. one of 5 raffle tickets winning if 260 tickets were sold.

B Find the probability of obtaining:

1. a double 2 when two ordinary dice are thrown,

2. a double 5 when two ordinary dice are thrown,

3. two draws out of two games of football if each result (win, draw, or loss) is equally likely,

4. three draws out of three games of football if each result is equally likely,

5. exactly two draws out of three games of football if each result is equally likely.

21 Simple Equations and Inequations

Equations

Exercise 1

Solve these equations:

1. $x + 5 = 12$
2. $c - 4 = 9$
3. $3k = 15$
4. $4t = 60$
5. $\dfrac{m}{5} = 7$
6. $2a + 3 = 15$
7. $4y - 1 = 19$
8. $5 + d = 17$
9. $6 + 2l = 12$
10. $4g - 5 = 11$
11. $2z - 7 = 1$

12. $3e + 2 = 8$
13. $5j + 3 = 18$
14. $14 = a + 2$
15. $6 = n - 4$
16. $14 = 2p$
17. $14 = 3z + 2$
18. $13 = 4x - 3$
19. $2f = 9$
20. $4h = 10$
21. $2s - 3 = 2$
22. $5 + 4k = 19$
23. $6q - 5 = 11$

24. $3u + 6 = 8$
25. $7l - 6 = 15$
26. $5w + 2 = 15$
27. $4n + 5 = 16$
28. $\dfrac{t}{2} - 4 = 3$
29. $\dfrac{x}{5} + 8 = 13$
30. $\dfrac{m}{3} - 1 = 8$

Exercise 2

Solve these equations:

1. $g + 7 = 2$
2. $h - 3 = {}^-7$
3. $n - 8 = {}^-1$
4. $2u = {}^-12$
5. $3w = {}^-15$
6. $6a = {}^-42$

7. $2t + 5 = 1$
8. $3k + 9 = 3$
9. $5d - 2 = {}^-12$
10. $4q - 11 = {}^-7$
11. $7q + 8 = {}^-13$
12. $4c + 19 = 3$

13. $3e + 14 = {}^-1$
14. $5l + 23 = 8$
15. $2f + 17 = 14$
16. $6m + 2 = {}^-8$
17. $7x - 23 = {}^-9$
18. $9p + 15 = 6$

Exercise 3

Solve these equations:

1. $5x + 9 - 2x + 1 = 19$
2. $2 + 2d - 4 + 3d = 18$

3. $4g - 3 - 2g + 14 = 23$
4. $1 + k - 10 + 3k = 11$

332

5. $6y - 1 + y - 2 = 25$

6. $9f - 9 - 6 - 7f = 21$

7. $12v - 2 - 8v + 12 = 38$

8. $t + 6t + 7 - 2t - 3 = 49$

9. $7p - 1 - 5p + 14 = 18$

10. $5h - 11 + 3h - 2 + 8 = 9$

11. $25 - 2b - 7 + 8b = 6$

12. $8z - 3z + 7 - z - 2 = {}^-15$

13. $3n - 9 + 9n - 5n - 7 = {}^-2$

14. $11 - 4a - 9 + 13a - 12 = {}^-19$

15. $8u + 23 - u + 6 - 3u = 15$

16. $c + 4 - 5c - 21 + 7c = 22$

Exercise 4

Find the value of:

1. ${}^-1 \times 4$

2. ${}^-1 \times 7$

3. ${}^-1 \times 5$

4. ${}^-1 \times 9$

5. ${}^-1 \times 8$

6. ${}^-1 \times 10$

7. ${}^-1 \times 15$

8. ${}^-1 \times 12$

9. ${}^-1 \times {}^-2$

10. ${}^-1 \times {}^-5$

11. ${}^-1 \times {}^-6$

12. ${}^-1 \times {}^-8$

13. ${}^-1 \times {}^-10$

14. ${}^-1 \times {}^-9$

15. ${}^-1 \times {}^-7$

16. ${}^-1 \times {}^-12$

Exercise 5

Work these out and compare the answers to all four parts of each question:

1. (a) ${}^-1 \times (6 - 3)$ (b) ${}^-(6 - 3)$ (c) ${}^-6 + 3$ (d) $3 - 6$

2. (a) ${}^-1 \times (9 - 4)$ (b) ${}^-(9 - 4)$ (c) ${}^-9 + 4$ (d) $4 - 9$

3. (a) ${}^-1 \times (7 - 1)$ (b) ${}^-(7 - 1)$ (c) ${}^-7 + 1$ (d) $1 - 7$

4. (a) ${}^-1 \times (10 - 2)$ (b) ${}^-(10 - 2)$ (c) ${}^-10 + 2$ (d) $2 - 10$

Note ${}^-1 \times (8 - 3) = {}^-8 + 3 = 3 - 8$

and ${}^-1 \times (8 - x) = {}^-8 + x = x - 8$

Exercise 6

Simplify the following:

e.g. ${}^-1 \times (15 - x) = {}^-15 + x = \underline{\underline{x - 15}}$

1. ${}^-1 \times (6 - x)$

2. ${}^-1 \times (7 - x)$

3. ${}^-1 \times (10 - x)$

4. ${}^-1 \times (4 - x)$

5. ${}^-1 \times (12 - x)$

6. ${}^-1 \times (20 - x)$

7. ${}^-1 \times (17 - x)$

8. ${}^-1 \times (1 - x)$

9. ${}^-1 \times (16 - x)$

10. ${}^-1 \times (14 - x)$

11. ${}^-1 \times (35 - x)$

12. ${}^-1 \times (25 - x)$

Exercise 7

Solve the following equations:

1. $8 - x = 5$
2. $4 - x = 1$
3. $12 - x = 9$
4. $14 - x = 6$
5. $2 - x = 8$
6. $3 - x = 7$
7. $5 - x = 12$
8. $9 - x = 9$
9. $6 - x = {}^-2$
10. $10 - x = {}^-4$
11. $3 - x = {}^-10$
12. $1 - x = {}^-1$

Exercise 8

Solve these equations:

1. $4m = 2m + 6$
2. $5y = 4y + 14$
3. $4k = 2 + 2k$
4. $3a = 12 - a$
5. $2n = 30 - n$
6. $7p = 12 - p$
7. $2c = 15 - 3c$
8. $2k + 9 = 5k$
9. $2t = 7t - 25$
10. $5d - 1 = 2d + 32$
11. $4b - 16 = 2b$
12. $9h - 20 = 4h$
13. $9e - 16 = 5e + 4$
14. $3q = 12 + q$
15. $5f = 16 - f$
16. $3u - 28 = 22 - 2u$
17. $14 + 5w = w + 14$
18. $l - 13 = 14 - 2l$
19. $3g - 8 = 2g - 5$
20. $3g - 8 = 5 - 2g$
21. $7x - 5 = 5x + 7$
22. $7 - t = 11 - 2t$
23. $29 - 8z = 14 - 3z$
24. $19 - 2v = 40 - 9v$

Equations Involving Brackets

Exercise 9

Solve these equations:

1. $2(x + 3) = 14$
2. $3(p - 6) = 12$
3. $4(x - 1) = 10$
4. $3(2y + 5) = 33$
5. $2(8 + k) = 24$
6. $4(2f - 8) = 24$
7. $5(3w - 7) = 10$
8. $3(t + 2) = 10$
9. $2(3n + 5) = 19$
10. $6(5t - 9) = 36$
11. $4(3y - 1) = 20$
12. $3(6z - 12) = 0$
13. $2(4p + 3) = 18$
14. $5(4k - 10) = 0$
15. $8(5a - 8) = 36$
16. $7(5 - 2m) = 7$

Exercise 10

Solve these equations:
1. $4(2h - 3) = 5h + 9$
2. $2(6y + 2) = 8y + 20$
3. $3(3i - 5) = 4(2i + 1)$
4. $2(5z - 8) = 3(2z + 4)$
5. $4 + 3v = 2(2v + 5) - 2v$
6. $5(2a - 1) = 3(3a + 7)$
7. $6(4p + 1) = 4(5p + 2)$
8. $3(7e - 2) = 5(3e + 6)$
9. $4(4n + 2) = 2(7n + 9)$
10. $5(3c - 2) + 8 = 3(4c + 7) - 2$
11. $7(2t - 3) = 4(3t + 1) - 19$
12. $6(3g + 2) = 5(5g - 3) + 13$

Exercise 11

In each of the following equations, find whether the given value of x satisfies the equation:

1. $4x - 5 = 11$	$x = 4$
2. $19 - 2x = 13$	$x = 3$
3. $15 - 3x = 12$	$x = 9$
4. $5x + 4 = x + 16$	$x = 5$
5. $2x + 7 = 15 - 2x$	$x = 4$
6. $5(2x + 3) = 65$	$x = 5$
7. $4(3x - 8) = 56$	$x = 7$
8. $5(3x - 7) = 4x + 9$	$x = 4$
9. $3(2x - 7) = 5 - 2x$	$x = 4$
10. $4(2x + 3) = 3(3x - 2)$	$x = 18$
11. $3x + 8 = 2$	$x = {}^-2$
12. $2x - 7 = {}^-9$	$x = {}^-1$
13. $5x + 3 = {}^-23$	$x = {}^-4$
14. $7x - 1 = {}^-13$	$x = {}^-2$
15. $5 - 4x = {}^-3$	$x = {}^-2$
16. $3x + 7 = 2x - 10$	$x = {}^-3$
17. $5x + 19 = 3 + x$	$x = {}^-4$
18. $2(3x + 5) = {}^-20$	$x = {}^-5$
19. $3(4 - 5x) = {}^-18$	$x = {}^-2$
20. $4(2x + 5) = 3x - 10$	$x = {}^-6$

Fractional Equations

Exercise 12

Solve the following equations:

1. $\dfrac{x}{2} = 10$

2. $\dfrac{x}{3} = 6$

3. $\dfrac{1}{2}x = 9$

4. $\dfrac{1}{4}x = 6$

5. $\dfrac{3x}{4} = 12$

6. $\dfrac{3x}{5} = 30$

7. $\dfrac{2}{3}x = 18$

8. $\dfrac{5}{6}x = 30$

9. $\dfrac{2x}{3} = 14$

10. $\dfrac{4x}{9} = 20$

11. $\dfrac{5x}{7} = 25$

12. $\dfrac{7x}{9} = 14$

13. $\dfrac{2x}{5} = 7$

14. $\dfrac{3}{7}x = 18$

15. $\dfrac{4}{5}x = 30$

16. $\dfrac{x}{4} = {}^-8$

17. $\dfrac{x}{3} = {}^-9$

18. $\dfrac{x}{^-6} = {}^-4$

19. $\dfrac{x}{^-5} = 7$

20. $\dfrac{x}{^-8} = {}^-7$

21. $\dfrac{x}{^-9} = 12$

22. $\dfrac{x}{^-8} = {}^-14$

23. $\dfrac{x}{12} = {}^-7$

24. $\dfrac{x}{15} = {}^-5$

Exercise 13

Solve the following equations:

1. $\dfrac{x}{4} = \dfrac{3}{2}$

2. $\dfrac{w}{12} = \dfrac{5}{4}$

3. $\dfrac{m}{9} = 2\dfrac{2}{3}$

4. $\dfrac{t}{5} = 1\dfrac{1}{2}$

5. $\dfrac{c}{6} = \dfrac{5}{4}$

6. $\dfrac{2k}{9} = \dfrac{4}{3}$

7. $\dfrac{3d}{2} = 4\dfrac{1}{2}$

8. $\dfrac{5n}{3} = 6\dfrac{2}{3}$

9. $\dfrac{3a}{4} = 7\dfrac{1}{2}$

10. $\dfrac{2z}{3} = 2\dfrac{2}{9}$

11. $\dfrac{3l}{5} = 5\dfrac{1}{10}$

12. $\dfrac{3u}{7} = \dfrac{6}{5}$

13. $\dfrac{4e}{5} = 1\dfrac{13}{15}$

14. $\dfrac{5}{8}x = 3\dfrac{3}{4}$

15. $\dfrac{5}{6}c = 4\dfrac{1}{2}$

Exercise 14

Solve the following equations:

1. $\dfrac{x}{4} + \dfrac{1}{2} = 2$ **11.** $\dfrac{5x}{6} + \dfrac{2x}{3} = 3$ **21.** $\dfrac{5}{6} - \dfrac{2x}{9} = \dfrac{1}{6}$

2. $\dfrac{x}{6} + \dfrac{1}{3} = 3$ **12.** $\dfrac{2x}{5} - \dfrac{x}{4} = 1$ **22.** $\dfrac{5x}{6} - \dfrac{5x}{8} = \dfrac{3}{4}$

3. $\dfrac{x}{6} + \dfrac{2}{3} = 7$ **13.** $\dfrac{4x}{5} - \dfrac{2}{3} = 2$ **23.** $\dfrac{2x}{3} + \dfrac{2x}{7} = \dfrac{4}{7}$

4. $\dfrac{x}{2} - \dfrac{3}{4} = 1$ **14.** $\dfrac{4x}{7} + \dfrac{x}{2} = 3$ **24.** $\dfrac{5}{6} - \dfrac{x}{10} = \dfrac{7}{10}$

5. $\dfrac{x}{5} + \dfrac{1}{2} = 2$ **15.** $\dfrac{x}{3} + \dfrac{3}{4} = 2$ **25.** $\dfrac{5x}{6} - \dfrac{7}{12} = \dfrac{11}{4}$

6. $\dfrac{x}{3} + \dfrac{x}{2} = 5$ **16.** $\dfrac{x}{2} - \dfrac{5}{6} = \dfrac{2}{3}$ **26.** $\dfrac{x}{2} - \dfrac{3}{4} = 3\tfrac{1}{4}$

7. $\dfrac{x}{4} - \dfrac{x}{5} = 3$ **17.** $\dfrac{x}{4} - \dfrac{7}{12} = \dfrac{2}{3}$ **27.** $\dfrac{4}{9} - \dfrac{x}{3} = \dfrac{5}{18}$

8. $\dfrac{3x}{5} - \dfrac{x}{3} = 2$ **18.** $x - \dfrac{7x}{10} = \dfrac{6}{5}$ **28.** $\dfrac{x}{4} + \dfrac{9}{10} = \dfrac{3}{20}$

9. $\dfrac{5x}{8} - \dfrac{x}{2} = 6$ **19.** $\dfrac{3}{4} - \dfrac{x}{8} = \dfrac{1}{2}$ **29.** $\dfrac{3x}{10} - \dfrac{4x}{5} = 2$

10. $\dfrac{5x}{6} - \dfrac{3x}{4} = 1$ **20.** $\dfrac{2x}{3} - \dfrac{7x}{12} = \dfrac{5}{6}$ **30.** $\dfrac{2x}{5} - \dfrac{5x}{6} = \dfrac{13}{15}$

Problems Leading to Equations

Exercise 15

For each problem, form an equation then solve it:

1. Petra had £d and spent £14 of it. If she had £9 left, find the value of d.

2. Robert had £$3k$ and spent £8 of it. If he had £13 left, find the value of k.

3. Find the value of u:

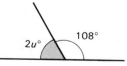

4. The width of a rectangle is 7 cm shorter than its length. If its width is 16 cm, find its length.

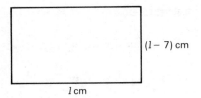

$(l - 7)$ cm

l cm

5. Dee thought of a number, doubled it then added 8. If her answer was 26, find the number thought of.

6. Two girls shared 43 sweets. If Elaine got $4t$ sweets and Helen got 17 sweets:
   (a) Find the value of t.
   (b) How many sweets did Elaine get?

7. There are b books on a shelf. If there were twice as many, a further 13 books would give 41 books altogether. How many books are there on the shelf?

8. Find the value of a:

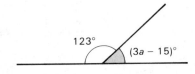

123°

$(3a - 15)°$

9. After travelling 48 miles, Lee had a further $6d$ miles to travel to complete his journey of 102 miles. Find the value of d.

10. I have $7m$ grams of sweets. After eating 36 g, I shall have 125 g left. Find the value of m.

Exercise 16

1. The perimeter of a rectangle is 26 cm, and its length is 3 cm more than its width. If the width is w cm:
   (a) Write an expression for:
      (i) the length,   (ii) the perimeter.
   (b) Form an equation and solve it to find the width of the rectangle.

2. The perimeter of a rectangle is 48 cm and its length is 3 times its width. If the width is b cm:
   (a) Write an expression for: (i) the length, (ii) the perimeter.
   (b) Form an equation and solve it to find the width of the rectangle.
   (c) Calculate the area of the rectangle.

3. Mrs Griffiths is now 4 times the age of her son. 9 years ago she was 19 years old. If her son is now s years old:
   (a) Write an expression in terms of s for:
      (i) Mrs Griffiths' present age,
      (ii) Mrs Griffiths' age 9 years ago.
   (b) Form an equation and solve it to find the son's present age.

4. Jack and Jill shared 84 marbles so that Jack received 6 times as many as Jill. If Jill received x marbles:
   (a) Write an expression for the number of marbles Jack received.
   (b) Write an equation and solve it to find the number of marbles Jill received.
   (c) How many marbles did Jack receive?

5. When a certain number is doubled then 7 subtracted, the result is the same as when 9 is added. Write an equation, then solve it to find the original number.

6. (a) Tracy saved £x per month for 5 months. She then spent £13. Write an expression for the amount of money Tracy has left from her savings.
   (b) If 3 months' savings at £x per month plus a further £9 gives the same amount that was left in part (a), write an equation then solve it to find Tracy's monthly savings.

Inequations

Exercise 17

For each question, list all possible answers:
1. I have one or more 10 p coins (but no other coins) in my pocket:
   (a) If I have less than 60 p, how much could there be?
   (b) If I have at least 40 p, but less than 90 p, how much could there be?

2. Mrs Hartley has only £1 coins in her purse:
   (a) If she has less than £7, how much might she have?
   (b) If she has at least £3, but less than £12, how much could she have?

3. A shop assistant sold up to 6 magazines. How many could she have sold?

4. A milkman delivered milk in up to 28 different streets. If he delivered to at least 23 different streets, in how many streets might he deliver milk?

5. Diana read at least three books last month. If she read 14 at the most, how many books might she have read?

Exercise 18

Throughout this exercise, take n to be a whole number. Find the solution set for each of the given *inequations*. When instructed, show the solution set on a number line.

A *e.g. 1* $n \leqslant 6$ Solution set $= \{0, 1, 2, 3, 4, 5, 6\}$

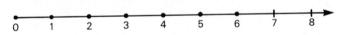

e.g. 2 $n > 4$ Solution set $= \{5, 6, 7, 8, \ldots\}$

Note The arrows suggest that the number lines continue. In *e.g. 2*, the arrow following the 8 means that all numbers after 8 are marked in the same way as 8, with a dot, and are therefore in the solution set.

1. $n < 8$	**4.** $n \leqslant 5$ (Show the answers on a number line.)
2. $n \geqslant 14$	**5.** $n > 9$ (Show the answers on a number line.)
3. $n > 3$	**6.** $n < 10$ (Show the answers on a number line.)

B 1. $4 < n < 12$	**4.** $3 \leqslant n < 9$ (Show on a number line.)
2. $9 \leqslant n \leqslant 15$	**5.** $1 < n < 10$ (Show on a number line.)
3. $18 < n \leqslant 24$	**6.** $12 < n \leqslant 18$ (Show on a number line.)

Exercise 19   Sector

For each question in Exercise 17, show the solution set using inequality signs ($<$, $\leqslant$, $>$ or $\geqslant$).

e.g. There were at least 6 tins in the cupboard and 19 at the most. How many could there be?

Let the number of tins in the cupboard $= n$.

A possible answer is: $6 \leqslant n \leqslant 19$.

Exercise 20

For each of the following, show the solution set using inequality signs:

1. 9 people each had from £3 to £14 on them. How much is that altogether?

2. A shop sells 6 to 19 bars of chocolate per day. How many are sold in 6 days?

3. A milkman delivered from 2 to 4 bottles of milk to each of 57 houses. How many bottles was that altogether?

4. A farmer had 76 sheep. If 29 of them had either 1, 2 or 3 lambs, what size could his flock be?

5. A girl keeps hens. On Monday she collects 49 eggs and on Tuesday 37 of the hens lay either 1 or 2 eggs. How many eggs could that be altogether for Monday and Tuesday?

Exercise 21

Throughout this exercise working need not be shown:

A If x is a *whole number*, find the smallest value of x:

1. $x + 5 > 9$	**6.** $\quad 2x \geqslant 9$	**11.** $2x - 6 > 8$
2. $x + 5 \geqslant 9$	**7.** $\quad 9x > 70$	**12.** $2x + 7 \geqslant 19$
3. $x - 9 > 7$	**8.** $\quad 7 - x < 4$	**13.** $3x + 2 > 25$
4. $\quad 3x \geqslant 15$	**9.** $\quad 7 - x \leqslant 4$	**14.** $5x - 3 > 17$
5. $\quad 3x > 15$	**10.** $12 - x \leqslant 2$	**15.** $4x + 9 \geqslant 23$

B If x is a *whole number*, find the largest value of x:

1. $x + 6 \leqslant 15$	**6.** $4x \leqslant 22$	**11.** $2x + 8 < 22$
2. $x + 6 < 15$	**7.** $8x < 58$	**12.** $3x - 1 \leqslant 17$
3. $x - 7 < 9$	**8.** $9 - x > 8$	**13.** $6x - 12 < 15$
4. $2x < 18$	**9.** $16 - x \geqslant 7$	**14.** $2x - 15 \leqslant 4$
5. $5x \leqslant 40$	**10.** $10 - x > 2$	**15.** $4x + 7 \leqslant 13$

Exercise 22

Throughout this exercise, take n to be a whole number. Find the solution set for each of the given inequations.

e.g. 1
$$n + 4 \leqslant 9$$
$$n \leqslant 5$$
Solution set $= \{0, 1, 2, 3, 4, 5\}$

$\left(\begin{array}{c}\text{Compare the equation}\\ n + 4 = 9 \\ \underline{\underline{n = 5}}\end{array}\right)$

e.g. 2
$$3n > 20$$
$$n > 6\tfrac{2}{3}$$
Solution set $= \{7, 8, 9, 10, \ldots\}$

$\left(\begin{array}{c}\text{Compare the equation}\\ 3n = 20 \\ \underline{\underline{n = 6\tfrac{2}{3}}}\end{array}\right)$

e.g. 3
$$2n - 5 \geqslant 1$$
$$2n \geqslant 6$$
$$n \geqslant 3$$
Solution set $= \{3, 4, 5, 6, 7, \ldots\}$

$\left(\begin{array}{c}\text{Compare the equation}\\ 2n - 5 = 1 \\ 2n = 6 \\ \underline{\underline{n = 3}}\end{array}\right)$

1. $n + 6 < 10$	**6.** $2n + 4 \leqslant 10$	**11.** $2n - 3 < 14$
2. $n - 4 \leqslant 5$	**7.** $3n - 10 > 20$	**12.** $4n + 6 < 28$
3. $n - 5 \geqslant 7$	**8.** $5n - 10 < 0$	**13.** $6n - 2 \geqslant 4$
4. $2n < 15$	**9.** $4n + 3 \geqslant 11$	**14.** $3n + 2 \geqslant 15$
5. $3n > 18$	**10.** $7n - 5 \leqslant 37$	**15.** $8n - 8 \leqslant 42$

Some inequations may not have a solution.

Consider $\qquad x + 4 < 2 \qquad$ where x is a whole number

so $\qquad\qquad x < {}^{-}2$

and the solution set $= \{\,\}$ (There are no whole numbers less than $^{-}2$.)

Note   Solution set $= \emptyset$ is also an acceptable answer, where the symbol for the empty set is used.

Consider the equation $x + 4 = 2$

$$\underline{\underline{x = {}^-2}}$$

(This equation would also have no solution, if x had to be a whole number.)

Exercise 23

Find the solution set for each of these inequations, where x is a whole number:

1. $x - 6 < 4$

2. $x + 4 < 6$

3. $x + 6 < 4$

4. $x - 2 > 12$

5. $8 + x \leqslant 3$

6. $2x \leqslant 1$

7. $5x \geqslant 8$

8. $4 - x > 9$

9. $2x - 2 \geqslant 17$

10. $4x + 6 \leqslant 2$

11. $3x + 2 < 5$

12. $3x + 9 > 26$

Revision Exercises XV to XXI

Revision Exercise XV

1. Draw a pair of axes where the x-values range from ⁻10 to ⁺10 and the y-values from ⁻8 to ⁺8:

   (a) Plot the points A(0, 6), B(6, 6) and C(4, 2). If A, B and C are three vertices of parallelogram ABCD, draw the parallelogram and write the co-ordinates of D.

   (b) P(0, ⁻4), Q(8, 0) and R(10, ⁻4) are three vertices of rectangle PQRS. Draw the rectangle and write the coordinates of S.

   (c) (⁻6, ⁻4) is the point of intersection of the diagonals of a square. One vertex is at (⁻4, 0). Find the co-ordinates of the other three vertices.

2. Draw another pair of axes as for question 1:

   (a) Draw and label the line $x = 7$.

   (b) Draw and label the line $y = ⁻3$.

   (c) Write the co-ordinates of the point of intersection of the lines in parts (a) and (b).

   (d) Draw and label the line $y = x - 5$.

   (e) Write the co-ordinates of the point of intersection of the graphs $y = x - 5$ and $x = 7$.

   (f) Draw and label the line $y = 2x - 6$.

   (g) Draw and label the line $y = 4 - 2x$.

   (h) Write the co-ordinates of the point of intersection of the graphs of:

   (i) $y = 4 - 2x$ and $y = x - 5$

   (ii) $y = 4 - 2x$ and $y = 2x - 6$.

344

3. Where would the graph of $y = 5x + 3$ cross the y-axis?

4. For the graph of $y = 4x - 7$, write:
   (*a*) the gradient,   (*b*) the y-intercept.

5. A graph has a gradient of 3 and a y-intercept of $^-8$. Write its equation.

6. Six graphs are shown. For each one, select from the following list the equation that best describes it.

$y = 2x$ $y = 3x + 3$
$y = 2x - 3$ $y = 2 - 3x$
$y = 2x + 3$ $y = ^-3x - 2$
$y = 3 - 2x$ $y = ^-3$
$y = 6x - 3$ $x = ^-5$
$y = 5x$ $y = ^-5$

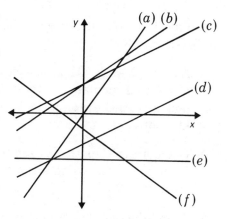

7. If $(3, k)$ and $(l, 7)$ lie on $y = 3x - 5$, then find the values of k and l.

8. Find the gradient of the straight-line segment that joins the points $(^-3, ^-4)$ and $(1, 12)$.

9. For the graph shown, write its equation:

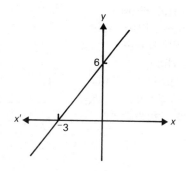

10. Sketch a graph of $y = 2x - 7$.

345

Revision Exercise XVI

1. Find the circumference of a circle with radius 6.8 cm, if $\pi = 3$.

2. Find the circumference of a circle with diameter 36 cm, giving the answer to two significant figures. (Use $\pi = 3.14$.)

3. A circle has a diameter of 7.5 m. Calculate its circumference using $\pi = 3.142$. Give your answer to three significant figures.

4. Find the circumference of a circle having a diameter of 84 cm. Use $\pi = 3\frac{1}{7}$.

5. A cyclist travels 30 laps of a circular cycle track that has a radius of 170 m. Calculate the total distance travelled. Use $\pi = 3.14$ and give the distance in kilometres rounded to the nearest kilometre.

6. Calculate the length of an arc of a circle with a diameter of 54 cm, if the arc subtends an angle of 120° at the centre of the circle. (Use $\pi = 3.14$.)

7. A circle has a radius of 24 mm; calculate its area using $\pi = 3.142$. Give your answer correct to three significant figures.

8. A metal plate has a diameter of 9 cm. Calculate the area of the plate to three significant figures using $\pi = 3.142$.

Revision Exercise XVII **M**

1. (a) Translate the given symbol 4 cm to the right and draw its image.
   (b) Translate the given symbol 1 cm to the left followed by 3 cm downwards, and draw its image.

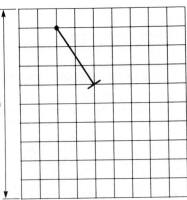

10 cm

2. Copy the following (the given squares represent 1 cm squares), then reflect each shape in the given mirror line:

(a)

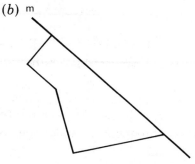

(b) m

3. A pentagon is labelled anticlockwise. If it is reflected in a mirror line, will its image be labelled clockwise or anticlockwise?

4. Copy the diagram, then draw the image of the given symbol after a 90° rotation clockwise about C.

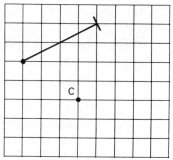

5. In the given diagram, explain why C is not the centre of rotation.

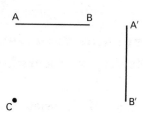

6. Find the co-ordinates of the images under the following transformations:

(a) PQ is translated 4 units downwards, where P is (3, 2) and Q is (4, ⁻1).

(b) △XYZ is translated 3 units to the left, followed by 7 units upwards; X is (⁻4, 2), Y is (⁻1, ⁻3) and Z is (3, ⁻1).

(c) △ABC is reflected in the x-axis; A is (⁻2, ⁻5), B is (0, ⁻1) and C is (3, ⁻3).

(d) △DEF is rotated 90° clockwise about the origin; D is (2, 7), E is (5, 1) and F is (1, 3).

347

7. (a) Describe the transformation:
$$G(3, 1) \longrightarrow G'(1, ^-3)$$
$$H(4, ^-2) \longrightarrow H'(^-2, ^-4)$$
$$I(^-1, ^-5) \longrightarrow I'(^-5, 1)$$

(b) Write the co-ordinates of the image of $J(^-2, 6)$ under the transformation in part (a).

8. Name the solid obtained when the shaded shape is rotated through $360°$ about the given line.

9. On squared paper, draw an enlargement of the given shape. Make each side twice as long.

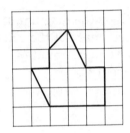

Revision Exercise XVIII

1. Find the value of:

(a) 7^2
(b) $2^4 \times 3^2$
(c) $\dfrac{4^4}{8^2}$

2. Find, without using a calculator, the value of:
(a) 2000^2
(b) 800^2
(c) 0.05^2
(d) 0.003^2

3. Use a calculator to find, to four significant figures:
(a) 2.76^2
(b) 498^2
(c) 0.53^2

4. Find the value of:
(a) $\left(\dfrac{7}{2}\right)^2$
(b) $\left(\dfrac{9}{10}\right)^2$
(c) $(1\tfrac{1}{4})^2$
(d) $\dfrac{12^2}{6}$

5. If $y = x^2 - 7$, find the value of y when x equals:

(a) 6   (b) $^-6$ (c) 2   (d) $^-2$ (e) $^-1$

6. $A = 6l^2$ gives the surface area of a cube with edges measuring l units. Find the surface area when length l equals:

(a) 3 m   (b) 5 cm   (c) 10 cm   (d) 1.2 m

7. Copy and check the given pattern, then write the next three steps:

$$1^3 = 1^2$$
$$1^3 + 2^3 + 1^3 = 1^2 + 3^2$$
$$1^3 + 2^3 + 3^3 + 2^3 + 1^3 = 3^2 + 6^2$$
$$1^3 + 2^3 + 3^3 + 4^3 + 3^3 + 2^3 + 1^3 = 6^2 + 10^2$$

and so on.

8. Write 208 as the sum of two squares.

9. Write 1225 as the product of two squares.

10. $\sqrt{69}$ lies between 8 and 9. Write, correct to one significant figure, two numbers between which the following square roots lie.

(a) $\sqrt{51}$ (b) $\sqrt{219}$ (c) $\sqrt{7165}$ (d) $\sqrt{0.5}$

11. Without using a calculator, find:

(a) $\sqrt{3600}$ (b) $\sqrt{0.000\,049}$ (c) $\sqrt{2.25}$

12. Find:

(a) $\sqrt{\dfrac{36}{25}}$ (b) $\sqrt{\dfrac{9}{64}}$ (c) $\sqrt{12\frac{1}{4}}$ (d) $\sqrt{36^2}$

13. Use a calculator to find, to four significant figures:

(a) $\sqrt{83.7}$ (b) $\sqrt{49\,800}$ (c) $\sqrt{0.0653}$

14. Simplify the following:

(a) $x^8 \times x^4$ (b) $y^7 \times y^3 \times y^9$ (c) $a^3 \times b^7 \times a^8 \times b$

15. Simplify:

(a) $3e^2 \times 8e^8$ (b) $4m^6 \times 5m^6$ (c) $9t^{13} \times 7t^9$

16. Simplify:

(a) $c^9 d \times c^5 d^4$ (b) $2g^4 h^9 \times 10h^6 g^7$ (c) $6k^3 l^{10} \times 3k^9 l^3$

17. Simplify:

(a) $x^{13} \div x^6$ 　　　(b) $\dfrac{35t^{10}}{5t^7}$ 　　　(c) $\dfrac{42u^7 w^5 z^{12}}{7u^2 w^4 z^8}$

18. Simplify:

(a) $(t^3)^7$ 　　　(b) $(2u^2)^4$ 　　　(c) $(3y^9)^3$

Revision Exercise XIX

1. Each exterior angle, A, of a regular polygon can be found by dividing 360 by the number of sides, n. We can write:

$$A = \frac{360}{n}$$

Use the formula to find each exterior angle of a 15-sided polygon.

2. Use $s = ut^2$ to find s when $u = 30$ and $t = 7$.

3. Power (measured in watts) can be found by dividing the work done (in joules) by the time taken (in seconds).

Find a formula giving the power P, in terms of W (work done) and t (time). Use the formula to find the power of a machine that does 3600 J work in 8 s.

4. An athlete trained for $3x$ hours each day. After $4d$ hours of training, how much is left to do?

5. Anthony had £$6x$. After spending £6, how much did he have left?

6. How many minutes are there in:
(a) 3 hours? 　　(b) u hours? 　　(c) $4m$ hours?

7. Write an expression in n for an odd number, where n is a whole number.

8. Find the missing numbers in: 4, 7, 12, $\boxed{?}$, 28, 39, $\boxed{?}$ ...

9. Copy the given sequence and underline the one term that is incorrect:

2, 5, 9, 14, 20, 26, 35, 44, ...

10. $T_n = 5n - 4$ gives the nth term of a sequence. Write the first seven terms.

11. Simplify the expressions:
(a) $x^2 - 7x + 3x - 6$
(b) $2p^2qr - 3qr^2p - 4r^2pq + qp^2r$

12. Multiply out:
(a) $2d(4e - 6)$ (b) $\frac{1}{3}(24k + 15l)$

13. Simplify:
(a) $(5t + 3u) + (4t - u)$
(b) $4(3m + 2n) + (2m - 6n)$

14. Multiply out: $^-3(6d - 7)$

15. Multiply out:
(a) $5c(3c - 4)$ (b) $^-6z(2z + 3)$ (c) $3v^2(v^2 + 2v - 8)$

16. Simplify: $8g - (5g - 6)$

17. Simplify:
(a) $(4y - 7) + (3y + 10)$
(b) $(5p + 6q) - (3p + 8q)$

18. Simplify:
(a) $16 + 4(3h - 5)$ (b) $18f - 2(7f - 6)$

19. Multiply out and simplify your answers:
(a) $s(s + 6) + 7(s - 3)$ (b) $w(w - 4) - 5(w - 4)$

20. Multiply out and simplify your answers:
(a) $(a + 9)(a - 3)$ (b) $(b - 4)(b - 3)$

21. By factorising, find the value of: $86 \times 63 + 86 \times 37$

22. Factorise:
(a) $18y - 12$ (b) $15x^2 + 9x$

23. Factorise: $m^2 - 36$

24. Without using a calculator, find the value of: $7.4^2 - 2.6^2$

Revision Exercise XX

1. Here are 15 sums of money:

    £4, £9, £8, £6, £3, £7, £9, £6,
    £8, £4, £7, £8, £7, £8, £5

    Find: (a) the mode, (b) the median, (c) the mean.

2. Kirsty obtained an average of 59% in eight tests. What was her total mark for the eight tests?

3. The mean age of six pupils is 13 years. If a 5-year-old leaves the group and a 17-year-old joins it, calculate the new mean age.

4. Write three numbers where the mode is 9 and the mean is 8.

5. Write four numbers where the mode is 6, the median is $6\frac{1}{2}$ and the mean is 7.

6. Find the mean of:
   (a) 8, 2, 9, 7, 4
   (b) 18, 12, 19, 17, 14
   (c) 68, 62, 69, 67, 64

7. Here are the ages (in years) of the residents of a village:

32	21	46	35	29	51	19	17	3	6	64	72
55	50	24	31	39	40	12	15	8	21	30	68
35	32	9	7	39	17	25	23	54	59	92	69
70	49	45	18	16	32	32	38	37	45	43	13
11	8	19	51	53	62	64	74	70	80	3	5
6	9	31	34	32	38	36	33	29	27	4	11
13	24	46	44	47	45	51	58	30	34	18	12
19	29	27	31	28	44	45	43	41	81	52	50
65	73	19	17	14	8	23	25	31	35	40	48
55	55	51	50	62	64	70	97	21	28	27	30
65	34	72	25	54	52	36	63	31	50	46	79
51	57	42	33	40	68	67	48	8	10	6	15
43	83	47	60	51	19	62	64	29	27	82	61
63	49	47	31	33	64	67	40	43	30		

    (a) Find the range.
    (b) Make a frequency table. Use the class intervals 0–9, 10–19, 20–29, 30–39, 40–49, 50–59, 60–69, 70–79, 80–89, 90–99.
    (c) Draw a histogram.
    (d) Give the modal class.

8. The following table shows the marks awarded to 12 competitors by two of the judges in a diving competition:

Competitor	1	2	3	4	5	6	7	8	9	10	11	12
Judge A	8	7	6	9	7	9	6	7.5	6.5	5.5	8	8.5
Judge B	7	7.5	6	8	6.5	8.5	6.5	8	7	5.5	8.5	8

(a) Draw a scattergram.
(b) Calculate the mean number of marks awarded by each judge, then plot them.
(c) Draw the line of best fit.
(d) Use your graph to find the probable mark awarded by Judge B when Judge A awarded 7 marks.

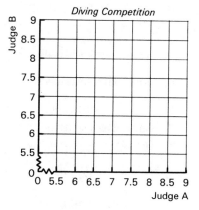

Diving Competition

9. What is the probability of obtaining exactly two tails when three coins are tossed? (The table produced in Exercise 22, p. 327 may be helpful.)

10. What is the probability of obtaining a 5 or a 6 when an ordinary die is thrown?

11. What is the probability of drawing out a jack or a queen from an ordinary pack of playing cards?

12. A bag contains 6 pieces of vanilla fudge, 8 pieces of walnut fudge and 7 pieces of raisin fudge. A piece of fudge is taken out of the bag at random, what is the probability that it is vanilla?

13. There are 6 black, 9 blue, 10 green and 5 red pen refills in a box. If one is removed at random, what is the probability that it is blue?

14. (a) Write two events where each has a probability of 1 of occurring.
(b) Write two events where each has a probability of 0 of occurring.

353

Revision Exercise XXI

1. Solve these equations:

(a) $h - 19 = 13$

(b) $6k = 36$

(c) $5t + 9 = 24$

(d) $\dfrac{n}{3} = 15$

(e) $\dfrac{m}{4} + 8 = 11$

2. Solve these equations:

(a) $p + 9 = 2$ (b) $8a = {}^-32$ (c) $3d + 17 = 8$

3. Solve the equation: $4x - 5 - x + 8 + 7x = 43$

4. Solve the equations:

(a) $13 - x = 4$ (b) $4 - x = 13$ (c) $7 - x = {}^-4$

5. Solve the equations:

(a) $4p - 5 = p + 7$ (b) $7 - 3q = 23 - 5q$

6. Solve the equation: $6(2y - 7) = 54$

7. Solve the equation: $4(3p - 1) = 5(2p + 4)$

8. (a) If $4x + 3 = 21 - 2x$, does $x = 3$?

(b) If $3(2x + 4) = 12$, does $x = {}^-4$?

9. Solve the following equations:

(a) $\dfrac{3x}{8} = 24$ (b) $\dfrac{t}{{}^-4} = {}^-9$ (c) $\dfrac{2z}{3} = 1\frac{5}{9}$

10. Solve the equations:

(a) $\dfrac{x}{2} - \dfrac{3x}{10} = \dfrac{4}{5}$ (b) $\dfrac{x}{8} + \dfrac{4}{5} = 1$

11. 2 classes shared 59 books. The first class got $4p$ books, while the second class got 27. Write an equation, then solve it to find the value of p.

12. Gavin saved £x. If he was then given a further £38, he would have 3 times as much as he had saved.

(a) Write an expression for the amount of money Gavin would have, after receiving the £38.

(b) Write an equation, then solve it, to find the amount of Gavin's savings.

13. Warren wrote at least 5 letters last month and 11 at the most:
  (*a*) How many letters might he have written?
  (*b*) Show the possible number of letters written using inequality signs.

14. Find the solution set, and show on a number line, where n is a whole number:
  (*a*) $n < 7$ (*b*) $8 \leqslant n \leqslant 13$

15. If n is a whole number:
  (*a*) Find the smallest value of n, where $2n - 4 \geqslant 8$.
  (*b*) Find the largest value of n, where $4n + 3 < 41$.

16. Find the solution sets where x is a whole number:
  (*a*) $x - 5 > 7$ (*e*) $x + 14 < 12$
  (*b*) $x + 2 \leqslant 11$ (*f*) $2x + 7 \geqslant 23$
  (*c*) $3x < 21$ (*g*) $6x - 2 > 15$
  (*d*) $5x \geqslant 14$ (*h*) $3x + 9 \leqslant 20$

22 Length, Volume, Capacity and Mass

Metric Conversions

Exercise 1

Copy and complete:

1.	2.7 cm = [?] mm	**20.**	5.4 ℓ = [?] cℓ
2.	9.3 m = [?] mm	**21.**	7 t = [?] kg
3.	3600 g = [?] kg	**22.**	5200 kg = [?] t
4.	980 cℓ = [?] ℓ	**23.**	58.7 m = [?] cm
5.	4.2 ℓ = [?] mℓ	**24.**	246 mℓ = [?] cℓ
6.	6.1 g = [?] mg	**25.**	9.01 kg = [?] g
7.	9400 cm = [?] m	**26.**	4.99 ℓ = [?] cℓ
8.	1.65 km = [?] m	**27.**	9.18 ℓ = [?] mℓ
9.	69 mℓ = [?] cℓ	**28.**	10.9 m = [?] cm
10.	12.4 kg = [?] g	**29.**	1.084 t = [?] kg
11.	86 g = [?] mg	**30.**	81 640 mℓ = [?] ℓ
12.	5630 m = [?] km	**31.**	3.72 km = [?] m
13.	790 mm = [?] cm	**32.**	7.08 ℓ = [?] cℓ
14.	12.84 m = [?] mm	**33.**	82 700 kg = [?] t
15.	5100 mg = [?] g	**34.**	4990 mg = [?] g
16.	1937 mℓ = [?] ℓ	**35.**	64.1 ℓ = [?] mℓ
17.	46 cℓ = [?] mℓ	**36.**	3312 cm = [?] m
18.	85 m = [?] mm	**37.**	50.6 cℓ = [?] mℓ
19.	48 600 m = [?] km	**38.**	196 g = [?] kg

Length

Exercise 2 Estimating

1. What is most likely to be 20 mm thick?
   A. a coin   B. a book   C. a brick   D. a pencil

2. What is likely to be about 10 m?
   A. the height of a tree
   B. the length of a cricket bat
   C. the width of a lorry
   D. the diameter of a tennis ball

3. The height of a chair seat is about:
   A. 1 m   B. 100 mm   C. 5 cm   D. 500 mm

4. The length of a 53-seater coach is about:
   A. 12 m   B. 18 m   C. 24 m   D. 30 m

5. The height of a small tin is about:
   A. 6 mm   B. 60 mm   C. 600 mm   D. 6 m

6. The diameter of a jam jar is about:
   A. 70 mm   B. 120 mm   C. 200 mm   D. 240 mm

7. The height of a house is about:
   A. 21 m   B. 15 m   C. 11 m   D. 7 m

8. The height of a table is about:
   A. 75 mm   B. 750 mm   C. 1.5 m   D. 20 cm

9. The length of a brick is about:
   A. 20 mm   B. 30 mm   C. 200 mm   D. 300 mm

10. The width of a car is about:
    A. 1.6 m   B. 2.8 m   C. 3.5 m   D. 4 m

Exercise 3

1. When a car of length 4.29 m is parked in a garage, there is a space of 85 cm in front of it. If the garage is 5.6 m long, how much space is behind the car?

2. Stuart threw a javelin 34.82 m. His sister threw the javelin 18.77 m. How much further did Stuart throw it?

3. The perimeter of the given field is 550 m. Find the missing distance.

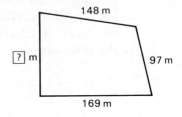

148 m

? m

97 m

169 m

4. Which is longer, 6000 cm or 600 m?

5. A metal carpet bar is 1 m long. What length is waste, if it is used at a doorway that is 857 mm wide?

6. A plank was 2.7 m long. What length remained, after pieces measuring 342 mm, 564 mm and 489 mm were cut off?

7. Andrea needed some material to make a dress. The length of material needed was twice the distance from shoulder to calf plus 70 cm (for long sleeves). What length of material did Andrea need to buy, if her measurement from shoulder to calf was 1.04 m?

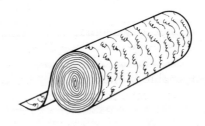

8. A length of plastic curtain rail measures 2.2 m. It is to be supported by nine equally spaced supports, where the support at each end is 2 cm from the end of the rail. How far apart should adjacent supports be?

358

9. Mrs Vaughan bought a 2 m length of plastic curtain rail. The length of rail needed was 1.92 m.

(a) How many centimetres of rail does she need to cut off?

(b) She needs to fit eight equally spaced supports throughout the length of 1.92 m. If the two end supports must be between 1 cm and 2 cm from the ends of the rail, how far from the ends should they be so that the distance between adjacent supports is a whole number of centimetres?

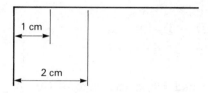

(c) If the supports are fitted as in part (b), how far apart should they be?

10.

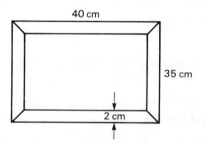

Fig. 1

(a) Mr Thexton wanted to frame a picture as in Fig. 1 above. The wood used was rectangular in cross-section and measured 2 cm by 1 cm (see Fig. 2). What is the smallest possible length of wood needed to make the given frame?

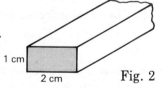

Fig. 2

(b) If Mr Thexton had decided to use a piece of wood having a cross-section as shown in Fig. 3, what is the smallest possible length of wood he would have needed?

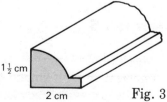

Fig. 3

359

Imperial Units of Length

The measurements made so far in this chapter have been in the *metric system*. The units used are called *metric units*. Before metrication (the change to the metric system) most measurements in Britain were in *imperial units*.

Using imperial units of length:

> 12 in = 1 ft
>
> 3 ft = 1 yd
>
> 1760 yd = 1 mile

Inches are marked along the edge of this page (subdivided into tenths of an inch) and along the edge of the opposite page (subdivided into 32nds and 16ths of an inch).

Exercise 4

1. How many inches are there in:
   (*a*) 2 ft?   (*b*) 7 ft?   (*c*) 12 ft

2. How many feet are there in:
   (*a*) 4 yd?   (*b*) 12 yd?   (*c*) 35 yd?

3. How many inches are there in:
   (*a*) 6 yd?   (*b*) 9 yd?   (*c*) 14 yd?

4. How many feet are there in:
   (*a*) 120 yd?   (*b*) 440 yd?   (*c*) 1 mile?

Exercise 5

Measure the lengths of six items (such as pencils or pens) using imperial units. If you do not have a suitable ruler or tape measure, use the inches marked along the edge of this page or the opposite page.

Volume of a Cuboid

Exercise 6

Copy and complete the sentences:

1.

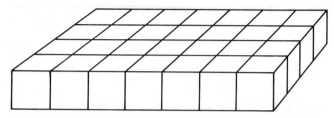

(a) There are ? small cubes in the diagram above.

(b) If there were 2 layers there would be ? small cubes.

(c) If there were 5 layers there would be ? small cubes.

(d) If each small cube has a volume of 1 cm³, the volume of the cuboid in the diagram above is ? cm³.

2.

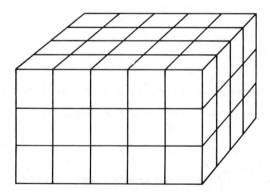

(a) There are ? small cubes in each layer of the cuboid above.

(b) There are ? layers.

(c) There are ? small cubes in the cuboid.

(d) If each small cube has a volume of 1 cm³, the volume of the cuboid is ? cm³.

Exercise 7

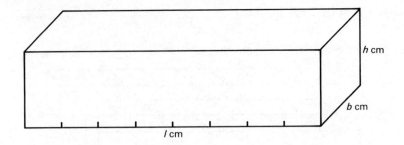

If a cuboid is l cm long, b cm wide and h cm high, then:

1. The number of 1 cm cubes in the length = [?].

2. The number of 1 cm cubes in the bottom layer of the cuboid = $l \times$ [?].

3. The total number of 1 cm cubes = $l \times$ [?] $\times$ [?].

4. The volume of the cuboid, $V = l \times$ [?] $\times$ [?].

Exercise 8

Calculate the volume of the cuboid given in each question:

1. 5 cm by 4 cm by 2 cm (as in the diagram)

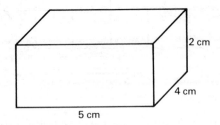

2. 6 cm by 3 cm by 2 cm
3. 6 cm by 5 cm by 3 cm

4. 8 cm by 5 cm by 4 cm

5. 7 m by 6 m by 2 m

6. 9 cm by 7 cm by 5 cm

7. 60 mm by 40 mm by 20 mm

8. 14 cm by 10 cm by 6 cm

9. 1.7 m by 1.2 m by 0.4 m

10. 5.3 m by 3.6 m by 1.9 m

11. 8.1 cm by 5.8 cm by 3.7 cm

12. $8\frac{1}{2}$ cm by $5\frac{3}{4}$ cm by $2\frac{1}{2}$ cm

Exercise 9

1.

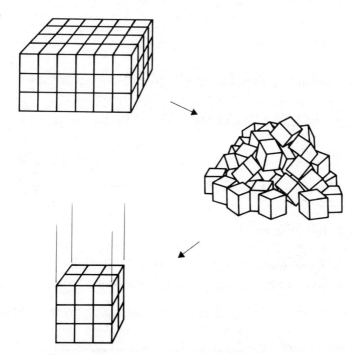

The cubes in the cuboid above have been re-arranged to form a new cuboid having six cubes as a base. How many cubes high is the new cuboid?

2. A cuboid measuring 9 cm by 8 cm by 2 cm is re-arranged to form a new cuboid of length 4 cm and width 3 cm. What is the height of the new cuboid?

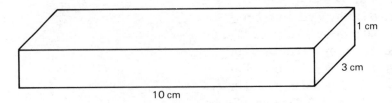

The diagram shows a cuboid with a volume of 30 cm³. (Note that a cuboid with length 3 cm, width 1 cm and height 10 cm is the same as that in the diagram, but in a different position.)

Sketch four more cuboids (all different) each having a volume of 30 cm³.

Exercise 11

1. The internal measurements of a cuboid-shaped box are:
   length = 8 cm, breadth = 7 cm, height = 3 cm.
   (a) How many 1 cm cubes would fit inside the box?

   (b) How many ½ cm cubes would fit inside the box?

2. Find the volume of:
   (a) a 2 cm cube   (d) a 10 cm cube
   (b) a 3 cm cube   (e) a 15 cm cube
   (c) a 6 cm cube   (f) a 20 cm cube

3. A 'rectangular' fish tank is 80 cm long, 30 cm wide and 30 cm high:
   (a) Calculate its volume.
   (b) If it is only three-quarters full of water, find the number of cubic centimetres of water in the tank.

4. A kitchen measures 10 ft by 8 ft by 8 ft. Calculate the number of cubic feet of air in the room.

5. A kitchen measures 3 m by 2.7 m by 2.4 m. Calculate the number of cubic metres of air in the room.

6. A net of a box is shown. When a box is made from this net, what volume would it have?

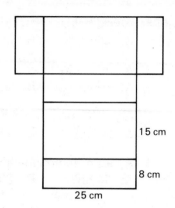

15 cm

8 cm

25 cm

Capacity

The *capacity* of a container is the amount of liquid it will hold.

Small amounts of liquid are usually measured in millilitres (mℓ), while large amounts of liquid are usually measured in litres (ℓ).

$$1000 \text{ mℓ} = 1 \text{ ℓ}$$
$$100 \text{ cℓ} = 1 \text{ ℓ}$$

In the imperial system, gallons (gal) are used for large amounts of liquid and pints (pt) for small amounts:

$$8 \text{ pt} = 1 \text{ gal}$$

Exercise 12

Choose the answer that is correct or almost correct:

1. A milk bottle holds:
    A. 4 ℓ   B. 20 ℓ   C. 600 mℓ   D. 20 mx

2. A teaspoonful of medicine is:
    A. 5 mℓ   B. 20 mℓ   C. 100 mℓ   D. 1 ℓ

3. A bucket holds:
    A. 1000 mℓ   B. 9 ℓ   C. 24 ℓ   D. 600 mℓ

4. A kettle holds:
    A. 1.7 ℓ   B. 3 ℓ   C. 6.6 ℓ   D. 4000 mℓ

365

5. A cup holds:

A. 200 mℓ   B. 50 mℓ   C. 400 mℓ   D. 100 mℓ

6. A bath holds:

A. 85 ℓ   B. 12 ℓ   C. 250 ℓ   D. 110 ℓ

7. A public swimming pool holds:

A. 250 ℓ   B. 2500 ℓ   C. 25 000 ℓ   D. 250 000 ℓ

8. A can of lemonade is:

A. 75 mℓ   B. 330 mℓ   C. 675 mℓ   D. 3.75 ℓ

9. A car's petrol tank holds:

A. 60 ℓ   B. 15 ℓ   C. 5 ℓ   D. 10 000 mℓ

10. A wash-basin holds:

A. 950 mℓ   B. 3 ℓ   C. 8 ℓ   D. 20 ℓ

Exercise 13

Choose the answer that is correct or almost correct:

1. A kettle holds:

A. 1 gal   B. 3 pt   C. 1 pt   D. $\frac{1}{2}$ pt

2. A tall, thin glass holds:

A. 1 gal   B. 3 pt   C. 1 pt   D. $\frac{1}{2}$ pt

3. A bath holds:

A. 100 pt   B. 15 gal   C. 35 gal   D. 55 gal

4. A watering-can holds:

A. 2 pt   B. 5 pt   C. 2 gal   D. 5 gal

5. A milkpan holds:

A. 8 pt   B. 4 pt   C. 2 pt   D. $\frac{1}{2}$ pt

Exercise 14

Copy the following list of containers. Write them one under the other. Alongside each container, write how many millilitres or litres it holds.

bucket, watering-can, kettle, saucepan, tea-pot, lemonade bottle, milk bottle, medicine bottle, shampoo bottle, glass tumbler, mug, cup, wineglass, wash-basin, washing-up bowl, perfume bottle, nail-polish bottle, teaspoon, tablespoon, winebottle, can of drink.

Exercise 15

1. I bought two dozen 500 mℓ cartons of milk. How many litres was that?

2. A mug holds 250 mℓ:
   (a) How many litres will five mugs hold?
   (b) How many mugs can be filled from 4 ℓ of water?

3. A milkpan holds 1.4 ℓ:
   (a) How many 200 mℓ cups can be filled from the milkpan?
   (b) How many 250 mℓ mugs can be filled from the milkpan?

4. A shop took delivery of four dozen cans of lemonade. How many litres of lemonade was that if each can held 330 mℓ?

5. A kettle holds 1.5 ℓ:
   (a) If I want to make 28 cups of tea where each cup holds 200 mℓ, how many times do I need to put the kettle on?
   (b) If I use 28, 250 mℓ mugs instead of cups, how many times do I need to put the kettle on?

6. Lynn must take two 5 mℓ spoonfuls of medicine three times a day. Each bottle holds 150 mℓ. How many days will two bottles last?

7. A wineglass holds 150 mℓ:
   (a) (i) How many glasses can be filled from a 1 ℓ bottle of wine?
       (ii) How much wine would be left over?
   (b) (i) Find the smallest number of 1 ℓ bottles needed to fill an exact number of glasses with no wine left over.
       (ii) How many glasses would be filled in part (i)?
   (c) (i) How many glasses can be filled from a 70 cℓ bottle of wine?
       (ii) How much wine would be left over?
   (d) (i) Find the smallest number of 70 cℓ bottles needed to fill an exact number of glasses with no wine left over.
       (ii) How many glasses would be filled in part (i)?

8. I have two sizes of containers. One holds 320 mℓ and the other holds 300 mℓ. How many of each must I use, if I want to completely fill all of them from 4 ℓ of water and not have any water left over?

Exercise 16

1. Change to pints:
   (a) 3 gal   (b) 16 gal   (c) 45 gal   (d) 72 gal

2. Change to gallons:
   (a) 32 pt   (b) 72 pt   (c) 200 pt   (d) 384 pt

3. If a wash-basin holds 14 pt, how many gallons of water will be used when the wash-basin has been filled four times?

4. A washing-up bowl holds $10\frac{1}{2}$ pt of water. How many times does it need to be filled to use 21 gal of water?

5. A bucket holds $1\frac{1}{2}$ gal while a watering-can holds 2 gal. How many time can the watering-can be filled from 20 full buckets of water?

6. If a kettle holds 3 pt and 10 cups hold $3\frac{1}{2}$ pt, how many cups can be filled from 7 full kettles of water?

Mass

The main metric unit of *mass** (often wrongly called weight) is the *kilogram* (kg). Other units of mass are the gram (g), milligram (mg) and metric tonne (t).

$$1\ t\ = 1000\ kg$$
$$1\ kg = 1000\ g$$
$$1\ g\ = 1000\ mg$$

Note   1 ℓ of water has a volume of 1000 cm^3 and has a mass of about 1 kg.

*See the glossary, p. 446.

Exercise 17

Copy these sentences but replace each question mark with t, kg, g or mg to make each sentence correct:

1. A jar of jam has a mass of 454 ? .

2. A teabag has a mass of 3 ? .

3. A packet of flour has a mass of 1.5 ? .

4. A drawing pin has a mass of 0.5 ? .

5. A loaf of bread has a mass of 800 ? .

6. A car has a mass of 1 ? .

7. A lorry has a mass of 10 ? .

8. A bar of chocolate has a mass of 100 ? .

Exercise 18

A Collect about ten different objects. Find the mass of each one. List the objects. Alongside each one, write its mass.

B Find the mass of about 20 common objects such as a jar of jam, a tin of fruit, a packet of tea, a suitcase, a bag of potatoes, and so on. The mass of a jar of jam is usually printed on the label. (This does not normally include the mass of the jar. You can weigh it if you wish to include the mass of the jar.)

Exercise 19

Choose the best answer:

1. An apple has a mass of about:
   A. 130 mg   B. 130 g   C. 500 mg   D. 500 g

2. A marble has a mass of about:
   A. 75 mg   B. 200 mg   C. 850 mg   D. 6 g

3. A woman has a mass of about:
   A. 25 kg   B. 150 kg   C. 55 kg   D. 940 g

4. A textbook has a mass of about:
   A. 540 mg   B. 5.4 g   C. 54 g   D. 540 g

5. A 10 p piece has a mass of about:
   A. 113 mg   B. 113 g   C. 1.13 g   D. 11.3 g

6. A new-born baby has a mass of about:
   A. 1 kg   B. 3 kg   C. 9 kg   D. 15 kg

7. A 53-seater coach has a mass of about:
   A. 7 t   B. 4 t   C. 1 t   D. 870 kg

8. A television set has a mass of about:
   A. 25 kg   B. 75 kg   C. 100 kg   D. 140 kg

9. An iron has a mass of about:
   A. 1.5 kg   B. 8 kg   C. 280 g   D. 890 mg

10. A cricket ball has a mass of about:
    A. 80 g   B. 420 g   C. 160 g   D. 420 mg

Exercise 20

1. A packet of sweets has a mass of 125 g:
   (a) Find the total mass of 6 packets.
   (b) How many packets have a total mass of 3 kg?

2. A textbook has a mass of 645 g. If you carry 20 of the books, what mass, in kilograms, are you carrying?

3. A box contains 24 jars of coffee. If each jar of coffee has a mass of 670 g and if the mass of the box is 490 g, find the total mass of the box of coffee.

4. A lift will carry a total mass of up to 1 t. Find the maximum number of people, each weighing 72 kg, that the lift will carry at the same time.

5. If £10 worth of 5 p pieces have a total mass of 1.131 kg, find the mass of one 5 p piece.

6. Find the total value of 1 kg of 20 p pieces if each 20 p piece has a mass of 5 g.

7. Which is heavier, £10 worth of 50 p pieces or 76 p worth of 2 p pieces, if each 50 p coin has a mass of 13.5 g and each 2 p coin has a mass of 7.128 g?

8. 1 cm^3 of brass has a mass of 8.4 g (we say that its *density* is 8.4 g/cm^3). Calculate the mass of a brass article having a volume of 14 cm^3.

The main units of mass in the imperial system are ounces (oz), pounds (lb), stones (st), hundredweights (cwt) and tons.

$$16 \, \text{oz} = 1 \, \text{lb}$$
$$14 \, \text{lb} = 1 \, \text{st}$$
$$112 \, \text{lb} = 1 \, \text{cwt}$$
$$20 \, \text{cwt} = 1 \, \text{ton}$$

Exercise 21

1. How many pounds are there in 1 ton?

2. How many stones are there in 1 cwt?

3. How many ounces are there in:
(a) 3 lb?   (b) 7 lb?   (c) $\frac{1}{2}$ lb?   (d) $\frac{3}{4}$ lb?

4. How many pounds are there in:

    (*a*) 3 st?   (*b*) 9 st   (*c*) 15 st?   (*d*) 19 st?

5. How many hundredweights are there in:

    (*a*) 4 tons?   (*b*) 9 tons?   (*c*) 15 tons?   (*d*) 20 tons?

6. Change to pounds:

    (*a*) 5 st 12 lb   (*b*) 7 st 8 lb   (*c*) 9 st 11 lb

Exercise 22

If 1 kg = 2.2 lb:

1. Change to pounds:

    (*a*) 6 kg   (*b*) 8 kg   (*c*) 3.5 kg   (*d*) 9.5 kg

2. Change to kilograms:

    (*a*) 66 lb   (*b*) 55 lb   (*c*) 9.9 lb   (*d*) 14.3 lb

Miscellaneous Units of Measure

Exercise 23

Copy these, but replace each box with $<$, $>$ or $=$ to make each statement correct:

1. 1 km ? 1 mile   **4.** 1 t ? 1 ton

2. 1 m ? 1 yd   **5.** 1 kg ? 1 lb

3. 1 ℓ ? 1 pt   **6.** 1 g ? 1 oz

Exercise 24

Container ships, lorries and railway flat cars carry three basic sizes of containers.

All three are 8 ft wide and 8 ft 6 in ($8\frac{1}{2}$ ft) high.

The three lengths are 40 ft, 30 ft and 20 ft.

Using 1 ft = 0.3048 m:

1. (a) Change the width of 8 ft to metres.
   (b) Change the height of 8 ft 6 in to metres.

2. Change the three different lengths of containers to metres.

Lorries and railway flat cars can carry containers up to a total length of 60 ft (a 40 ft and a 20 ft, two 30 ft, and so on):

3. Change 60 ft to metres.

Some trailers are 2.5 m wide:

4. Calculate the amount of space in millimetres left on each side of a trailer when the 8 ft wide container is placed centrally on the trailer.

5. Calculate in cubic feet the volumes of all three sizes of container.

6. Calculate in cubic metres the volumes of all three sizes of container.

A 6-wheeled tractor unit (lorry without a trailer) has a mass of 7.6 t. A 4-wheeled tractor unit has a mass of 6.72 t. A 30 ft trailer has a mass of 4.08 t and an empty 30 ft container has a mass of 3.48 t. A 6-wheeled tractor unit can pull a maximum of 38 t including its own mass while a 4-wheeled tractor unit can pull a maximum of 32.5 t.

7. Find the largest mass of goods that can be carried in a 30 ft container pulled by:
   (a) a 6-wheeled tractor unit,
   (b) a 4-wheeled tractor unit.

Containers can be stacked five high. The bottom container can stand a maximum load of 80 t:

8. If all containers have the same mass, find the maximum mass of each.

9. If the bottom container has a mass of 23 t, the second 18.2 t, the third 16.7 t and the fourth 24.5 t, calculate the mass of the top container if the bottom container supports its maximum load.

A container ship of about 35 000 t can carry up to 800 of the largest containers:

10. If the average mass of these containers is 21.7 t, calculate the load carried by the ship.

11. If the maximum mass of a container is 26.19 t, calculate the maximum load carried by the ship.

12. A small coaster carries sixty 40 ft containers each of mass 28.6 t, fifty 30 ft containers each having a mass of 24.5 t and twenty 20 ft containers each with a mass of 17.9 t. Calculate the load carried by the ship.

Miscellaneous Information

The longest animal ever recorded is the bootlace worm. In 1864, one measuring more than 55 m (180 ft) was washed ashore at St Andrews, Fifeshire, Scotland.

The main span of the Humber Estuary Bridge measures 1410 m (4626 ft).

In Austria, the Arlberg road tunnel is 14 km (8.7 miles) long.

The heaviest recorded man in Great Britain was William Campbell who was born in Glasgow in 1856 and died in 1878. He was 191 cm (6 ft 3 in) tall and had a mass of 340 kg (53 st 8 lb). His waist measured 216 cm (85 in) and his chest 244 cm (96 in). His coffin had a total mass of 680 kg (107 st 2 lb).

The largest blue whale ever recorded was 33.58 m long. Another blue whale of length 29.48 m was believed to have a total mass of 177 t (174 tons). A 27.6 m blue whale taken by the Slava whaling fleet in the Antarctic on 17 March 1947 had a tongue that weighed 4.29 t (4.22 tons).

23 Conversion Graphs and Tables

Conversion Graphs

8 km is about the same distance as 5 miles.

We can write $8\text{ km} \approx 5\text{ miles}$.
Also, $\qquad 80\text{ km} \approx 50\text{ miles}$

The relationship between kilometres and miles can be shown on a graph:

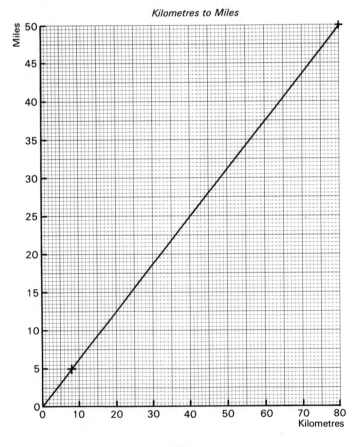

Kilometres to Miles

Exercise 1

1. Copy the graph shown on the previous page. (Do not forget the title.) Use a scale of 1 cm to 5 km and 2 cm to 5 miles.

2. Use your graph to change:
   (a) 40 km into miles
   (b) 16 km into miles
   (c) 76 km into miles
   (d) 60 km into miles

   (e) 20 miles into kilometres
   (f) 45 miles into kilometres
   (g) 35 miles into kilometres
   (h) 12.5 miles into kilometres

Exercise 2

A Draw another graph to convert kilometres into miles. This time, draw the graph so that a distance of up to 16 kilometres can be converted to miles. Use a scale of 1 cm to 1 km and 2 cm to 1 mile. Use 8 km = 5 miles and 16 km = 10 miles.

1. Use your graph to convert to miles:
   (a) 12 km   (b) 6.4 km   (c) 8.8 km   (d) 13.6 km

2. Use your graph to convert to kilometres:
   (a) 2.5 miles   (b) 8 miles   (c) 6 miles   (d) 9.5 miles

B Draw a graph to convert pounds to kilograms.
Use a scale of 1 cm to 5 lb and 2 cm to 5 kg.
Use 5 kg = 11 lb and 40 kg = 88 lb.

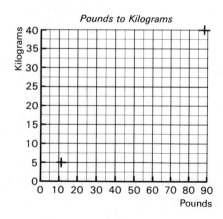

Pounds to Kilograms

From your graph:

1. Change to kilograms:

   (*a*) 55 lb   (*d*) 20 lb

   (*b*) 44 lb   (*e*) 75 lb

   (*c*) 77 lb   (*f*) 46 lb

2. Change to pounds:

   (*a*) 10 kg   (*d*) 30.9 kg

   (*b*) 30 kg   (*d*) 24.1 kg

   (*c*) 15 kg   (*f*) 5.9 kg

C Draw a conversion graph to change litres to gallons. Use a scale of 1 cm to 5 ℓ and 1 cm to 1 gal. Use 50 ℓ = 11 gal.

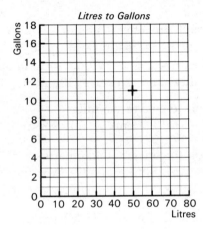

Now use your graph to:

1. Change to gallons:

   (*a*) 30 ℓ (*d*) 70 ℓ

   (*b*) 80 ℓ (*e*) 45 ℓ

   (*c*) 20 ℓ (*f*) 18 ℓ

2. Change to litres:

   (*a*) 8.8 gal   (*d*) 13 gal

   (*b*) 13.2 gal   (*e*) 10 gal

   (*c*) 2.2 gal   (*f*) 5.5 gal

D Draw a conversion graph to change pounds sterling to Greek drachmas. Use a scale of 1 cm to £1 and 1 cm to 200 drachmas. Use £10 = 2400 drachmas.

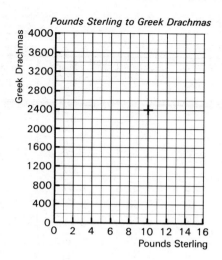

Now use your graph to:

1. Change to drachmas:
   (a) £5
   (b) £12
   (c) £16

   (d) £14
   (e) £7.50
   (f) £1.50

2. Change to pounds:
   (a) 3600 drachmas
   (b) 960 drachmas
   (c) 2640 drachmas

   (d) 1680 drachmas
   (e) 600 drachmas
   (f) 1560 drachmas

Conversion Tables

A table can be used to convert one unit to another. Four different conversion tables are given on the next page. Look at the first table of length. Look carefully at the row of figures having an 8 in the centre column.

The row gives	centimetres	cm or in	inches
	20.32	8	3.15

This row shows that: 8 cm = 3.15 in
It also shows that: 8 in = 20.32 cm

(Note that the values are more accurate in the tables than on the graphs you have drawn.)

379

Conversion Tables

Length			Mass		
centimetres	cm or in	inches	kilograms	kg or lb	pounds
2.54	1	0.39	0.45	1	2.20
5.08	2	0.79	0.91	2	4.41
7.62	3	1.18	1.36	3	6.61
10.16	4	1.58	1.81	4	8.82
12.70	5	1.97	2.27	5	11.02
15.24	6	2.36	2.72	6	13.23
17.78	7	2.76	3.18	7	15.43
20.32	8	3.15	3.63	8	17.64
22.86	9	3.54	4.08	9	19.84
25.40	10	3.94	4.54	10	22.05
50.80	20	7.87	9.07	20	44.09
76.20	30	11.81	13.61	30	66.14
101.60	40	15.75	18.14	40	88.18
127.00	50	19.69	22.68	50	110.23
254.00	100	39.37	45.36	100	220.46

Length			Capacity		
kilometres	km or miles	miles	litres	ℓ or gal	gallons
1.61	1	0.62	4.55	1	0.22
3.22	2	1.24	9.09	2	0.44
4.83	3	1.86	13.64	3	0.66
6.44	4	2.49	18.18	4	0.88
8.05	5	3.11	22.73	5	1.10
9.66	6	3.73	27.28	6	1.32
11.27	7	4.35	31.82	7	1.54
12.87	8	4.97	36.37	8	1.76
14.48	9	5.59	40.91	9	1.98
16.09	10	6.21	45.46	10	2.20
32.19	20	12.43	90.92	20	4.40
48.28	30	18.64	136.38	30	6.60
64.37	40	24.85	181.84	40	8.80
80.47	50	31.07	227.30	50	11.00
160.93	100	62.14	454.60	100	22.00

Exercise 3

Use the tables on the previous page to change:

A centimetres to inches:
    1. 4 cm   **2.** 7 cm   **3.** 8 cm   **4.** 30 cm   **5.** 100 cm

B inches to centimetres:
    1. 3 in   **2.** 8 in   **3.** 9 in   **4.** 20 in   **5.** 100 in

C kilometres to miles:
    1. 7 km   **2.** 9 km   **3.** 20 km   **4.** 40 km   **5.** 100 km

D miles to kilometres:
    1. 5 miles   **2.** 8 miles   **3.** 30 miles   **4.** 40 miles   **5.** 100 miles

E pounds to kilograms:
    1. 6 lb   **2.** 8 lb   **3.** 20 lb   **4.** 40 lb   **5.** 100 lb

F kilograms to pounds:
    1. 2 kg   **2.** 5 kg   **3.** 30 kg   **4.** 40 kg   **5.** 100 kg

G litres to gallons:
    1. 4 ℓ   **2.** 7 ℓ   **3.** 9 ℓ   **4.** 30 ℓ   **5.** 100 ℓ

H gallons to litres:
    1. 1 gal   **2.** 5 gal   **3.** 9 gal   **4.** 20 gal   **5.** 100 gal

Exercise 4

Some values are not in the conversion tables.

e.g.   Convert 46 km into miles.
        From the table, 40 km = 24.85 miles
        and   6 km =   3.73 miles
        so   46 km = 28.58 miles

Use the given tables to convert:

1. 52 km to miles   **3.** 35 cm to inches
2. 26 kg to pounds   **4.** 12 gal to litres

5. 44 ℓ to gallons
6. 80 miles to kilometres
7. 15 in to centimetres
8. 58 lb to kilograms
9. 63 ℓ to gallons
10. 71 kg to pounds

11. 99 in to centimetres
12. 138 km to miles
13. 112 lb to kilograms
14. 87 cm to inches
15. 263 miles to kilometres
16. 185 gal to litres

Exercise 5

Use the given conversion tables for the following:

1. (a) 5 cm = $\boxed{?}$ in

   (b) 50 cm = 10×5 cm = $10 \times$ the answer to part (a) = $\boxed{?}$ in

   (c) From the tables, 50 cm = $\boxed{?}$ in

   (d) Explain why the answers to parts (b) and (c) are different.

2. (a) 49 lb = 40 lb + 9 lb
           = $\boxed{?}$ kg + $\boxed{?}$ kg
           = $\boxed{?}$ kg

   (b) 49 lb = 50 lb − 1 lb
           = $\boxed{?}$ kg − $\boxed{?}$ kg
           = $\boxed{?}$ kg

   (c) Explain why the answers to parts (a) and (b) are different.

24 Vectors

Displacement Vectors

Exercise 1

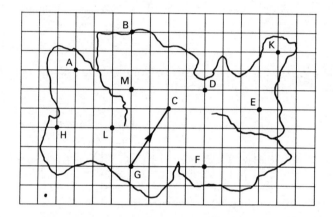

On the map above, a journey from G to C can be written as

$$\overrightarrow{GC} = \begin{pmatrix} 2 \\ 3 \end{pmatrix}$$

Other journeys are: $\overrightarrow{CK} = \begin{pmatrix} 6 \\ 3 \end{pmatrix}$, $\overrightarrow{AB} = \begin{pmatrix} 3 \\ 2 \end{pmatrix}$, $\overrightarrow{CB} = \begin{pmatrix} ^-2 \\ 4 \end{pmatrix}$

$$\overrightarrow{DE} = \begin{pmatrix} 3 \\ ^-1 \end{pmatrix}, \quad \overrightarrow{DC} = \begin{pmatrix} ^-2 \\ ^-1 \end{pmatrix}, \quad \overrightarrow{DF} = \begin{pmatrix} 0 \\ ^-4 \end{pmatrix}$$

Write the following journeys in the same way as above:

1. D to K	**5.** L to H	**9.** C to L
2. L to C	**6.** G to M	**10.** E to B
3. F to E	**7.** B to M	**11.** A to G
4. H to L	**8.** M to A	**12.** K to D

383

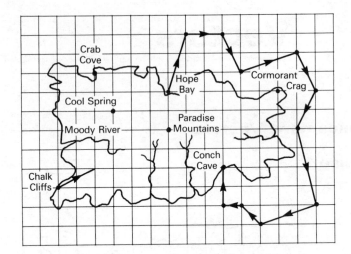

1. A sea journey from Hope Bay to Conch Cave is shown on the map above. The route can be written as:

$$\binom{1}{3}, \binom{2}{0}, \binom{1}{-2}, \binom{?}{1}, \binom{1}{?}, \binom{?}{-2},$$

$$\binom{?}{?}, \binom{-3}{?}, \binom{?}{?}, \binom{?}{?}, \binom{?}{?}$$

Copy and complete the above route.

2. (a) Copy the given map.
   (b) Here is a route to some treasure:

$$\binom{2}{1}, \binom{2}{0}, \binom{0}{1}, \binom{-1}{2}, \binom{3}{-2}, \binom{1}{2}, \binom{-2}{0}, \binom{3}{1}, \binom{3}{-1}, \binom{-2}{-1}, \binom{0}{-2}$$

On your copy of the map, start at Chalk Cliffs and mark the route to the treasure. $\left(\text{The first stage of the journey, } \binom{2}{1}, \text{ is shown.} \right)$

In this chapter we have been using *displacement vectors*.

To describe a straight journey we need to know the distance travelled (the *magnitude* of the journey), and its *direction*.

A *vector* is defined as having both *magnitude* (size) and *direction*.

Exercise 3

In each question the vectors describe a journey from the given place to another place on the map below. Find the place at the end of each journey.

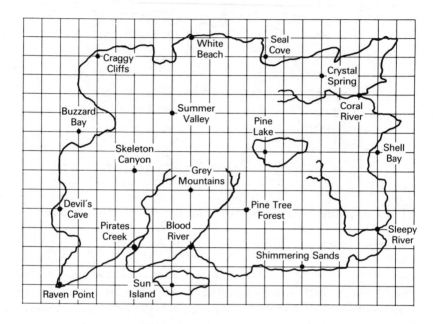

1. $\begin{pmatrix} 2 \\ 2 \end{pmatrix}$, $\begin{pmatrix} 2 \\ -1 \end{pmatrix}$, $\begin{pmatrix} 1 \\ 0 \end{pmatrix}$, $\begin{pmatrix} 1 \\ 2 \end{pmatrix}$, $\begin{pmatrix} 2 \\ 1 \end{pmatrix}$, $\begin{pmatrix} -1 \\ -3 \end{pmatrix}$ from Devil's Cave

2. $\begin{pmatrix} -1 \\ 3 \end{pmatrix}$, $\begin{pmatrix} 2 \\ 1 \end{pmatrix}$, $\begin{pmatrix} -3 \\ 0 \end{pmatrix}$, $\begin{pmatrix} 5 \\ 2 \end{pmatrix}$, $\begin{pmatrix} -2 \\ -3 \end{pmatrix}$, $\begin{pmatrix} 1 \\ 0 \end{pmatrix}$ from Skeleton Canyon

3. $\begin{pmatrix} -2 \\ 0 \end{pmatrix}$, $\begin{pmatrix} -4 \\ -2 \end{pmatrix}$, $\begin{pmatrix} 1 \\ -2 \end{pmatrix}$, $\begin{pmatrix} 4 \\ 1 \end{pmatrix}$, $\begin{pmatrix} 0 \\ 1 \end{pmatrix}$, $\begin{pmatrix} 3 \\ 1 \end{pmatrix}$ from Crystal Spring

4. $\begin{pmatrix} -3 \\ 2 \end{pmatrix}$, $\begin{pmatrix} 3 \\ 1 \end{pmatrix}$, $\begin{pmatrix} 0 \\ 2 \end{pmatrix}$, $\begin{pmatrix} 2 \\ 3 \end{pmatrix}$, $\begin{pmatrix} 2 \\ -5 \end{pmatrix}$, $\begin{pmatrix} -1 \\ -1 \end{pmatrix}$, $\begin{pmatrix} 1 \\ 4 \end{pmatrix}$

   from Shimmering Sands

5. $\begin{pmatrix} -2 \\ -1 \end{pmatrix}$, $\begin{pmatrix} 1 \\ -4 \end{pmatrix}$, $\begin{pmatrix} 3 \\ -2 \end{pmatrix}$, $\begin{pmatrix} 2 \\ -4 \end{pmatrix}$, $\begin{pmatrix} -5 \\ 1 \end{pmatrix}$, $\begin{pmatrix} -1 \\ 2 \end{pmatrix}$, $\begin{pmatrix} -3 \\ -4 \end{pmatrix}$ from Seal Cove

Copy the following map on to squared paper. You may use larger squares to obtain a larger map.

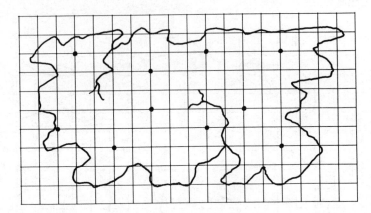

The ten points marked on the map are the starting points of ten different journeys. Question 1 gives the vector $\overrightarrow{AA'} = \begin{pmatrix} 5 \\ 2 \end{pmatrix}$. Label one of the ten points on your map as A, then find, mark and label the end point A'. Note that you must carefully select the point A so that AA' is drawn with a straight-line segment, the line segment does not cross a river and the point A' does not land in the sea.

Show all the journeys on your copy of the map. None of them should cross rivers or end in the sea as explained above.

1. $\overrightarrow{AA'} = \begin{pmatrix} 5 \\ 2 \end{pmatrix}$

6. $\overrightarrow{FF'} = \begin{pmatrix} -5 \\ 0 \end{pmatrix}$

2. $\overrightarrow{BB'} = \begin{pmatrix} -1 \\ -2 \end{pmatrix}$

7. $\overrightarrow{GG'} = \begin{pmatrix} 6 \\ -2 \end{pmatrix}$

3. $\overrightarrow{CC'} = \begin{pmatrix} -2 \\ 3 \end{pmatrix}$

8. $\overrightarrow{HH'} = \begin{pmatrix} -3 \\ 4 \end{pmatrix}$

4. $\overrightarrow{DD'} = \begin{pmatrix} 3 \\ 0 \end{pmatrix}$

9. $\overrightarrow{II'} = \begin{pmatrix} -3 \\ 2 \end{pmatrix}$

5. $\overrightarrow{EE'} = \begin{pmatrix} -3 \\ -3 \end{pmatrix}$

10. $\overrightarrow{KK'} = \begin{pmatrix} 2 \\ -3 \end{pmatrix}$

Exercise 5 ▬▬▬▬▬▬▬▬▬ M

In the diagram, *all* the arrows show the vector $\begin{pmatrix} 3 \\ 2 \end{pmatrix}$.

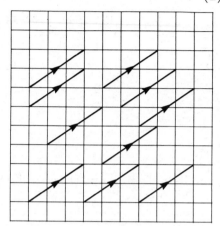

On squared paper, draw three arrows to show each of these vectors:

1. $\begin{pmatrix} 4 \\ 1 \end{pmatrix}$ **3.** $\begin{pmatrix} {}^-2 \\ {}^-1 \end{pmatrix}$ **5.** $\begin{pmatrix} 2 \\ {}^-5 \end{pmatrix}$ **7.** $\begin{pmatrix} {}^-1 \\ {}^-4 \end{pmatrix}$

2. $\begin{pmatrix} {}^-4 \\ 3 \end{pmatrix}$ **4.** $\begin{pmatrix} 3 \\ 0 \end{pmatrix}$ **6.** $\begin{pmatrix} 0 \\ 2 \end{pmatrix}$ **8.** $\begin{pmatrix} {}^-3 \\ 2 \end{pmatrix}$

Exercise 6 ▬▬▬▬▬▬▬▬▬

In each question, a vector and the co-ordinates of its starting point have been given.

Find the co-ordinates of its end point.

e.g. $\begin{pmatrix} 5 \\ 3 \end{pmatrix}$, $(2, 3)$

End point is $\underline{\underline{(7, 6)}}$

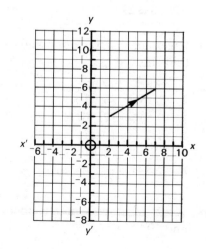

Try to answer these without plotting the points:

1. $\begin{pmatrix} 3 \\ 4 \end{pmatrix}$, $(2,1)$ **4.** $\begin{pmatrix} ^-2 \\ 3 \end{pmatrix}$, $(2,^-3)$ **7.** $\begin{pmatrix} ^-6 \\ 1 \end{pmatrix}$, $(5,^-5)$

2. $\begin{pmatrix} 4 \\ 6 \end{pmatrix}$, $(3,^-2)$ **5.** $\begin{pmatrix} ^-1 \\ ^-5 \end{pmatrix}$, $(4,2)$ **8.** $\begin{pmatrix} 8 \\ ^-3 \end{pmatrix}$, $(^-4,2)$

3. $\begin{pmatrix} 1 \\ 5 \end{pmatrix}$, $(^-3,^-1)$ **6.** $\begin{pmatrix} 5 \\ 0 \end{pmatrix}$, $(^-2,1)$ **9.** $\begin{pmatrix} ^-2 \\ ^-10 \end{pmatrix}$, $(^-5,^-1)$

Exercise 7

Given a vector and its end point, find the co-ordinates of its starting point:

1. $\begin{pmatrix} 4 \\ 3 \end{pmatrix}$, $(6,9)$ **4.** $\begin{pmatrix} 4 \\ ^-6 \end{pmatrix}$, $(1,2)$ **7.** $\begin{pmatrix} 8 \\ ^-5 \end{pmatrix}$, $(2,^-9)$

2. $\begin{pmatrix} 5 \\ 1 \end{pmatrix}$, $(2,6)$ **5.** $\begin{pmatrix} ^-9 \\ 4 \end{pmatrix}$, $(^-12,5)$ **8.** $\begin{pmatrix} ^-2 \\ ^-1 \end{pmatrix}$, $(^-6,^-7)$

3. $\begin{pmatrix} 1 \\ 4 \end{pmatrix}$, $(^-2,^-1)$ **6.** $\begin{pmatrix} ^-14 \\ ^-10 \end{pmatrix}$, $(^-8,^-17)$ **9.** $\begin{pmatrix} ^-15 \\ 13 \end{pmatrix}$, $(^-4,9)$

Exercise 8

A Given the starting point and the end point of a displacement vector, find the vector:

	Start	End			Start	End
1.	$(2,4)$	$(5,9)$		**6.**	$(^-1,^-6)$	$(^-5,^-3)$
2.	$(0,2)$	$(2,^-6)$		**7.**	$(0,0)$	$(8,4)$
3.	$(4,7)$	$(^-1,1)$		**8.**	$(0,0)$	$(2,^-9)$
4.	$(^-3,9)$	$(8,11)$		**9.**	$(0,0)$	$(^-8,^-2)$
5.	$(7,^-4)$	$(4,^-2)$		**10.**	$(0,0)$	$(^-7,5)$

B Write what you notice about the answers to questions 7, 8, 9 and 10.

Translation Vectors

Translations can be described using vectors. The diagram shows an L-shape that has been translated 4 squares to the right and 3 squares upwards. The vector $\begin{pmatrix} 4 \\ 3 \end{pmatrix}$ describes the translation.

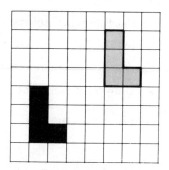

Exercise 9

In the diagram, A has been translated to A'. The pair of coordinates for the object A, is (3, 2) while the image A', is (6, 7).

The vector for this translation is
$$\begin{pmatrix} 3 \\ 5 \end{pmatrix}$$

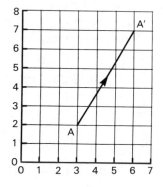

The *component** 3 gives the number of squares moved across while 5 gives the number of squares moved upwards.

A Given a translation vector and a point, find the image of that point under the given translation:

1. $\begin{pmatrix} 5 \\ 3 \end{pmatrix}$, $(1, {}^-4)$

2. $\begin{pmatrix} 6 \\ 5 \end{pmatrix}$, $({}^-1, {}^-2)$

3. $\begin{pmatrix} 7 \\ {}^-3 \end{pmatrix}$, $({}^-2, 7)$

4. $\begin{pmatrix} {}^-3 \\ 9 \end{pmatrix}$, $(8, {}^-2)$

5. $\begin{pmatrix} {}^-8 \\ {}^-7 \end{pmatrix}$, $(1, 1)$

6. $\begin{pmatrix} 3 \\ {}^-7 \end{pmatrix}$, $({}^-6, 1)$

*See the glossary, p. 444.

B **1.** Onto what point would the translation vector $\begin{pmatrix} ^-2 \\ 6 \end{pmatrix}$ map each of the following points?

(a) (4, 3)   (b) (1, $^-$6)   (c) (0, $^-$9)   (d) ($^-$4, $^-$4)

2. Copy and complete:

(a) $\begin{pmatrix} 5 \\ 2 \end{pmatrix}$ maps ($^-$2, $^-$6) $\longrightarrow$ ([?], [?])

(b) $\begin{pmatrix} 1 \\ ^-2 \end{pmatrix}$ maps (4, $^-$5) $\longrightarrow$ ([?], [?])

3. What translation vector maps:
(a) ($^-$2, $^-$1) onto (6, 5)?
(b) (8, 1) onto ($^-$2, $^-$3)?
(c) ($^-$1, 6) onto ($^-$6, 6)?
(d) ($^-$5, 3) onto ($^-$1, $^-$4)?
(e) (0, 0) onto (6, $^-$12)?
(f) (9, $^-$1) onto (0, 0)?

4. Copy and complete:

(a) $\begin{pmatrix} 3 \\ 2 \end{pmatrix}$ maps ([?], [?]) $\longrightarrow$ (1, $^-$1)

(b) $\begin{pmatrix} 12 \\ ^-10 \end{pmatrix}$ maps ([?], [?]) $\longrightarrow$ (3, $^-$6)

(c) $\begin{pmatrix} ^-2 \\ 7 \end{pmatrix}$ maps ([?], [?]) $\longrightarrow$ (0, 8)

(d) $\begin{pmatrix} ^-10 \\ ^-16 \end{pmatrix}$ maps ([?], [?]) $\longrightarrow$ ($^-$7, $^-$12)

(e) $\begin{pmatrix} 4 \\ ^-2 \end{pmatrix}$ maps ($^-$3, [?]) $\longrightarrow$ ([?], $^-$3)

(f) $\begin{pmatrix} ^-9 \\ ^-8 \end{pmatrix}$ maps ([?], 16) $\longrightarrow$ ($^-$4, [?])

390

Exercise 10

Draw a pair of axes as shown:
$^-8 \leqslant x \leqslant {}^+8$ and $^-6 \leqslant y \leqslant {}^+14$

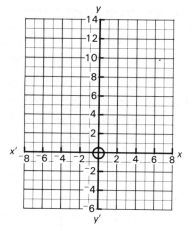

A 1. Plot the points L($^-2, 3$),
M($^-4, ^-1$) and N($2, ^-2$) then
join them to give triangle LMN.

2. Translate $\triangle$LMN to position

L'M'N' using the vector $\begin{pmatrix} 5 \\ 2 \end{pmatrix}$.

3. Translate $\triangle$L'M'N' to position

L''M''N'' using the vector $\begin{pmatrix} 1 \\ 6 \end{pmatrix}$.

4. Which vector would have translated $\triangle$LMN directly to image
position L''M''N''?

5. (a) Find a rule connecting the vectors in questions 2, 3 and 4.
(b) Test your rule using your own shapes and your own vectors.

B 1. Use the vector $\begin{pmatrix} 2 \\ 3 \end{pmatrix}$ to map P → P' where P is the point ($^-7, 8$).
What are the co-ordinates of P'?

2. Use the vector $\begin{pmatrix} 4 \\ 2 \end{pmatrix}$ to map P' → P''. Find the co-ordinates of P''.

3. Which vector maps P to P''?

4. (a) Find a rule connecting the vectors in questions 1, 2 and 3.
(b) Test your rule using your own choice of points and vectors.

C Repeat part B where Q is the point ($^-6, 6$) and where $\begin{pmatrix} ^-1 \\ ^-3 \end{pmatrix}$ maps Q
onto Q' and $\begin{pmatrix} 4 \\ 2 \end{pmatrix}$ maps Q' onto Q''. In question 3, find which vector
maps Q onto Q''.

391

Exercise 11

A *e.g. 1* $\begin{pmatrix} 3 \\ 5 \end{pmatrix} + \begin{pmatrix} 3 \\ 2 \end{pmatrix} = \begin{pmatrix} 6 \\ 7 \end{pmatrix}$ *e.g. 2* $\begin{pmatrix} 2 \\ {}^{-}4 \end{pmatrix} + \begin{pmatrix} {}^{-}3 \\ {}^{-}1 \end{pmatrix} = \begin{pmatrix} {}^{-}1 \\ {}^{-}5 \end{pmatrix}$

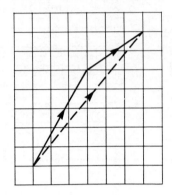 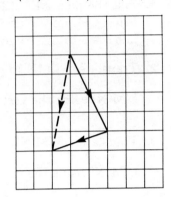

Add the following vectors and show your results on a graph:

1. $\begin{pmatrix} 4 \\ 1 \end{pmatrix} + \begin{pmatrix} 2 \\ 3 \end{pmatrix}$ **4.** $\begin{pmatrix} {}^{-}2 \\ 2 \end{pmatrix} + \begin{pmatrix} 4 \\ 3 \end{pmatrix}$

2. $\begin{pmatrix} 3 \\ 2 \end{pmatrix} + \begin{pmatrix} 0 \\ {}^{-}2 \end{pmatrix}$ **5.** $\begin{pmatrix} {}^{-}3 \\ {}^{-}1 \end{pmatrix} + \begin{pmatrix} 1 \\ 5 \end{pmatrix}$

3. $\begin{pmatrix} 5 \\ 2 \end{pmatrix} + \begin{pmatrix} {}^{-}2 \\ 4 \end{pmatrix}$ **6.** $\begin{pmatrix} {}^{-}6 \\ 3 \end{pmatrix} + \begin{pmatrix} 2 \\ {}^{-}5 \end{pmatrix}$

B Add these vectors:

1. $\begin{pmatrix} 5 \\ 9 \end{pmatrix} + \begin{pmatrix} 10 \\ 8 \end{pmatrix}$ **5.** $\begin{pmatrix} 14 \\ {}^{-}9 \end{pmatrix} + \begin{pmatrix} 7 \\ 7 \end{pmatrix}$ **9.** $\begin{pmatrix} {}^{-}9 \\ {}^{-}7 \end{pmatrix} + \begin{pmatrix} {}^{-}7 \\ {}^{-}9 \end{pmatrix}$

2. $\begin{pmatrix} 7 \\ 4 \end{pmatrix} + \begin{pmatrix} {}^{-}5 \\ 3 \end{pmatrix}$ **6.** $\begin{pmatrix} {}^{-}12 \\ 11 \end{pmatrix} + \begin{pmatrix} {}^{-}2 \\ {}^{-}7 \end{pmatrix}$ **10.** $\begin{pmatrix} {}^{-}13 \\ {}^{-}16 \end{pmatrix} + \begin{pmatrix} {}^{-}4 \\ 15 \end{pmatrix}$

3. $\begin{pmatrix} 6 \\ 1 \end{pmatrix} + \begin{pmatrix} {}^{-}8 \\ {}^{-}10 \end{pmatrix}$ **7.** $\begin{pmatrix} {}^{-}15 \\ {}^{-}18 \end{pmatrix} + \begin{pmatrix} 9 \\ {}^{-}7 \end{pmatrix}$ **11.** $\begin{pmatrix} 8 \\ {}^{-}4 \end{pmatrix} + \begin{pmatrix} 8 \\ {}^{-}4 \end{pmatrix}$

4. $\begin{pmatrix} {}^{-}3 \\ 12 \end{pmatrix} + \begin{pmatrix} 3 \\ {}^{-}12 \end{pmatrix}$ **8.** $\begin{pmatrix} 21 \\ {}^{-}9 \end{pmatrix} + \begin{pmatrix} {}^{-}11 \\ 11 \end{pmatrix}$ **12.** $\begin{pmatrix} 17 \\ {}^{-}14 \end{pmatrix} + \begin{pmatrix} {}^{-}17 \\ 14 \end{pmatrix}$

Exercise 12

Answer these:

1. (*a*) Find $\begin{pmatrix} 4 \\ 2 \end{pmatrix} + \begin{pmatrix} 1 \\ 6 \end{pmatrix}$ and show your results on a graph.

(*b*) Find $\begin{pmatrix} 1 \\ 6 \end{pmatrix} + \begin{pmatrix} 4 \\ 2 \end{pmatrix}$ and show your results on a graph.

(*c*) Does $\begin{pmatrix} 4 \\ 2 \end{pmatrix} + \begin{pmatrix} 1 \\ 6 \end{pmatrix} = \begin{pmatrix} 1 \\ 6 \end{pmatrix} + \begin{pmatrix} 4 \\ 2 \end{pmatrix}$?

2. (*a*) Does $\begin{pmatrix} ^-3 \\ 5 \end{pmatrix} + \begin{pmatrix} 4 \\ 1 \end{pmatrix} = \begin{pmatrix} 4 \\ 1 \end{pmatrix} + \begin{pmatrix} ^-3 \\ 5 \end{pmatrix}$?

(*b*) Show your results on a graph.

3. (*a*) Does $\begin{pmatrix} ^-6 \\ ^-2 \end{pmatrix} + \begin{pmatrix} 3 \\ ^-4 \end{pmatrix} = \begin{pmatrix} 3 \\ ^-4 \end{pmatrix} + \begin{pmatrix} ^-6 \\ ^-2 \end{pmatrix}$?

(*b*) Show your results on a graph.

4. Copy and complete:

(*a*) $\begin{pmatrix} 3 \\ 7 \end{pmatrix} + \begin{pmatrix} 4 \\ 1 \end{pmatrix} = \begin{pmatrix} 4 \\ 1 \end{pmatrix} + \begin{pmatrix} \boxed{?} \\ \boxed{?} \end{pmatrix}$

(*b*) $\begin{pmatrix} 2 \\ ^-8 \end{pmatrix} + \begin{pmatrix} ^-1 \\ 3 \end{pmatrix} = \begin{pmatrix} ^-1 \\ \boxed{?} \end{pmatrix} + \begin{pmatrix} \boxed{?} \\ ^-8 \end{pmatrix}$

(*c*) $\begin{pmatrix} ^-6 \\ ^-5 \end{pmatrix} + \begin{pmatrix} ^-4 \\ 9 \end{pmatrix} = \begin{pmatrix} \boxed{?} \\ 9 \end{pmatrix} + \begin{pmatrix} ^-6 \\ \boxed{?} \end{pmatrix}$

(*d*) $\begin{pmatrix} ^-9 \\ 1 \end{pmatrix} + \begin{pmatrix} 2 \\ ^-10 \end{pmatrix} = \begin{pmatrix} 2 \\ ^-10 \end{pmatrix} + \begin{pmatrix} \boxed{?} \\ \boxed{?} \end{pmatrix}$

Exercise 13

Copy and complete:

1. $\begin{pmatrix} 4 \\ 8 \end{pmatrix} + \begin{pmatrix} 7 \\ \boxed{?} \end{pmatrix} = \begin{pmatrix} \boxed{?} \\ 14 \end{pmatrix}$ **2.** $\begin{pmatrix} 3 \\ \boxed{?} \end{pmatrix} + \begin{pmatrix} ^-2 \\ 4 \end{pmatrix} = \begin{pmatrix} \boxed{?} \\ 13 \end{pmatrix}$

3. $\begin{pmatrix} 5 \\ -1 \end{pmatrix} + \begin{pmatrix} \boxed{?} \\ 6 \end{pmatrix} = \begin{pmatrix} 1 \\ \boxed{?} \end{pmatrix}$
    8. $\begin{pmatrix} \boxed{?} \\ -9 \end{pmatrix} + \begin{pmatrix} -12 \\ 15 \end{pmatrix} = \begin{pmatrix} 6 \\ \boxed{?} \end{pmatrix}$

4. $\begin{pmatrix} \boxed{?} \\ -5 \end{pmatrix} + \begin{pmatrix} 7 \\ \boxed{?} \end{pmatrix} = \begin{pmatrix} 5 \\ -9 \end{pmatrix}$
    9. $\begin{pmatrix} 8 \\ -12 \end{pmatrix} + \begin{pmatrix} \boxed{?} \\ \boxed{?} \end{pmatrix} = \begin{pmatrix} 0 \\ 0 \end{pmatrix}$

5. $\begin{pmatrix} 12 \\ \boxed{?} \end{pmatrix} + \begin{pmatrix} \boxed{?} \\ -4 \end{pmatrix} = \begin{pmatrix} 8 \\ -14 \end{pmatrix}$
    10. $\begin{pmatrix} -13 \\ -14 \end{pmatrix} + \begin{pmatrix} \boxed{?} \\ \boxed{?} \end{pmatrix} = \begin{pmatrix} 0 \\ 0 \end{pmatrix}$

6. $\begin{pmatrix} -10 \\ 17 \end{pmatrix} + \begin{pmatrix} \boxed{?} \\ \boxed{?} \end{pmatrix} = \begin{pmatrix} -6 \\ 13 \end{pmatrix}$
    11. $\begin{pmatrix} \boxed{?} \\ \boxed{?} \end{pmatrix} + \begin{pmatrix} -15 \\ 6 \end{pmatrix} = \begin{pmatrix} 0 \\ 0 \end{pmatrix}$

7. $\begin{pmatrix} \boxed{?} \\ \boxed{?} \end{pmatrix} + \begin{pmatrix} 13 \\ -9 \end{pmatrix} = \begin{pmatrix} 10 \\ -11 \end{pmatrix}$
    12. $\begin{pmatrix} \boxed{?} \\ \boxed{?} \end{pmatrix} + \begin{pmatrix} 16 \\ -17 \end{pmatrix} = \begin{pmatrix} 0 \\ 0 \end{pmatrix}$

Exercise 14

1.

	Mon	Tue	Wed	Thu	Fri	Sat	Sun
Cycling	2	3	0	$2\frac{1}{2}$	2	3	4
Swimming	1	0	2	$\frac{1}{2}$	$1\frac{1}{2}$	2	0

The table above shows the number of hours per day that someone spends cycling and swimming. The information can be written as vectors.

If the vector $\begin{pmatrix} 3 \\ 2 \end{pmatrix}$ stands for Saturday:

(a) Which day does $\begin{pmatrix} 3 \\ 0 \end{pmatrix}$ stand for?

(b) Why does $\begin{pmatrix} 1\frac{1}{2} \\ 2 \end{pmatrix}$ not stand for Friday?

(c) Which vector stands for Friday?

(d) The total time spent cycling and swimming on Saturday and Sunday can be worked out as follows:

$$\begin{pmatrix} 3 \\ 2 \end{pmatrix} + \begin{pmatrix} 4 \\ 0 \end{pmatrix} = \begin{pmatrix} 7 \\ 2 \end{pmatrix}$$

This shows that 7 h were spent cycling and 2 h were spent swimming. By adding vectors, show the total times spent cycling and swimming:
   (i) on Monday and Tuesday,
   (ii) on Thursday and Friday,
   (iii) for the full week.

2. The table shows the number of tins of beans, soup, tuna, fruit and jars of jam used during three months.

The vector $\begin{pmatrix} 4 \\ 5 \\ 3 \\ 4 \\ 1 \end{pmatrix}$ shows January's groceries.

	Nov	Dec	Jan
Beans	8	6	4
Soup	5	7	5
Tuna	4	6	3
Fruit	4	5	4
Jam	1	2	1

(a) Write the vector for December.
(b) By adding vectors, find the totals for the months of November and December.
(c) Using vectors, find the totals for the three months.

Exercise 15

1. A bus is 12 m long. The distance between two bus stops is 800 m. The bus starts with the driver opposite the first bus stop then stops again when the driver is opposite the second bus stop. How far has:
(a) the driver travelled?
(b) a passenger on the back seat travelled?
(c) a passenger sitting 6.5 m from the back of the bus travelled?

2. A train travels a certain journey. Who travels further, a person in the first carriage or someone in the last carriage?

3. A ship sails from J to K, the vector for the journey being $\begin{pmatrix} -2 \\ 7 \end{pmatrix}$.

It then sails to L in the direction given by the vector $\begin{pmatrix} 1 \\ -4 \end{pmatrix}$.

(a) What vector gives the journey back to J from L?
(b) What vector gives the direct journey from J to L?

4. An aeroplane flew from P to Q, the journey vector being $\begin{pmatrix} 9 \\ -6 \end{pmatrix}$.

It then flew to R in the direction given by the vector $\begin{pmatrix} -9 \\ 2 \end{pmatrix}$.

(a) What vector gives the journey back to P from R?
(b) What vector gives the direct journey from P to R?
(c) In what direction is R from P?

25 Simultaneous Equations

Simultaneous Equations (Where Neither Equation Needs to be Multiplied

Exercise 1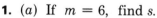

A A man and his son practised a balancing act. The boy stood on the man's head and their total height was 11 ft. If we let the man's height be m ft and his son's height s ft, then $m + s = 11$.

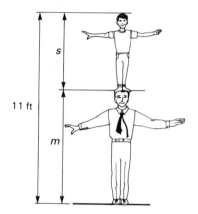

11 ft

1. (a) If $m = 6$, find s.
   (b) If $m = 6.1$, find s.
   (c) If $m = 5.8$, find s.
   (d) If $s = 4.8$, find m.
   (e) If $s = 5$, find m.
   (f) If $s = 5.2$, find m.

2. Write three more possible pairs of values for m and s.

B A man has two sons who are the same height. In their balancing act their total height was 16 ft. We can write $m + 2s = 16$

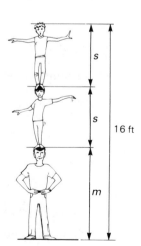

16 ft

1. (a) If $s = 4.8$, find m.
   (b) If $s = 5$, find m.
   (c) If $s = 5.2$, find m.
   (d) If $m = 6$, find s.
   (e) If $m = 6.1$, find s.
   (f) If $m = 5.8$, find s.

2. Write three more possible pairs of values for m and s.

C Which pair of answers to part B are the same as a pair of answers to part A?

D If the men in parts A and B have the same height, and if all three boys have the same height, then:

$$m + 2s = 16$$
and $$m + s = 11$$

1. How tall are the boys? (The diagram may help.)

2. How tall are the men?

Note   If $$m + 2s = 16 \qquad [1]$$

and $$m + s = 11 \qquad [2]$$

Equation [1] — Equation [2] gives $$s = 5$$

Substituting in [2] $$m + s = 11$$

so $$m + 5 = 11$$

$$m = 6$$

so $m = 6$ and $s = 5$

that is, the men are 6 ft tall and the boys 5 ft tall.

The two equations have been solved *simultaneously*.

398

Exercise 2

Solve these pairs of simultaneous equations:

A **1.** $m + 2s = 15$
$m + s = 10\frac{1}{2}$

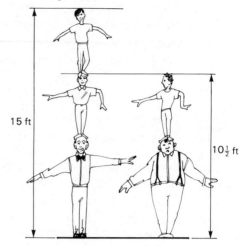

2. $m + 4s = 25\frac{1}{2}$
$m + 3s = 20\frac{1}{2}$

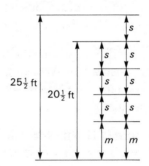

B **1.** $m + 6s = 15$
$m + 5s = 13$

2. $3m + s = 19$
$2m + s = 14$

3. $5m + 3s = 28$
$4m + 3s = 26$

4. $4x + 2y = 26$
$3x + 2y = 23$

5. $4t + 2u = 20$
$6t + 2u = 22$

6. $5c + 3d = 20$
$2c + 3d = 8$

7. $6k + l = 21$
$6k + 4l = 48$

8. $v + 2w = 8$
$v + 8w = 17$

9. $3a + 7b = 45$
$2a + 7b = 37$

10. $4p + 5q = 63$
$9p + 5q = 73$

11. $7e + 3f = 18$
$3e + 3f = 12$

12. $4g + 9h = 32$
$4g + 2h = 18$

Exercise 3

1. If we let one fried egg cost e p and one sausage s p, then if one fried egg and two sausages cost 95 p, we can write $e + 2s = 95$. If two fried eggs and two sausages cost £1.30, this can be written as $2e + 2s = 130$.

    (a) Solve simultaneously the equations:

    $$e + 2s = 95$$
    $$2e + 2s = 130$$

    (b) What does one fried egg cost?

    (c) What does one sausage cost?

2. (a) Five large packs and two small packs of wood screws hold 87 screws altogether. Write an equation to show this if a large pack holds l screws and a small pack holds s screws.

    (b) Three large packs and two small packs of wood screws hold 57 screws altogether. Write this as an equation.

    (c) Solve simultaneously the equations formed in parts (a) and (b), then write the number of screws in each size pack.

3. Six pencils and seven rulers cost £2.45 while six pencils and two rulers cost £1.30. Working in pence, write two equations then solve them simultaneously to find the cost of:

    (a) a ruler, (b) a pencil.

4. The sum of two numbers is 53. One of the numbers when added to 5 times the other number, gives 129. Form two equations then solve them to find both numbers.

5. One large and three small chocolate bars have a total mass of 365 g while four of the large and three of the small chocolate bars have a total mass of 740 g. Write two equations then solve them simultaneously to find the mass of each type of chocolate bar.

Exercise 4

Which pair of values satisfies both equations simultaneously?

1. $x + 4y = 12$
    $3x + 4y = 20$

    A. $x = 4, \ y = 3$
    B. $x = 1, \ y = 8$
    C. $x = 4, \ y = 2$
    D. $x = 2, \ y = 4$

2. $2a + 5b = 25$
  $2a + 8b = 34$

A. $a = 10, \ b = 1$
B. $a = 1, \ b = 4$
C. $a = 9, \ b = 2$
D. $a = 5, \ b = 3$

3. $7p + 2q = 46$
  $7p + 6q = 54$

A. $p = 4, \ q = 9$
B. $p = 2, \ q = 6$
C. $p = 6, \ q = 2$
D. $p = 5, \ q = 5$

4. $9k + 5l = 42$
  $3k + 5l = 24$

A. $k = 3, \ l = 4$
B. $k = 4, \ l = 1$
C. $k = 3, \ l = 3$
D. $k = 6, \ l = 1$

5. $2d + 5e = 34$
  $4d + 3e = 40$

A. $d = 7, \ e = 4$
B. $d = 4\frac{1}{2}, \ e = 5$
C. $d = 12, \ e = 2$
D. $d = 2, \ e = 6$

6. $m + 7n = 15$
  $2m + 5n = 21$

A. $m = 1, \ n = 2$
B. $m = 2, \ n = 2$
C. $m = 4, \ n = 3$
D. $m = 8, \ n = 1$

Simultaneous Equations (Where One Equation Needs to be Multiplied)

Consider the equations:

$$2d + 3e = 19 \qquad [1]$$
$$6d + 7e = 51 \qquad [2]$$

Note In this instance, when we subtract one equation from the other, neither letter will disappear. However, if the first equation is multiplied by 3 we obtain $6d + 9e = 57$, which has the same number of ds as equation [2]. Now, the subtracting method will work. The worked example is as follows.

e.g.

$$2d + 3e = 19 \qquad [1]$$
$$6d + 7e = 51 \qquad [2]$$

$3 \times [1]$ $6d + 9e = 57 \qquad [3]$

$[3] - [2]$ $2e = 6$

$\therefore$ $e = 3$

Substitute in [1] $2d + 3e = 19$

When $e = 3$ $2d + 9 = 19$

so $2d = 10$

and $d = 5$

Check in [2]   LHS* $= 6d + 7e$

$$= 6 \times 5 + 7 \times 3$$
$$= 30 + 21$$
$$= 51$$
$$= \text{RHS*} \qquad \text{So } \underline{d = 5 \text{ and } e = 3}$$

Exercise 5

Solve the following pairs of simultaneous equations:

1. $2x + 3y = 16$
$\quad 4x + 7y = 34$

2. $2r + 3s = 17$
$\quad 5r + 9s = 44$

3. $g + 3h = 16$
$\quad 3g + 7h = 40$

4. $6a + 5b = 32$
$\quad a + 2b = 10$

5. $8u + 7v = 29$
$\quad 4u + 5v = 19$

6. $3v + 10w = 29$
$\quad 4v + 5w = 22$

7. $4k + 3l = 38$
$\quad 5k + 6l = 52$

8. $2d + e = 12$
$\quad 10d + 7e = 72$

9. $6p + 5q = 15$
$\quad 2p + 3q = 9$

10. $2m + 3n = 10$
$\quad 5m + 12n = 34$

Exercise 6

For each of the following problems, form two equations then solve them simultaneously.

1. Two pairs of compasses and five protractors cost £3.10, while four pairs of compasses and two protractors cost £4.28. By working in pence, find the cost of:

    (*a*) a protractor,   (*b*) a pair of compasses.

*LHS means left-hand side and RHS means right-hand side.

2. Two dance and three theatre tickets cost £50 altogether, while one theatre and five dance tickets cost £47. Find the cost of:
(*a*) a dance ticket,   (*b*) a theatre ticket.

3. In a competition, a team that won three games and drew five were awarded 38 points, while a team that won six and drew two games were awarded 44 points. How many points were there for:
(*a*) a draw?   (*b*) a win?

4. It took Mr Pearce 44 min to plant four bushes and one tree, and it took him 48 min to plant three bushes and two trees. (Each tree took the same length of time and each bush took the same length of time.) How long did it take to plant:
(*a*) a bush?   (*b*) a tree?

5. Two pens and six pencils cost £2.80, while four pens and three pencils cost £3.80. Find the cost of each.

26 Travel Graphs and Average Speed

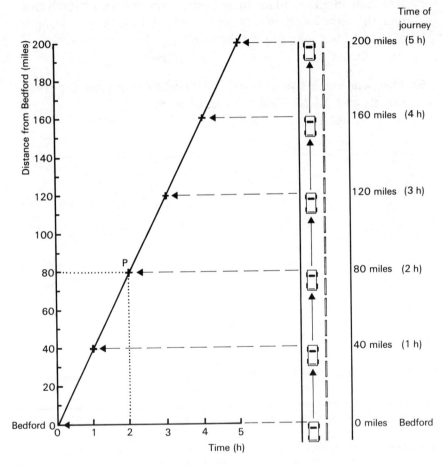

On the right of the diagram above, a car is travelling at a steady 40 m.p.h. The distance/time graph shown on the left illustrates the journey. The point labelled P shows that the car is 80 miles from its starting place (Bedford) after 2 h.

Using the graph, find:

1. the distance the car is from Bedford after:
   (a) 3 h   (b) 5 h   (c) $1\frac{1}{2}$ h

2. the time taken for the car to travel:
   (a) 160 miles   (b) 100 miles   (c) 140 miles

Exercise 2

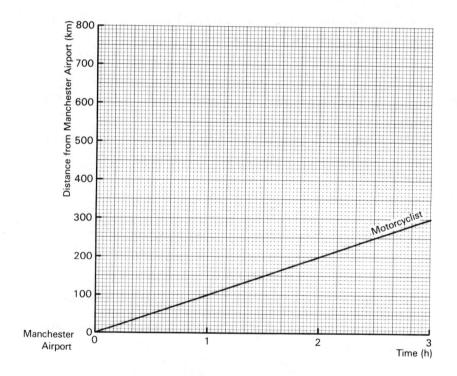

A 1. Copy the pair of axes shown above.

2. A motorcyclist set off from Manchester Airport and travelled at a steady 100 km/h. This is shown on the graph above (100 km after 1 h, 200 km after 2 h, 300 km after 3 h).

Copy the graph and label it as shown.

B Each of the following left Manchester Airport at the same time as the motorcyclist in part A, and travelled in the same direction. Draw a graph for each journey, using the same pair of axes as for part A. Label each graph.

1. a helicopter flying at a steady 150 km/h,

2. a car travelling at a steady 80 km/h,

3. a bus travelling at a steady 60 km/h,

4. a cyclist cycling at a steady 15 km/h,

5. a pedestrian walking at a steady 6 km/h,

6. an aeroplane flying at a steady 600 km/h (only part of this graph will fit using the axes drawn).

C Answer the following questions using the graphs drawn in parts A and B.

1. How far was the motorcyclist from Manchester Airport after:
(a) 2 h? (b) $1\frac{1}{2}$ h? (c) $2\frac{3}{4}$ h?

2. How far was the bus from Manchester Airport after:
(a) $\frac{1}{2}$ h? (b) 1 h 20 min? (c) $2\frac{1}{4}$ h?

3. How far was the car from Manchester Airport after:
(a) 2 h? (b) $2\frac{1}{2}$ h? (c) 45 min?

4. How far was the helicopter from Manchester Airport after:
(a) 3 h (b) $\frac{1}{2}$ h? (c) 2 h 40 min?

5. How long did it take the helicopter to be 300 km from Manchester Airport?

6. How long did it take the motorcyclist to be:
(a) 250 km from Manchester Airport?
(b) 75 km from Manchester Airport?

7. How long did it take the aeroplane to be:
(a) 300 km from Manchester Airport?
(b) 700 km from Manchester Airport?
(c) 450 km from Manchester Airport?

8. How long did it take the pedestrian to walk 10 km from Manchester Airport?

9. How far was the car ahead of the bus after 3 h?

10. How far was the bus ahead of the cyclist after 2 h?

11. How far was the motorcyclist ahead of the car after 75 min?

12. How far ahead of the helicopter was the aeroplane after 36 min?

D Explain how to recognise which of the journeys shown on a distance/time graph is the fastest.

Average Speed

$$\text{Average speed} = \frac{\text{total distance travelled}}{\text{total time taken}}$$

Exercise 3

A Find the average speed in miles per hour (m.p.h.) for a journey of:

1. 150 miles in 3 h
2. 240 miles in 4 h
3. 108 miles in 3 h
4. 224 miles in 7 h
5. 402 miles in 6 h

6. 72 miles in $1\frac{1}{2}$ h
7. 175 miles in $2\frac{1}{2}$ h
8. 18 miles in 20 min
9. 30 miles in 40 min
10. 80 miles in 100 min

B Find the average speed in kilometres per hour (km/h) for a journey of:

1. 320 km in 4 h
2. 90 km in 2 h
3. 324 km in 3 h
4. 472 km in 8 h
5. 564 km in 6 h

6. 38 km in 30 min
7. 175 km in $3\frac{1}{2}$ h
8. 15 km in 10 min
9. 44 km in 40 min
10. 70 km in 50 min

Exercise 4

A For each journey shown, find the speed in the units stated:

1.

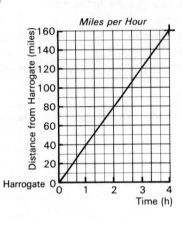

Miles per Hour

3.

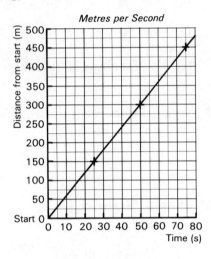

Metres per Second

2.

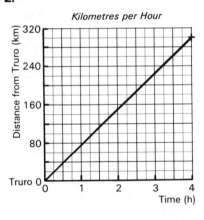

Kilometres per Hour

4.

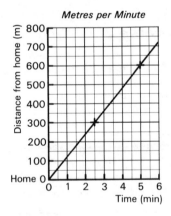

Metres per Minute

B 1. Draw a pair of axes as shown opposite. Use a scale of 4 cm to 1 h on the time axis and 1 cm to 10 miles on the distance axis.

408

Draw a graph to show a journey of 125 miles in $2\frac{1}{2}$ h. Find the average speed in miles per hour.

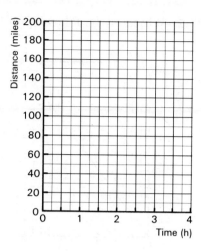

2. Draw a pair of axes where the time ranges from 0 h to 4 h (use a scale of 4 cm to 1 h), and the distance ranges from 0 km to 400 km (use a scale of 1 cm to 20 km). Draw a graph to show a journey of 360 km in 4 h. Find the average speed in kilometres per hour.

3. (a) Draw a pair of axes as for part A, question 3.
   (b) Draw a graph to show an average speed of 7 m/s.
   (c) From your graph, find the distance travelled in 35 s.
   (d) From your graph, find the time taken to travel 455 m.

Exercise 5

1. Which of the following two graphs shows the faster journey?

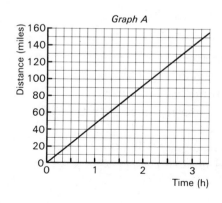

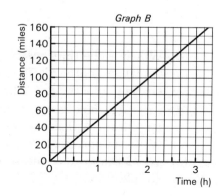

2. Which of the following two graphs shows the faster journey?

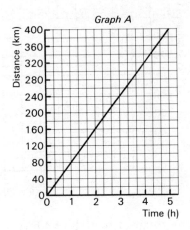

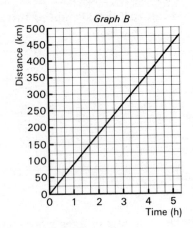

3. The graph shows four different journeys all starting from the same place at the same time:

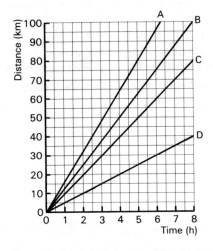

(a) Which is the third fastest journey?

(b) On which journey is 75 km travelled in 6 h?

(c) On which journey is 75 km travelled in $7\frac{1}{2}$ h?

(d) After 5 h, how many more kilometres have been travelled on journey A than on journey D?

(e) Write the speeds of all four journeys in kilometres per hour.

(f) Write the ratio of the speed of B to the speed of C in its simplest form.

410

Exercise 6

The graph shows a cycle journey from Leicester to Gainsborough:

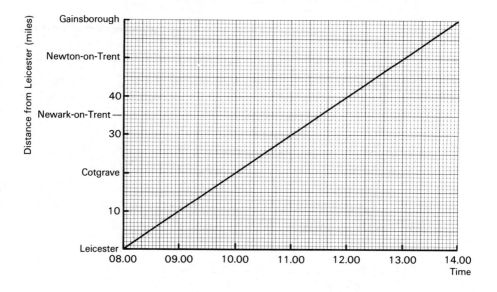

1. At what time did the cyclist leave Leicester?

2. At what time did the cyclist arrive at Cotgrave?

3. How far is Cotgrave from Leicester?

4. How far is Newark-on-Trent from Leicester?

5. At what time did the cyclist arrive at Newark-on-Trent?

6. At what time did the cyclist arrive at Newton-on-Trent?

7. How far is Newton-on-Trent from Cotgrave?

8. How far is Gainsborough from Leicester?

9. How long did the cyclist take to travel from Leicester to Gainsborough?

10. What was the cyclist's average speed for the journey?

Exercise 7

1. A cyclist set off from Etchingham at 9 o'clock in the morning. The graph and diagram show the journey.

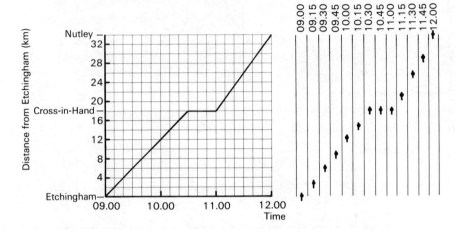

(*a*) How far was the cyclist from Etchingham after:
    (i) 30 min?
    (ii) 1 h?
    (iii) $1\frac{1}{2}$ h?
    (iv) $1\frac{3}{4}$ h?
    (v) 2 h?
    (vi) $2\frac{1}{2}$ h?
    (vii) 3 h?

(*b*) What does the horizontal part of the graph mean?
(*c*) How far is Cross-in-Hand from Etchingham?

(d) How far is Nutley from Cross-in-Hand?

(e) For how long did the cyclist stop?

(f) What was the cyclist's average speed:
   (i) from Etchingham to Cross-in-Hand?
   (ii) from Cross-in-Hand to Nutley?

2. Clifford walked from his home to his friend's house, where he waited for his friend to get ready. They then travelled by bus to a disco. The graph below shows the journey.

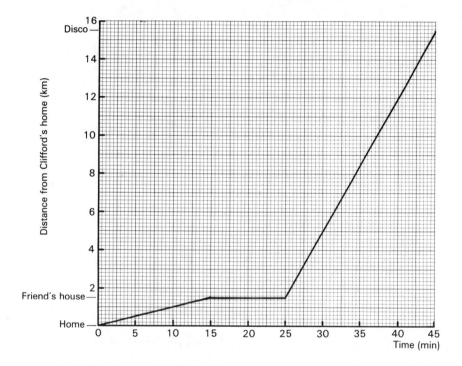

(a) How long did Clifford take to walk to his friend's house?

(b) How far is it from Clifford's home to his friend's house?

(c) What was Clifford's average walking speed between his home and his friend's house?

(d) How long did Clifford wait at his friend's house?

(e) How far is it from his friend's house to the disco?

(f) How long did the bus journey take from his friend's house to the disco?

(g) What was the average speed of the bus?

(h) How far was Clifford from home after half an hour?

413

3. The following graph shows Mr Gilbert's car journey from Brighton to Leeds:

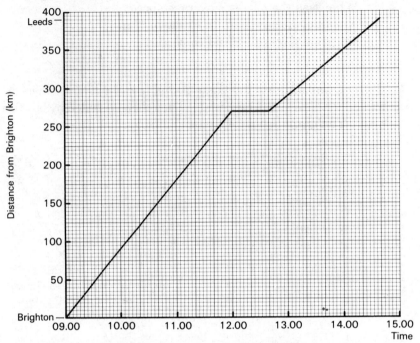

(a) How far is it from Brighton to Leeds?

(b) At what time did Mr Gilbert arrive in Leeds?

(c) At what time did Mr Gilbert stop for lunch?

(d) For how many minutes did Mr Gilbert stop?

(e) How far was the lunch stop from Leeds?

(f) Calculate the average speed from Brighton to the lunch stop.

(g) Calculate the average speed from the lunch stop to Leeds.

Exercise 8   Interpreting Sketch Graphs

e.g.

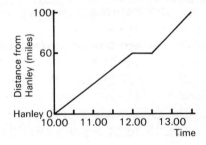

414

e.g. The motorist left Hanley at 10 o'clock in the morning. She travelled for 2 h at a steady 30 m.p.h., after which she stopped at 12 o'clock for $\frac{1}{2}$ h. Her stop was at a café that was 60 miles from Hanley. She set off again at 12.30, and travelled a further 40 miles at a steady 40 m.p.h. She arrived at her destination one hour later, at half-past one in the afternoon.

Interpret the following sketch graphs as in the example above. Mention distances, times and average speeds.

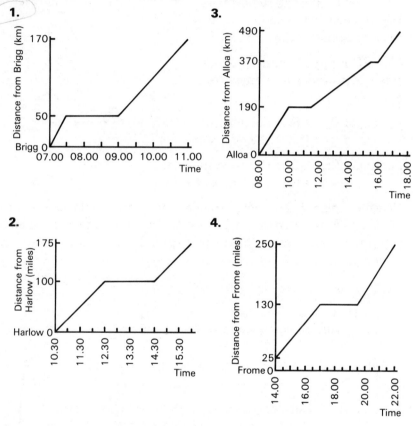

1.

2.

3.

4.

27 The Tangent Ratio in Trigonometry

In right-angled triangle PQR, where angle R is the right-angle, PQ is called the *hypotenuse*. It is the side opposite the right-angle.

Side PR is *opposite* angle Q and side QR is *adjacent* to (next to) angle Q.

For angle Q: PR is the *opposite* side.
                  QR is the *adjacent* side.

For angle P: QR is the opposite side.
                  PR is the adjacent side.

Consider angle Q. There are two sides next to this angle but only one of them, QR, is called the adjacent side. The other side, PQ, which is opposite the right-angle, has its own special name, the *hypotenuse*.

Exercise 1

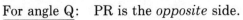

A In each triangle, which side is the hypotenuse?

1.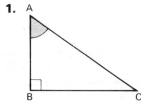

2.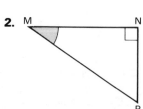

3.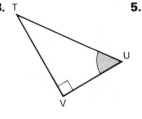

4.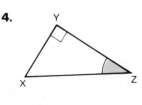

5.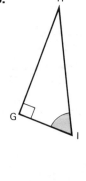

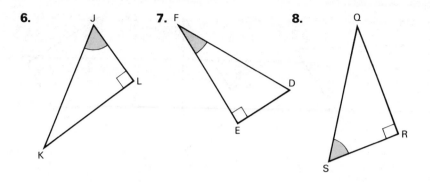

B For each triangle in part A, which side is opposite the shaded angle?

C For each triangle in part A, considering the shaded angle, which side is the adjacent side?

Exercise 2

For each triangle, write whether the side marked with the question mark is the hypotenuse, the opposite side or the adjacent side, in relation to the shaded angle:

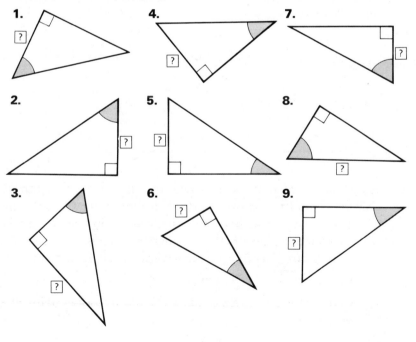

10.

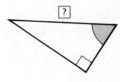

11.

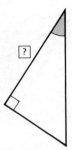

12.

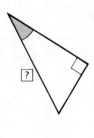

Exercise 3

A **1.** In the given right-angled triangle ABC, $\widehat{ACB} = 32°$:

(*a*) Measure the opposite side, AB.

(*b*) Measure the adjacent side, BC.

(*c*) Work out $\dfrac{\text{opp.}}{\text{adj.}}$.

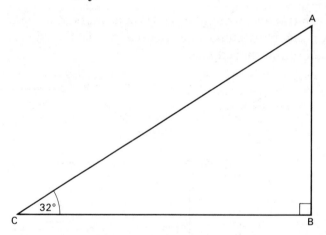

(*d*) Using a calculator that has a 'tan' key on it, find tan 32° and round the answer to three decimal places. To do this, first make sure that the calculator is in 'degree mode'. Although we have measured angles in degrees, angles may be measured in *radians* or in *grades*. When in 'degree mode', key in $\boxed{\text{AC}}$ $\boxed{3}$ $\boxed{2}$ $\boxed{\text{tan}}$.

(*e*) Compare the answers to parts (*c*) and (*d*), then write what you notice.

2. (*a*) Draw three more right-angled triangles, all different sizes. In each triangle, one angle should measure 32°.

(*b*) For each triangle, in relation to the 32° angle, measure the opposite and adjacent sides then work out $\dfrac{\text{opp.}}{\text{adj.}}$, giving each answer correct to one decimal place.

(*c*) Find tan 32° correct to one decimal place.

(*d*) Compare the answers to parts (*b*) and (*c*), then write what you notice.

B **1.** In the given right-angled triangle XYZ, $\widehat{XZY} = 40°$:

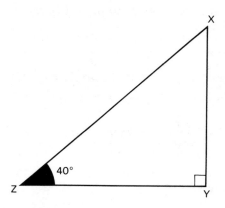

(*a*) Measure opposite side, XY.

(*b*) Measure adjacent side, YZ.

(*c*) Work out $\dfrac{\text{opp.}}{\text{adj.}}$.

(*d*) Using a calculator, find tan 40° to two decimal places.

(*e*) Compare the answers to parts (*c*) and (*d*), then write what you notice.

2. (*a*) Draw three different right-angled triangles in which one of the angles measures 40°.

(*b*) For each triangle, in relation to the 40° angle, measure the opposite and adjacent sides; then work out $\dfrac{\text{opp.}}{\text{adj.}}$ giving each answer correct to one decimal place.

(*c*) Find tan 40° correct to one decimal place.

(*d*) Compare the answers to parts (*b*) and (*c*), then write what you notice.

C 1. Draw five different right-angled triangles in which the angles, other than the right-angle, are different. Label each triangle PQR, where angle $Q = 90°$.

2. For each triangle:
   (a) Measure angle R.
   (b) Measure PQ (opp.).
   (c) Measure QR (adj.).
   (d) Work out $\dfrac{\text{opp.}}{\text{adj.}}$, giving the answer to one decimal place.
   (e) Find $\tan \widehat{R}$ on a calculator and write the answer correct to one decimal place.
   (f) Compare the answers to parts (d) and (e) then write what you notice.

From Exercise 3 you should have discovered that for any right-angled triangle:

$$\tan \theta = \frac{\text{opp.}}{\text{adj.}} \quad \text{or more simply,} \quad \tan = \frac{\text{opp.}}{\text{adj.}}$$

Calculator Practice

Exercise 4

Find (correct to four decimal places):

1. $\tan 25°$	**6.** $\tan 74°$	**11.** $\tan 82.1°$
2. $\tan 19°$	**7.** $\tan 63.2°$	**12.** $\tan 50.9°$
3. $\tan 54°$	**8.** $\tan 77.5°$	**13.** $\tan 71.4°$
4. $\tan 45°$	**9.** $\tan 23.7°$	**14.** $\tan 10.3°$
5. $\tan 7°$	**10.** $\tan 14.6°$	**15.** $\tan 36.8°$

If $\tan \theta = 0.74$, then angle θ can be found by keying in:

$$\boxed{\text{AC}} \; \boxed{\cdot} \; \boxed{7} \; \boxed{4} \; \boxed{\text{INV}} \; \boxed{\tan}$$

or on some calculators, $\boxed{\text{AC}} \; \boxed{\cdot} \; \boxed{7} \; \boxed{4} \; \boxed{\text{arc}} \; \boxed{\tan}$

or perhaps $\boxed{\text{AC}} \; \boxed{\cdot} \; \boxed{7} \; \boxed{4} \; \boxed{\text{F}} \; \boxed{\tan^{-1}}$

Try it. You should find that $\theta = 36.5°$, correct to one decimal place.

Exercise 5

Find angle θ correct to one decimal place if:

1. $\tan \theta = 0.561$ **5.** $\tan \theta = 2.023$ **9.** $\tan \theta = 1.043$
2. $\tan \theta = 0.888$ **6.** $\tan \theta = 0.795$ **10.** $\tan \theta = 2.344$
3. $\tan \theta = 3.133$ **7.** $\tan \theta = 9.677$ **11.** $\tan \theta = 0.52$
4. $\tan \theta = 1.45$ **8.** $\tan \theta = 0.36$ **12.** $\tan \theta = 1.2$

Exercise 6   Calculating Angles

A In each right-angled triangle, find the required angle giving each answer in degrees (correct to one decimal place):

e.g.   Find angle N.

In right-angled triangle LMN:

Since $\tan = \dfrac{\text{opp.}}{\text{adj.}}$

$$\tan \widehat{N} = \frac{LM}{MN} = \frac{5.32}{3.8} = 1.4$$

since $\tan \widehat{N} = 1.4$

$\widehat{N} = \underline{\underline{54.5°}}$ (to 1 d.p.)

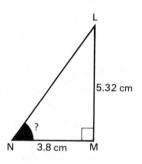

1.

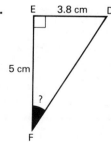

2.

3.

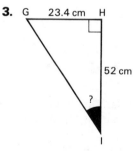

4.

5.

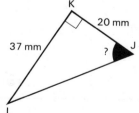

6.

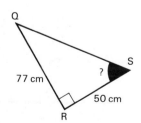

421

7.

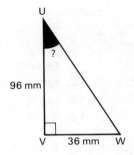

8.

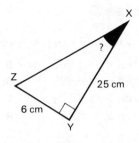

B 1. A ladder is placed against a vertical wall so that it reaches 4.8 m up the wall. If its foot is on level ground and 2 m from the wall, find the angle the ladder makes with the ground. Give the answer correct to one decimal place.

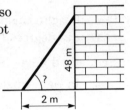

2. A ship sailed 8 km due north followed by 4 km due east. Calculate the bearing of the finishing port from the starting port, giving the answer correct to the nearest degree.

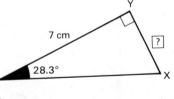

Exercise 7 Calculating the Opposite Side

A In each right-angled triangle, calculate the required side giving the answer correct to three significant figures:

e.g. Find side XY in the given triangle.

In right-angled triangle XYZ,

since $\tan = \dfrac{\text{opp.}}{\text{adj.}}$

$\tan 28.3° = \dfrac{XY}{7}$

so $XY = 7 \tan 28.3°$

$XY = \underline{\underline{3.77 \text{ cm}}}$ (to 3 s.f.)

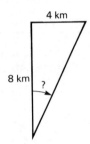

422

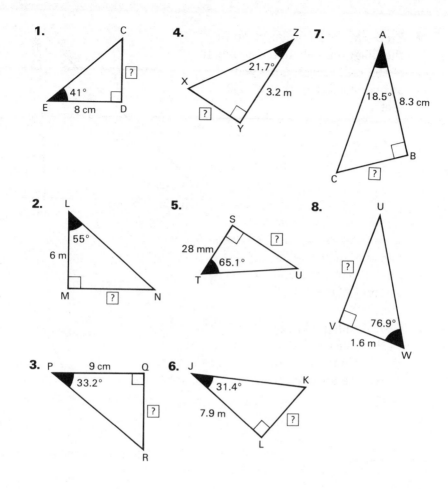

1.
C
?
41°
E 8 cm D

4.
Z
21.7°
X
3.2 m
?
Y

7.
A
18.5° 8.3 cm
B
?
C

2.
L
55°
6 m
M ? N

5.
S
?
28 mm
65.1°
T U

8.
U
?
V
76.9°
1.6 m
W

3. P 9 cm Q
33.2°
?
R

6. J
31.4°
7.9 m K
?
L

B **1.** From a point 82 m from the foot of a Cypress tree, the angle of elevation of the top of the tree is 23°. Calculate the height of the tree.

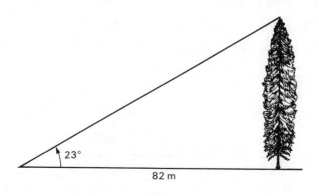

23°
82 m

2. From the information given in the diagram, calculate the height of the radio mast. Give your answer correct to the nearest metre.

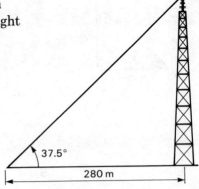

37.5°

280 m

Revision Exercises XXII to XXVII

Revision Exercise XXII

1. Copy and complete:

(a) 24 mm = $\boxed{?}$ cm

(b) 6.2 m = $\boxed{?}$ cm

(c) 7490 mm = $\boxed{?}$ m

(d) 2.6 km = $\boxed{?}$ m

(e) 9.1 ℓ = $\boxed{?}$ cℓ

(f) 186 mℓ = $\boxed{?}$ cℓ

(g) 6920 cℓ = $\boxed{?}$ mℓ

(h) 3.25 ℓ = $\boxed{?}$ mℓ

(i) 96.5 g = $\boxed{?}$ mg

(j) 0.84 kg = $\boxed{?}$ g

(k) 29 300 kg = $\boxed{?}$ t

(l) 68 100 g = $\boxed{?}$ kg

2. (a) The length of a car is about:

A. 2.4 m B. 4.3 m C. 180 cm D. 920 mm

(b) A mug holds about:

A. 250 mℓ B. 150 ℓ C. 1.5 ℓ D. 9.5 mℓ

(c) A packet of tea has a mass of about:

A. 125 mg B. 825 mg C. 125 g D. 785 g

3. A piece of wood is 2 m long. Eight equal lengths are cut off, leaving 160 mm waste. How long is each length that has been cut off?

4. (a) How many inches are there in 5 ft?

(b) How many feet are there in 7 yd?

(c) How many inches are there in 8 yd?

(d) How many feet are there in 880 yd?

5. If I fill four 300 mℓ glasses, six 250 mℓ glasses and seven 200 mℓ glasses with lemonade, how many litres of lemonade do I use?

6. If ten glasses hold $4\frac{1}{2}$ pt, how many gallons do 80 similar glasses hold?

7. A marble paperweight is cuboid-shaped and measures 8 cm by 5 cm by 1.5 cm:

    (*a*) Calculate its volume.

    (*b*) If marble has a density of 2.6 g/cm³, calculate the mass of the paperweight.

8. Given that 14 lb = 1 st, change 8 st 13 lb to pounds.

9. If 1 kg = 2.2 lb, change:

    (*a*) 7 kg to pounds,   (*b*) 132 lb to kilograms.

10. Which is longer, 1 in or 1 cm?

Revision Exercise XXIII

A Draw a graph to convert pints to litres. Use a scale of 2 cm to 5 pt and 1 cm to 1 ℓ. Use 4 ℓ = 7 pt. Use your graph to:

1. Change to litres:

    (*a*) 35 pt   (*d*) $10\frac{1}{2}$ pt

    (*b*) 21 pt   (*e*) $3\frac{1}{2}$ pt

    (*c*) 28 pt   (*f*) $15\frac{3}{4}$ pt

2. Change to pints:

    (*a*) 8 ℓ   (*d*) 14 ℓ

    (*b*) 10 ℓ   (*e*) 5 ℓ

    (*c*) 18 ℓ   (*f*) 3 ℓ

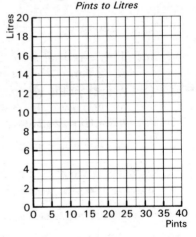

Pints to Litres

B Use the conversion table opposite to change:

1. °C to °F:

    (*a*) 100 °C   (*c*) 10 °C   (*e*) 60 °C   (*g*) ⁻15 °C

    (*b*) 0 °C   (*d*) 30 °C   (*f*) 15 °C   (*h*) ⁻20 °C

2. °F to °C:

    (*a*) 90 °F   (*c*) 35 °F   (*e*) 25 °F   (*g*) ⁻10 °F

    (*b*) 5 °F   (*d*) 0 °F   (*f*) 70 °F   (*h*) ⁻5 °F

Temperature

°Celsius	°C or °F	°Fahrenheit
‾28.9	‾20	‾4
‾26.1	‾15	5
‾23.3	‾10	14
‾20.6	‾5	23
‾17.8	0	32
‾15	5	41
‾12.2	10	50
‾9.4	15	59
‾6.7	20	68
‾3.9	25	77
‾1.1	30	86
1.7	35	95
4.4	40	104
10	50	122
15.6	60	140
21.1	70	158
26.7	80	176
32.2	90	194
37.8	100	212
43.3	110	230

Revision Exercise XXIV

1. Which vectors are shown by the arrows?

(a)   (b)

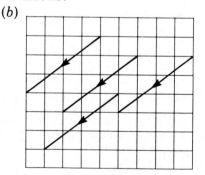

2. On squared paper, draw arrows to show these vectors (one arrow for each vector is acceptable):

(a) $\begin{pmatrix} 5 \\ 2 \end{pmatrix}$ (b) $\begin{pmatrix} ^-3 \\ ^-3 \end{pmatrix}$ (c) $\begin{pmatrix} 2 \\ ^-4 \end{pmatrix}$ (d) $\begin{pmatrix} ^-1 \\ 6 \end{pmatrix}$

3. Given a vector and its starting point, find the co-ordinates of its end point:

(a) $\begin{pmatrix} 4 \\ 2 \end{pmatrix}$, ($^-$5, 7)   (b) $\begin{pmatrix} 3 \\ -2 \end{pmatrix}$, (5, 4)   (c) $\begin{pmatrix} -9 \\ -3 \end{pmatrix}$, (2, 6)

4. Given a vector and its end point, find the co-ordinates of its starting point:

(a) $\begin{pmatrix} 2 \\ 6 \end{pmatrix}$, (2, 0)   (b) $\begin{pmatrix} -3 \\ -9 \end{pmatrix}$, ($^-$5, $^-$4)   (c) $\begin{pmatrix} -1 \\ 14 \end{pmatrix}$, ($^-$8, 4)

5. Given the starting point and the end point of a displacement vector, find the vector:

	(a)	(b)	(c)	(d)
Start	(3, 1)	(12, 5)	(0, 0)	(0, 0)
End	(2, 8)	(13, 0)	(6, $^-$3)	($^-$2, 14)

6. (a) Find the image of the point ($^-$7, 4) under the translation vector $\begin{pmatrix} 5 \\ -1 \end{pmatrix}$.

(b) What translation vector would map (0, 0) onto ($^-$9, 1)?

(c) $\begin{pmatrix} 5 \\ -8 \end{pmatrix}$ maps ($\boxed{?}$, $\boxed{?}$) $\longrightarrow$ (11, $^-$1).

7. If $\begin{pmatrix} 4 \\ 3 \end{pmatrix}$ maps A onto A$'$ and $\begin{pmatrix} 2 \\ 7 \end{pmatrix}$ maps A$'$ onto A$''$, which vector maps A onto A$''$?

8. Work out $\begin{pmatrix} 5 \\ -4 \end{pmatrix} + \begin{pmatrix} -1 \\ 7 \end{pmatrix}$ and graph your results:

9. Work out:

(a) $\begin{pmatrix} 10 \\ -6 \end{pmatrix} + \begin{pmatrix} -1 \\ 17 \end{pmatrix}$ (b) $\begin{pmatrix} 15 \\ 0 \end{pmatrix} + \begin{pmatrix} -12 \\ -2 \end{pmatrix}$ (c) $\begin{pmatrix} -14 \\ -19 \end{pmatrix} + \begin{pmatrix} -13 \\ 12 \end{pmatrix}$

10. Copy and complete: $\begin{pmatrix} 5 \\ -6 \end{pmatrix} + \begin{pmatrix} -8 \\ 4 \end{pmatrix} = \begin{pmatrix} -8 \\ 4 \end{pmatrix} + \begin{pmatrix} \boxed{?} \\ \boxed{?} \end{pmatrix}$

11. Copy and complete:

(a) $\begin{pmatrix} 9 \\ \boxed{?} \end{pmatrix} + \begin{pmatrix} \boxed{?} \\ 13 \end{pmatrix} = \begin{pmatrix} 7 \\ 18 \end{pmatrix}$
(b) $\begin{pmatrix} ^-17 \\ 12 \end{pmatrix} + \begin{pmatrix} \boxed{?} \\ \boxed{?} \end{pmatrix} = \begin{pmatrix} 0 \\ 0 \end{pmatrix}$

12. The table shows the number of hours spent sleeping, eating, working and at leisure, during one week:

	Mon	Tue	Wed	Thur	Fri	Sat	Sun
Sleeping	$7\frac{1}{2}$	7	7	8	$6\frac{1}{2}$	6	8
Eating	2	$1\frac{1}{2}$	2	$2\frac{1}{2}$	2	4	3
Working	8	8	$3\frac{1}{2}$	$7\frac{1}{2}$	7	3	0
Leisure	$6\frac{1}{2}$	$7\frac{1}{2}$	$11\frac{1}{2}$	6	$8\frac{1}{2}$	11	13

(a) Give Friday's activities as a vector.

(b) Which day does the vector $\begin{pmatrix} 7 \\ 2 \\ 3\frac{1}{2} \\ 11\frac{1}{2} \end{pmatrix}$ show?

(c) By adding vectors, find the totals for Monday and Tuesday.
(d) Use vectors to find the totals for Thursday, Friday and Saturday.

Revision Exercise XXV

1. Solve the simultaneous equations:
(a) $3x + 7y = 29$
$3x + 6y = 27$

(b) $5m + 2n = 24$
$3m + 2n = 18$

2. At a concert, three seats in the circle and four seats in the stalls cost £68; while five seats in the circle and four seats in the stalls cost £92. Write two equations then solve them simultaneously, to find the cost of a seat in:
(a) the circle,
(b) the stalls.

3. Which of the pairs of values satisfies both equations simultaneously?

$$x + 4y = 14$$
$$5x + 4y = 38$$

A. $x = 2, \quad y = 3$
B. $x = 4, \quad y = 2\frac{1}{2}$
C. $x = 6, \quad y = 2$
D. $x = 10, \quad y = 1$

4. Solve simultaneously: $\quad 3g + 5h = 31$
$$4g + 15h = 58$$

5. Two adults and five children paid a total of £23 to visit a stately home, while four adults and three children paid £25:
(a) What is the cost per child?
(b) What is the cost per adult?

Revision Exercise XXVI

1. Find the average speed, in miles per hour, for a journey of:
(a) 195 miles in 5 h,   (b) 140 miles in $3\frac{1}{2}$ h.

2. Find the average speed, in kilometres per hour, for a journey of:
(a) 236 km in 4 h,   (b) 50 km in 40 min.

3. Find the average speed shown on the given graph, giving the answer in miles per hour.

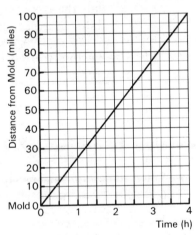

4. Draw a pair of axes where the time ranges from 0 to 10 s. (Use a scale of 2 cm to 1 s) and the distance ranges from 0 to 80 m (use a scale of 1 cm to 5 m). Draw a graph to show a journey of 60 m in $7\frac{1}{2}$ s. Find the average speed, in metres per second.

5. Mr G. O. North travelled from Portsmouth to Birmingham and then to Carlisle. The following graph shows his journey.

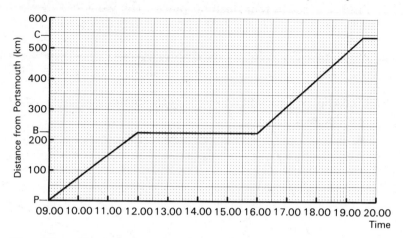

Key: P = Portsmouth, B = Birmingham, C = Carlisle.

(a) How far is Birmingham from Portsmouth?
(b) How long did Mr North spend in Birmingham?
(c) At what time did Mr North arrive in Carlisle?
(d) How far is Carlisle from Birmingham?
(e) How long did the journey from Birmingham to Carlisle take?
(f) Calculate the average speed from Portsmouth to Birmingham.
(g) Calculate the average speed from Birmingham to Carlisle.

6.

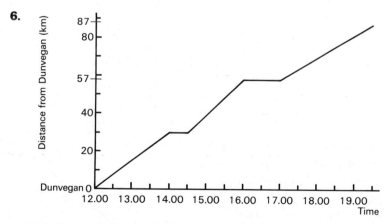

Describe fully the journey shown by the graph above. Give distances, times and average speeds.

Revision Exercise XXVII

1. Find, correct to four decimal places, the value of:
   (a) $\tan 36°$ (b) $\tan 22.3°$ (c) $\tan 68.7°$

2. Find angle θ correct to one decimal place:
   (a) $\tan \theta = 3.84$ (b) $\tan \theta = 0.246$ (c) $\tan \theta = 1.032$

3. Find the required angles giving each answer in degrees correct to one decimal place:
   (a) 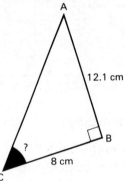   (b)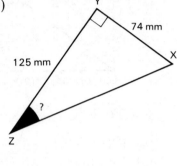

4. Calculate the required sides giving answers correct to three significant figures:
   (a) 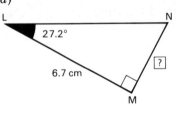   (b)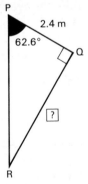

5. The angle of elevation of the top of a telegraph pole from a point on level ground, 11 m from the foot of the pole, is 35.6°. Calculate, to three significant figures, the height of the pole.

432

Appendix 1
Capital Letters

Symmetry (pp. 1, 40)

Appendix 2
Sets

Set notation　　**(p. 7)**

e.g. 1　$\mathscr{E} = \{\, x : x = 4n\ \text{where } n \text{ is even}\}$ can be read as:

The universal set | is | the set of values of x | such that | x | is equal to | 4 times the value of n | where | n | is | even

In this case, $\mathscr{E} = \{8,\quad 16,\quad 24,\quad 32,\quad 40, \ldots\}$

when　$n =$ 　2　　4　　6　　8　　10

$4n =$ 　4×2　4×4　4×6　4×8　4×10

e.g. 2　　$\mathscr{E} = \{t : 14 \leqslant t < 20\ \text{where } t \text{ is a whole number}\}$

so　$\mathscr{E} = \{14, 15, 16, 17, 18, 19\}$

Appendix 3
Calculators

(p. 44)

Clearing the Display

$\boxed{\text{C}}$ ($\boxed{\text{ON}|\text{C}}$ or $\boxed{\text{CE}}$ or $\boxed{\text{CE/C}}$ on some calculators) On many calculators, $\boxed{\text{C}}$ is used to clear the last number that was keyed in.

$\boxed{\text{AC}}$ This key usually clears everything from the calculator except for the memory. On certain calculators, $\boxed{\text{AC}}$ may also clear the memory. Some calculators do not have an $\boxed{\text{AC}}$ key. On those, pressing $\boxed{\text{C}}$ (or $\boxed{\text{CE/C}}$ or $\boxed{\text{ON}|\text{C}}$) twice normally clears everything from the calculator except the memory.

The Memory Keys

$\boxed{\text{MR}}$ ($\boxed{\text{RCL}}$ or $\boxed{\text{RM}}$) This key ReCaLls what is in the calculator's Memory and shows it in the display. The number that was in the display is lost, but the number in the memory remains. Some calculators, use the key $\boxed{\text{MRC}}$ or $\boxed{\text{M}^{\text{R}}_{\text{C}}}$ which work in the same way as the $\boxed{\text{MR}}$ key when first pressed, but usually clear the memory when pressed twice (see $\boxed{\text{MC}}$).

$\boxed{\text{Min}}$ ($\boxed{\text{STO}}$ or $\boxed{\text{MS}}$ on some calculators) This key normally STOres in the Memory the number that is shown on the display. Any previous number that was in the memory is lost, but the number in the display stays the same. On some calculators, possibly older models, this key stores the calculation so far.

Key in: $\boxed{\text{AC}}$ $\boxed{8}$ $\boxed{\div}$ $\boxed{2}$ $\boxed{\text{Min}}$ $\boxed{\text{AC}}$ $\boxed{\text{MR}}$

If the display shows 2 then $\boxed{\text{Min}}$ stores the displayed number.

If the display shows 4 then $\boxed{\text{Min}}$ stores the calculation so far.

(Throughout this series of books, I have let $\boxed{\text{Min}}$ store the number shown on the display.)

To store the calculation so far,

key in: $\boxed{\text{AC}}$ $\boxed{8}$ $\boxed{\div}$ $\boxed{2}$ $\boxed{=}$ $\boxed{\text{Min}}$
                                        ↑
                    This key causes the answer
                    of the calculation so far to
                    appear on the display.

$\boxed{\text{Min}}$ stores this result in the memory.

Keying in $\boxed{\text{AC}}$ $\boxed{\text{MR}}$ should now display 4. The sequence $\boxed{\text{AC}}$ $\boxed{9}$ $\boxed{\text{Min}}$ $\boxed{\text{AC}}$ $\boxed{4}$ $\boxed{\text{Min}}$ $\boxed{\text{AC}}$ will store 4 in the memory and leave 0 on the display (9 is lost). Try it. (Depress $\boxed{\text{MR}}$ afterwards to check that 4 is now in the memory.)

$\boxed{\text{MC}}$ ($\boxed{\text{CM}}$ on some calculators) This key clears the memory without clearing the display. Other ways of clearing the memory are: $\boxed{\text{AC}}$ $\boxed{\text{Min}}$ or $\boxed{\text{MRC}}$ $\boxed{\text{MRC}}$ or $\boxed{\text{M}_\text{C}^\text{R}}$ $\boxed{\text{M}_\text{C}^\text{R}}$, but these methods affect the display. (Remember, on calculators without an $\boxed{\text{AC}}$ key, $\boxed{\text{AC}}$ can probably be replaced by $\boxed{\text{C}}$ $\boxed{\text{C}}$ or $\boxed{\text{ON|C}}$ $\boxed{\text{ON|C}}$ or $\boxed{\text{CE/C}}$ $\boxed{\text{CE/C}}$.)

$\boxed{\text{M+}}$ ($\boxed{\text{SUM}}$ on some calculators) This key adds the displayed number to the number already in the memory. Clear the memory first, then key in:

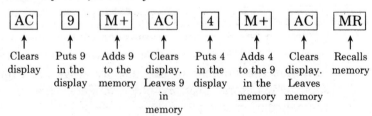

$\boxed{\text{AC}}$	$\boxed{9}$	$\boxed{\text{M+}}$	$\boxed{\text{AC}}$	$\boxed{4}$	$\boxed{\text{M+}}$	$\boxed{\text{AC}}$	$\boxed{\text{MR}}$
↑	↑	↑	↑	↑	↑	↑	↑
Clears display	Puts 9 in the display	Adds 9 to the memory	Clears display. Leaves 9 in memory	Puts 4 in the display	Adds 4 to the 9 in the memory	Clears display. Leaves memory	Recalls memory

The last key $\boxed{MR}$ in the previous sequence should cause 13 to appear in the display.

Make certain you know the difference between $\boxed{Min}$ and $\boxed{M+}$ (that is, $\boxed{STO}$ and $\boxed{SUM}$ on some calculators).

Note $\boxed{M+}$ can be used instead of $\boxed{Min}$ as long as you CLEAR THE MEMORY FIRST.

So $\boxed{MC}\,\boxed{M+}$ is the same as $\boxed{Min}$.

$\boxed{M-}$ This key subtracts the displayed number from the number number already in the memory.

Note $\boxed{MR}\,\boxed{M-}$ should clear the memory and $\boxed{MR}\,\boxed{M-}\,\boxed{AC}$ should clear the memory and the display.

If your calculator does not have the key $\boxed{M-}$ but has $\boxed{M+}$ and $\boxed{+/-}$, then $\boxed{+/-}\,\boxed{M+}$, can be used instead of $\boxed{M-}$.

Appendix 4
Computer Programs

Finding the value of pi   (pp. 239–241)

John Wallis series
```
1Ø    REM WALLIS SERIES TO APPROXIMATE PI
2Ø    LET  P = 2
3Ø    LET  N = 1
4Ø    LET  C = (N + 1)/N
5Ø    LET  P = P * C
6Ø    PRINT N, P
7Ø    LET  N = N + 1
8Ø    LET  C = N/(N + 1)
9Ø    LET  P = P * C
1ØØ   PRINT N, P
11Ø   LET  N = N + 1
12Ø   IF  N > 2ØØØØØ THEN  GOTO 14Ø
13Ø   GOTO 4Ø
14Ø   END
```

Note   On some computers, you may be able to miss out GOTO in line 12Ø.)

Leibnitz series
```
1Ø    REM LEIBNITZ SERIES TO APPROXIMATE PI
2Ø    LET  P = Ø
3Ø    LET  A = Ø
4Ø    LET  D = 1
5Ø    LET  J = 1
6Ø    FOR N = 1 TO 2ØØØØØ
7Ø        LET  A = A + J/D
8Ø        LET  P = 4 * A
9Ø        PRINT N, P
1ØØ       LET  J = J * (−1)
11Ø       LET  D = D + 2
12Ø   NEXT N
13Ø   END
```

John Wallis and Lord Brouncker series

```
1∅    REM CONTINUED FRACTIONS AND PI
2∅    FOR N = 3 TO 1∅∅
3∅        LET X = 2 * N − 3
4∅        LET Y = X * X/2
5∅        LET Y = Y + 2
6∅        LET X = X − 2
7∅        LET Y = X * X/Y
8∅        IF X = 1 THEN GOTO 1∅∅
9∅        GOTO 5∅
1∅∅       LET P = 4/(1 + Y)
11∅       PRINT N, P
12∅   NEXT N
13∅   END
```

Note   On some computers, you may be able to miss out GOTO in
         line 8∅.)

A. Sharp series

```
1∅    REM H3 SHARP/PI
2∅    LET R = SQR(12)
3∅    LET P = R
4∅    LET J = −1
5∅    FOR N = 2 TO 2∅
6∅        LET Q = R * J/(3↑(N − 1) * (2 * N − 1))
7∅        LET P = P + Q
8∅        PRINT N, P
9∅        LET J = J * (−1)
1∅∅   NEXT N
11∅   END
```

Euler series

```
1∅    REM H4 EULER/PI
2∅    LET P = 2
3∅    LET J = −1
4∅    FOR N = 2 TO 2∅
5∅        LET I = 2 * N − 1
6∅        LET Q = 4 * J/(I * 2↑I)
7∅        LET P = P + Q
8∅        PRINT N, P
9∅        LET J = J * (−1)
1∅∅   NEXT N
11∅   END
```

Note   For some computers it may be necessary (or better):
         (i) to change END into STOP,
         (ii) to use the TAB statement when printing.

Glossary

ASCII (p. 132)

ASCII stands for American Standard Code for Information Interchange. Each symbol on a key of a computer keyboard (e.g. A to Z, 0 to 9 and others such as + or −) is called a *character*. Each character is changed into a binary code such as ASCII. Although ASCII is based on a 7-bit character (a *bit* is a binary digit), 8 bits are normally used (some computer books will give further information on this).

broken scale (p. 321)

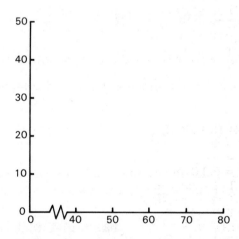

The diagram shows a broken scale used on the 'horizontal' axis. It is used when the full range of values will not fit on an axis. In the example, 0 to 80 is shown on the horizontal axis. Since 0 to 80 will not fit completely, unless a small scale is used, and since only the range of values from 40 to 80 is needed, the scale is broken, as shown, between 0 and 40. A larger scale can then be used.

co-domain (p. 197)

Note that some books refer to the co-domain as the 'range' or the 'range set'. However, the range is the set of elements in the co-domain that are actually used.

In the mapping shown below:

> the domain is $\{1, 2, 3\}$
> the co-domain is $\{1, 2, 3, 4, 5, 6\}$
> the range is $\{2, 4, 6\}$

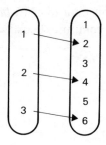

component of a vector (p. 389)

Each value in a vector is called a component. In the vector $\begin{pmatrix} 3 \\ 4 \end{pmatrix}$, 3 is the first component and 4 is the second component.

credit card (pp. 83, 176)

A credit card is a plastic card that can be used for making payments. The credit card holder signs the card as soon as he or she receives it.

When using the card to pay for something, a slip is signed by the cardholder for the amount payable. The credit-card company sends a monthly statement to each card holder listing all such payments. The total amount for the month (or part of it) should then be paid to the credit-card company.

event   (p. 327)

An event is the occurrence of a set of outcomes. In a statistical experiment, the probability of an event is the probability of a set of outcomes happening.

histogram   (p. 316)

A histogram looks like a bar chart; but in a *bar chart* the *length* of each block shows the frequency, while in a *histogram* the frequency is shown by the *area* of each block.

When each block or bar has the same width, a histogram is the same as a bar chart. The difference will be more clearly shown in book 3E.

integers   (p. 282)

An integer is a member of the set $\{\ldots, {}^{-}3, {}^{-}2, {}^{-}1, 0, 1, 2, 3, \ldots\}$. 1, 2, 3, ... are positive integers and ${}^{-}1, {}^{-}2, {}^{-}3, \ldots$ are negative integers.

interior angles   (p. 4)

Interior angles are angles that are inside a polygon.

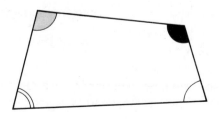

mapping   (p. 196)

A mapping is a relation in which *every* member of the first set is linked by some rule to one or more members of the second set. On p. 194, Exercise 1, question 4 does not show a mapping since the number 12 in the first set is not used. In Exercise 2, on p. 195, question 4 is *not* a mapping.

Note   Some texts define a mapping differently. Such texts would probably define a mapping and a function as being the same. All texts probably agree on the definition of a function. A function is defined on p. 197.

mass   (p. 368)

Mass is the amount of matter in a body. It is often confused with weight, which is a force. For example, on the Earth, the weight of a body is the force with which it is attracted towards the centre of the Earth (the force of gravity). On the Moon, the force of gravity is less than on Earth, so the weight of a body is less on the Moon than on Earth. However, the mass of the body remains the same.

natural numbers   (p. 1)

The natural numbers have long been accepted as being the set of counting numbers: $\{1, 2, 3, 4, 5, \ldots\}$ which does not include zero. More recently, some bodies have included zero in the set of natural numbers.

Throughout this course, I have taken the natural numbers to be the counting numbers.

Note that some examining groups include zero as a natural number and therefore take whole numbers and natural numbers to be one and the same: $\{0, 1, 2, 3, 4, 5, \ldots\}$.

Make certain you know which definition you need for your course.

outcome   (p. 326)

In a statistical experiment, an outcome is a happening. For example, in tossing a coin, the outcome could be a head or it could be a tail.

p.a.   (p. 176)

p.a. means 'per annum' (that is, 'per year' or 'each year').

plane surface   (p. 4)

A plane surface is a flat surface.

probability   (p. 330)

Probability is a measure of how likely an event is.
If all outcomes are equally likely we can write:

the probability of an event

$$= \frac{\text{the number of ways the event can happen}}{\text{the total number of possible outcomes}}$$

For example, in taking a card from a pack of cards there are 52 possible outcomes (there are 52 cards). Each outcome is equally likely. (Each card has the same chance of being selected.) Since there are 4 kings in the pack there are 4 ways a king can be selected.

$$\text{The probability of a king} = \frac{4}{52} = \frac{1}{13}$$

The values used in measuring probability vary between 0 and 1. A probability of 0 means that it is impossible for the event to happen; whereas if the probability of an event is 1, that event is certain to happen.

real numbers   (p. 220)

A real number is a number that can be written as a decimal
5, 2.8, $^-3$, $2\frac{1}{2}$, $\sqrt{2}$ are all real numbers.

sterling   (p. 99)

Sterling is British money as distinguished from foreign money.

subtended (p. 249)

To be opposite to.

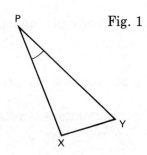

Fig. 1

In Fig. 1, the line XY subtends the angle P. We can also say that angle P has been subtended by line XY.

In Figs. 2 and 3, angle P has been subtended by arc XY.

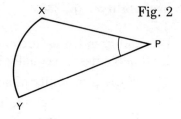

Fig. 2

In Fig. 3, arc XY subtends an angle P at the circumference of the circle.

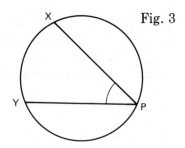

Fig. 3

weight

See mass.

whole numbers (p. 6)

The set of whole numbers is $\{0, 1, 2, 3, 4, 5, 6, \ldots\}$.